THE
NIGHTINGALE
TRAINING SCHOOL

THE
NIGHTINGALE
TRAINING SCHOOL
1860–1996

Roy Wake

HAGGERSTON PRESS

First published 1998
by Haggerston Press,
38 Kensington Place, London W8
Unauthorised duplication contravenes
applicable legislation

Printed and bound in Great Britain
by T. J. International, Padstow

ISBN 1 869812 17 4

All orders for this book to:

The Nightingale Fellowship
Gassiot House
2 Lambeth Palace Road
London SE1 7EW

This history is dedicated
to the memory of a special Nightingale –
an example to us all

Miss Rosamond A Hone OBE

1913–1995

Principal Tutor
of The Nightingale Training School
1955–1972

Contents

Illustrations

Foreword

The Purpose of this book is to act as a permanent reminder of our unique heritage as graduates of the Nightingale Training School and to celebrate the work of so many nurse managers, teachers and staff who made such a training possible.

As recounted in the book, the loss of the Nightingale School as a centre for the training of nurses was a sadness to us all. However, those of us who work in the NHS know that change is integral to its culture, the skill being to recognise how to influence the process and so obtain the best possible outcome. From the time it was made clear that the School could not 'stand alone', a dedicated effort has been made to ensure a continuation of training which recognises that a well informed nurse is more competent to practice and deliver essential nursing care – this the Nightingale Institute is committed to supporting.

It is hard to envisage what Florence Nightingale or indeed Dame Alicia Lloyd Still and others would have thought about the immense changes in health care delivery since the Nightingale Training School first opened. I do know that, though they would have challenged many of the decisions taken in the interests of nurse education and nursing care, they would have supported the continuance of nurse education and the part it has to play in the development of improved nursing care.

Our celebration on 11th May 1996 was a thanksgiving for the privilege of having been part of the Nightingale Training School, and Nightingales from all corners of the world, together with close collegues of the Nightingale School, met together for a joyous day of thanks, commemoration and recollection.

This History will ensure the Nightingale Training School is never forgotten, as it becomes a treasured possession of Nightingales the world over as well as an essential requirement for nursing libraries.

Natalie Tiddy
President,
Nightingale Fellowship

The Badge of the Nightingale Training School

The badge was introduced by Dame Alicia Lloyd Still in 1925. Its design is taken from the eight-pointed cross of the *Knights of the Hospital of St John of Jerusalem*. Its four arms symbolise the Cardinal Virtues – *Prudence, Temperance, Justice and Fortitude* – and its points represent the *Eight Beatitudes* which spring from the practice of those virtues. The *Colour Blue* was chosen as being the colour of the *Ribbon of the Order of Merit* of Miss Nightingale. The inclusion of the *Tudor Rose, Fleur-de-Lis* and the *Shield with the Sword of St Paul* afford a link with the *Hospital Coat of Arms*. The centre of the design portrays the head of *Miss Nightingale* in relief, with the words *'Schola Sancti Thomae'*.

Preface

An unexpected message to telephone Roisin Tierney led to meetings with her and Natalie Tiddy and to the writing of this book. The normal practice of historians is to undertake research and investigation before seriously beginning to write a narrative. In this case, the time scale under which the Nightingale Fellowship wished to operate, and my initial ignorance about the School and its history, have meant establishing a different working method. This has required learning as one goes, and absorbing into the narrative information coming from the answers to the questionnaire sent out to members of the Fellowship, which arrived during the course of writing.

At first it was thought that a great deal of work on the early history of the School would have to be done in the Greater London Record Office or, by arrangement, on documents brought from there to the County Record Office in Winchester, but an early meeting with Dr Monica Baly shewed that there was no point in going over the work that she had done so painstakingly and in such detail. Her kindness at that time was invaluable and much appreciated, and she has been generous in allowing her work to be greatly drawn on, and in personal help and advice.

Slowly it became clear that, in the time available, more would be learnt about the School from the 1930s onwards by talking with people or reading the answers to the questionnaire than from any other sources. The Fellowship *Journal*, in its recording of events since 1925, has been the other indispensable quarry. Beyond this, there has had to be a wide reading in the field generally – and a bringing to bear of one's own knowledge as an historian – in order to arrive at what one hopes is a fair and accurate account of the School in context from 1860 to 1996.

The questionnaire has brought in an extraordinary richness of response. Many have replied well beyond the questions asked, with diaries, photographs, books, tapes; some answers have led to interviews, and one has wondered more than once how far and often one should travel. It has seemed as if the opportunity to reminisce and to evaluate has appealed much more to older Nightingales. Amongst their replies have been found sentences that suddenly capture the imagination, for example, one recalling the bombing of September 1940:

13

I was sleeping in the basement of Gassiot House when we had a direct hit. Trying to get out resulted in dislodging large lumps of rubble fearfully onto someone else. My head wound was treated by Peter Spilsbury who was killed two days later. Previous to that night we slept in the basement corridor where rats ran along the overhead pipes. Sharing this 'dormitory' with us was Florence Nightingale's maid then in her nineties.

Or again, from another trained in the later 1940s:

I was privileged to be the first Gold Medallist after the War (1947). I have the medal on my mantelpiece. I also have an oval-shaped, pearl and diamond chips set in gold brooch given to me by my great-aunt Fanny Wynne which she wore at the neck of her uniform and which can be seen in the old photographs of Florence Nightingale with her nurses. My great-aunt is one of them.

One of the questions asked was 'What led you to enter the Nightingale School?' The answers have been many and varied; very often it was a matter of family connections – daughters following mothers, nieces following aunts, doctors in the family – but every now and then, a particular one caught the attention, like that from a collateral descendant of Florence Nightingale. Another told that

I grew up at Embley Park, the childhood home of Florence Nightingale. My father was headmaster of the boys' boarding school and we lived in the building.

Suddenly and late, a piece of information could arrive not mentioned by anyone else:

Rules were there for a reason. Perhaps it was odd that counterpanes had to be folded just so, but who remembers that day and night nurses had to fold them differently so that, at a glance, it could be known whether a sleeping or unconscious patient had been attended to and had had his bed made or not?

It did prove harder to hear from or meet younger students. Eventually a stop had to be put to incorporating more information from the answers to the questionnaire, but they form a unique archive for the Fellowship that may be of use to others. It will be readily understood that, from so many contributions, much was unavoidably repetitive, but all those who answered can rest assured that what they wrote has been read carefully. It would have made for awkward reading to have named every contributor when quoted, and it is to be hoped that the general line of quoting anonymously will be accepted and appreciated; there are a few justifiable exceptions. In the same sense, it has seemed better not to name every Ward Sister or Tutor, praised or criticised, most of whom certainly made unforgettable impressions on their students. There are some pen-portraits that stand out.

The Ward Sisters were supreme commanders, feared by student nurses and unfortunate Housemen alike, but respected and sometimes even liked – Miss Rosamond Hone, whom we worshipped, Miss Shelton, Miss Gamlen, are to be remembered particularly.

Some things run through every decade in answer after answer, above all the intense pride in being a Nightingale. In each generation people were proud to wear the uniforms and the Badge. It is also to be hoped that readers will not become bored at the repetition of this pride, but it is a theme present from the earlier times, right up to the closing of the School.

I am sincerely very proud of being a Nightingale. Both medical staff and patients are impressed, and I appreciate my 'old school' training – in comparison to colleagues my standards are of a *much* higher standard than theirs, from lesser training hospitals.

I am in no position to compare and contrast the Nightingale training with that of other major teaching hospitals. It is highly likely that their students are just as proud of their Schools. Indeed one senior Nightingale has said that this pride is not permissible if it becomes exclusive and arrogant. Nevertheless, if readers were able to go through the questionnaires as I have they would have to accept that pride rings like a bell across the generations. Almost all have said that being recognised as a Nightingale – usually by the wearing of the Badge – has often enhanced their career prospects, and not infrequently embarrassed them.

It will be noticed that a marked distaste for what is seen by many as a falling of standards in recent years makes itself felt, exemplified by attitudes to uniform, patients and nursing practices.

For obvious reasons, those trained during the Second World War have especially vivid memories; it was the high moment of nursing seen as a service to humanity and not as a career. They lived out a saying of Dame Alicia Lloyd Still's to a young woman: 'Remember, nurse, you are giving your youth to the sick.' Forced inwards on themselves, they formed close friendships, many of which have lasted a lifetime. They were knit together by a common loathing of Park Prewett – in later years only Lambeth Nurses' Home provoked anything like the same strength of feeling – and it would seem that they felt no need for 'counselling', which later generations were to be offered, because they drew strength from each other. It was a training, as they say repeatedly, that prepared them for all that was to happen to them in later life.

Only the most heartfelt thanks can be given to all those who have been willing to help and who have introduced me to an area of social and nursing history with which I was hitherto unfamiliar. Some rather formidable people have been met and many new friends made. Some names stand out because without them nothing of value could have been written:

Natalie Tiddy, Roisin Tierney, Monica Baly, Sheila Garrett, Peggy Nuttall, Joan Lucking, the Fellowship Secretary; then come Belinda Atkinson, Alex Attewell, Janice Cackett, Ursula Cowell, Jane Easterbrook, Professor Macleod Clark, Bryan McSwiney, Sue Norman, Mary Richardson, Richard Sawyer, Carol Wilson.

Miss Cullen gathered a group of Nightingales to meet and talk at the beginning and towards the end of the writing, and their insights were refreshing, informative and confirmed much of what had been told by other people.

It was essential from my point of view that the Fellowship should engage Roger Hudson of the Haggerston Press as editor and publisher. Previous experience of working with him had shewn the indispensability of his professionalism, his wide range of historical knowledge and his immovable integrity. Once author and editor have agreed a final text, so much more work remains to be done in the printing and publishing.

Lastly, Mrs Audrey Atter has often been co-author rather than mere assistant, present at every interview, note-taking, following up with a great deal of reading, and involved at every stage in the construction of the narrative.

It has been a most enjoyable book to write, but quite a difficult one, not least because the School has changed so much over the years, at first in an organic evolutionary sense, but then from the early 1980s into a series of not obviously connected forms, although the present Director of the Nightingale Institute is determined that its adherence to the highest standards should stem from that of FN herself. I am well aware that the book will be read and scrutinised in a very particular way by many readers who are themselves part of the School's history. I hope that they find it accurate, fair and readable.

Roy Wake
July 1997

Introduction

'Go your way straight to God's work, in simplicity and
singleness of heart.' (Florence Nightingale: *Notes on Nursing*)

No one reading this book should expect a new life of Florence Nightingale. Nor is it a history of nursing, but of one distinctive Training
School founded in her name and shadow, financed with money from the
Nightingale Fund, and which ceased to exist as a separate entity on
May 10th, 1996. That said, some reassessment of the achievement and
influence of Florence Nightingale is necessary and unavoidable, and
many readers may be somewhat surprised to see what they were. A
legend has been created which must be examined. Until blindness over-
came her at the beginning of the new century and her mental clarity
began to fade, the School was one part of her many-sided activities, and
'Nightingales', for so they have always been called, have never ceased to
refer and defer to her. Her influence was always felt though it was intermittent, often exercised from a distance and not always, it must be said,
in the best interests of the School. From the very beginnings of the
work on this book one encountered quite opposing views: on the one
hand, the continuing devotion to her memory, signified in commemora-
tions and celebrations acknowledging her shining influence and guiding
spirit; on the other hand, some trenchant views, either that she was
irrelevant or that her influence had been exaggerated or even invented.

A service is held annually on the nearest Sunday to her birthday in
East Wellow Church, near to what was the Nightingale family home at
Embley Park in Hampshire. She is buried in the family grave in the
churchyard. On 12th May 1996 the fairly recently-appointed Vicar
reflected on the impossibility of his avoiding FN – and by and large so
she will be referred to in this book. After all, these are the letters she
insisted were to be carved on her gravestone. He had looked for someone with whom to compare her and had arrived at Lady Thatcher. For
my part, I saw greater similarities with someone whose life I had been
studying in connection with a previous book of mine: Mary Ward
(1585–1645), the Foundress of the Institute of the Blessed Virgin Mary
(IBVM). She was an interesting model of someone who had devoted
herself to establishing an honourable public way of life for women that

took them out of the shadow of men, someone who had asked the key question, 'What can women do?' It needs to be pointed out that until certainly the 18th century, such women would, unavoidably, be within the world of religious orders. Even in that century, the few lay women who tried to strike out on an independent line were regarded as wildly eccentric, and most only 'got away with it' because they were aristocratic. Many readers will pause here and ask: who was Mary Ward, and what makes it appropriate to see her as an aptly comparable woman with FN?

Mary Ward was born into a time of persecution of Catholics by the Elizabethan Government. Her family wanted a good marriage for her, but she felt called to a life of service to God and humanity. In the circumstances of the time, this meant that she had to become a Religious, which was impossible in England and therefore required her to abandon her family and to live abroad. After some restless years, she became convinced that her vocation was to form a completely new community of women Religious who would not live an enclosed life but rather be free, wearing ordinary clothes and following a flexible pattern of prayer and worship. She wanted women to be able to respond to whatever the need was perceived to be. She spent her life exploring and finding answers to her own question: *'What can women do?'*

At the heart of her life of unceasing struggle was the incomprehension and hostility of men. When she died it must have seemed that she had failed, but a small group of women devoted to her were determined to continue the work. Out of this came the Institute of the Blessed Virgin Mary and the foundation of schools and colleges that were eventually to span the world. One year before Florence Nightingale died in 1910, the Institute was finally given Papal approval. Although separated by two and a half centuries, both women were determined to establish the full dignity of *what women can do*, but in no sense as imitation men. There is a telling and memorable scene recorded by one of Mary Ward's band when, in either December 1617 or 1618, the following incident occurred:

> While Mr Sackville was commending us . . . Fr Minister, who was present, answered: 'It is true, while they are in their first fervour, but fervour decays, and when all is done *they are but women.* Fervour not being in the feelings.'
> She said, 'There is a will to do well which women may have as

well as men. There is no such difference between men and women. Yet women, may they not do great matter? It is not the taking of vows or the approval of Superiors that gives security . . . it is not learning that I commend to you, but knowledge, true knowledge which you all may have if you love and seek it . . . I implore you, for God's sake to love the truth. Love verity.'[1]

Florence Nightingale had never heard of Mary Ward, but parallels between the two are striking. Each woman left a secure and well-to-do home. Each was determined not to marry. Mary Ward lived her life in great poverty, whereas Florence Nightingale was a woman of means, on 'dining terms with half the Cabinet'. Moreover she was a very clever woman, who had received an unusual personal education from her father which made her rather formidable to would-be-suitors. She was quite familiar with current philosophical ideas as much as with politics. Nevertheless, both she and Mary Ward came gradually to the conviction that there was some special duty to carry out: Mary Ward would have used the word vocation with ease; Florence Nightingale would not have found it alien.

Both were convinced that they had heard God calling them. In 1611, Mary Ward, 'alone and in some extraordinary repose of mind . . . not by sound of voice but intellectually', received a clear call to the pattern of her life. In a private note, Florence Nightingale wrote: 'On February 7th, 1837, God spoke to me and called me to His service.' This was not an inward revelation.[2] She heard an objective voice, outside herself, speaking to her in human words. Nearly forty years later, in 1874, she wrote that her 'voices' had spoken to her four times. In March 1849, when she was visiting Egypt: 'God called me in the morning and asked me what I would do good for Him, for Him alone without the reputation.' On May 12th that same year she wrote: 'Today I am 30, the age Christ began His mission. Now no more childish things. No more love. No more marriage. Now Lord let me think only of Thy will, what Thou willest me to do. Oh Lord Thy will, Thy will.'[3] Both women came slowly over some years to a final, clear conviction of what was to be done, and from then onwards gave their whole lives to it. Florence Nightingale had to pursue her vocation whilst always having demanding obligations to her mother and sister. She remained loyal to them to the end, but nothing deflected her from her 'calling', a word that she used throughout her life.

Views of Florence Nightingale ranged from the angel with the lamp to the interfering manipulative woman who was a nuisance and a hindrance, resented, like Mary Ward, because she was a woman. Each wished to show that women as women, and not as imitation men, could undertake large and far-reaching endeavours. It was certainly a hostile world in both cases; the current social structures presented towering obstacles. The two of them are part of a long history, and their achievements have helped to make it possible for some to believe that Mary Ward's question has been answered: women can do whatever men can do.

Florence Nightingale seems to have wanted to be free of Church and Churches, though she was a close friend of Henry Edward Manning, the second Catholic Archbishop of Westminster, and did consider becoming a Catholic. She never took the step and veered away to more personal religious thinking. Manning had concluded already that she was not likely to give her *obedience* to the Church. Even so, a proper study of her thinking and her work brings a realisation that she came to see herself as a foundress of a movement that was quasi-religious. In her *Notes on Nursing*, she wrote:

> It is true we make 'no vows'. But is a vow necessary to convince us that the true spirit for learning any art, most especially an act of charity, aright, is not a disgust to everything or something else? Do we really place the love of our kind (and of nursing as one branch of it) so low as this? . . . You do not want the effect of your good things to be, 'how wonderful for a woman!' nor would you be deterred from good things by hearing it said, 'yes, but she ought not to have done this, for it is not suitable for a woman'. But you want to do the thing that is good whether it is 'suitable for a woman' or not. It does not make a thing good, that it is remarkable that a woman should have been able to do it. Neither does it make a thing bad, which would have been good had a man done it, that it has been done by a woman. Oh, leave these jargons and go your way straight to God's work, in simplicity and singleness of heart.

Florence Nightingale was a difficult woman to work with and for. Her letters show how critical she could be of nearly all the women in her life. Poverty was not necessarily required, but Chastity and Obedience certainly were. Again, in *Notes on Nursing*, she wrote:

It seems a commonly received idea among men, and even among women themselves, that it requires nothing but a disappointment in love, the want of an object, a general disgust and incapacity for other things, to turn a woman into a good nurse . . . The everyday management of a large ward, let alone of a hospital do not come by inspiration to the lady disappointed in love.[4]

An analogy can be seen between the organisation of a religious congregation and her ideas for what evolved as the Nightingale Training School for Nurses, and this analogy remains valid throughout its history, long after her death. There was the same sense of a totally demanding vocation into a novitiate through to full profession. There were to be dedicated groups of women, bound together under obedience, to be sent and used wherever most needed. Into this came a continuous care for the personal development and education of each nurse. The famous Nightingale Badge was, surprisingly, given for the first time only in 1925, an outward symbol of a dedicated life. It is heavy with religious significance. The four arms of the eight-pointed cross of the Knights of the Hospital of St John of Jerusalem symbolise the Cardinal Virtues of prudence, temperance, justice and fortitude, the points representing the eight Beatitudes. Since 1925, the School has perpetuated this sense of a dedicated life through the awarding of the Badges, emphasising that they were a personal award and symbol, not to be treated lightly; indeed, regulations were published about the strict procedure to be followed were a badge to be lost and a replacement to be required.

The call that came in 1854 from Sidney Herbert, the Secretary at War, asking Florence Nightingale to take a group of nurses to Scutari in Turkey to bring order and hope to the wounded from the Crimea in hospital there, happened because he knew that she had already committed herself to the study and practice of nursing. This had first begun to take formal shape as a result of her stay at Kaiserswerth in 1851, a Lutheran Religious foundation for the care of the sick. There she got to know something of the work of the Catholic Sisters of Charity in Paris, whose premises she would have entered in 1853 (wearing a religious habit), if she had not been called back to nurse her grandmother; indeed, she made two further attempts to enter the Maison de la Providence and did spend a fortnight there.

It is commonly thought that Florence Nightingale returned from the Crimean War with clearly formulated ideas about nursing, the training of nurses and nursing as a noble profession fit for educated women, for which a large sum of money had been raised already to make her plans come true. This was, emphatically, not the case. Her dedication to nursing is indisputable, but her first preoccupation, and perhaps the presiding one of her whole life, was the care of soldiers and the planning and organisation of hospitals. The establishment of a Training School for nurses was arrived at by more compromises than might have been expected from such a strong-willed woman, and took shape over the passage of quite some years. Syllabuses were arrived at slowly, out of the experience of early Nightingales. If one takes a curriculum to be the public statement of what an educational institution *intends*, then the elucidation of detail – how are the aims to be achieved – took place over no less than twenty years. Intermittent though her involvement in the Training School was, she was involved, and no one could claim that she was not well-informed about its affairs, certainly from the time of the crisis of 1872. The School has borne her name for 136 years, and even now the new arrangements are still carried out under it, though the Nightingale Institute, a completely new organisation, is no longer even housed on its old site. The Badge bears her profile; wreaths are laid, anniversaries commemorated, and it is the Nightingale Fellowship that has asked for this book to be written.

It does no proper service to Florence Nightingale, however, to claim more for her than is substantiated. Stories, even legends gather round significant and great people, and what may be presented as unbroken and consistent achievement from 1860 onwards becomes, on closer examination, a much more complicated and at times a more hesitant or unclear story. At some point revisionist historians always move in, but in the case of Florence Nightingale the serious re-thinking has come only recently. In 1984 Miss Monica Baly submitted a thesis for the degree of Ph.D. at London University in which she put forward her conclusions after the most thorough-going search through the primary sources that had been done up to that time. The thesis was made into a book: *Florence Nightingale and the Nursing Legacy*, published in 1986.[5] Revisionism, after all, is the essence of historical study and Dr Baly is the first major revisionist.

Florence Nightingale and the Training School bearing her name undoubtedly have had a momentous influence reaching to every part of the world. If one were seeking the briefest summing up of what she stood for in nursing it would be: the establishment of nursing as an autonomous profession – she would have said 'calling' because she did not like the word 'profession'. This 'calling' had to have a moral base, and sanitation was at the centre of the work.

Introductions are not for conclusions. The purpose of this book is to stand as a written record for those who already know the story, or most of it, and also to bring those who do not into a realisation of the truth and the value of their inheritance.

CHAPTER ONE

Florence Nightingale

Most people come to hear about Florence Nightingale when studying 19th century British history, and in particular the Crimean War. Their text book may well have an illustration of 'The Lady with the Lamp', and that she was a heroine, one of the few people to come out of the War with a high reputation, might register. But then what? She lived to be 90, and when she died in 1910, many at the time were surprised that she had survived so long, and many continue to be surprised. But not everyone has studied 19th-century history and, under the present arrangements of the National Curriculum, History is not compulsory after fourteen. One must admit furthermore that the young can be noticeably unobservant and uninquisitive.

Those whose interest may have been aroused might well turn for more information, a little later in life, to Lytton Strachey's *Eminent Victorians*. Indeed, visitors to the Florence Nightingale Museum at St Thomas' Hospital, a notable teaching as well as research centre, are able to buy, as a separate booklet, the section on Florence Nightingale from that book. It is puzzling that an institution centred on her work should sell so derogatory and spiteful a portrait, without any accompanying corrective. *Eminent Victorians* was published in May 1918, to instant acclaim, and has been frequently reprinted. In it, Strachey chose four people who represented to him what he disliked about Victorian England: Cardinal Manning, Florence Nightingale, Dr Arnold, the Headmaster of Rugby, and General Gordon. His distaste for all of them is expressed in what is regarded by some as most elegant and entertaining prose, which went down well in the post-war world, when the age of 'de-bunking' was setting in, and it was fun to ridicule the world before 1914. In the disillusionment and weariness brought by the War, people reached for explanations of its causes. Many accepted Strachey's exposures of what he thought were the hypocrisies and pretensions of Victorian England. He was mildly acquainted with newly-fashionable ideas in psychology (his brother and sister-in-law trained under Freud) and so attempted a novel interpretation of his characters, very largely to their detriment. Instead of the two- or three-volume biographies popular in the 19th century came sharp and amusing essays by a clever man determined to make mischief. 'I've been reading *Eminent Victorians*,' wrote Rudyard Kipling. 'It seems to me downright wicked in its heart.'[1] Bertrand Russell asked whether, 'In stripping away so effectively the pious camouflage of his parents' world, was he not replacing one kind of falsity with another, substituting their piety with what a future Master of Balliol was to call a "contemptible snigger"?'[2]

Strachey had been invited to write FN's official biography, but turned this down and the task was undertaken by Sir Edward Cook. His book, *The Life of Florence Nightingale*, appeared in two volumes in 1913. This was the official biography that has impressed so many writers since, many of whom who have found it difficult to get away from the portrait presented. In January 1914, Strachey told his brother, James, 'I have just been reading the book I might have written – the Life of F Nightingale. I'm glad I didn't, as I couldn't have satisfied anybody. She was a terrible woman – though powerful. And certainly a wonderful book might have been made out of her, from the cynical point of view. Of course the Victorian age is fairly reeking all over it. What a crew they were!'[3] So, what did Strachey write about her a few years later? One quotation must suffice to show how Strachey's intense dislike distorted everything about her.

> Beneath her cool and calm demeanour lurked fierce and passionate fires. As she passed through the wards in her plain dress, so quiet, so unassuming, she struck the casual observer simply as the pattern of a perfect lady; but the keener eye perceived something more than that – the serenity of high deliberation in the scope of the capacious brow, the sign of power in the dominating curve of the thin nose, and the traces of a harsh and dangerous temper – something peevish, something mocking and yet something precise – in the small and delicate mouth. There was humour in the face; but the curious watcher might wonder whether it was humour of a very pleasant kind; might ask himself, even as he heard the laughter and marked the jokes with which she cheered the spirits of her patients, what sort of sardonic merriment this same lady might not give vent to, in the privacy of the chamber.[4]

Noel Annan, in his book *Our Age*, asserts:

> He [Strachey] did not deny that her work was magnificent. He sim-
> ply removed the picture of the Lady with the Lamp and drew in its
> place the portrait of a commanding, ruthless bird of prey destroying
> anybody standing in her path whether friend or foe, who treated
> human beings . . . as objects to be manipulated to her ends . . . [Stra-
> chey was saying that] By suppressing her genuine erotic nature
> Florence Nightingale transformed herself into a megalomaniac who,
> so far from inaugurating a new era in the care of patients, set her face
> against the findings of medical science.[5]

One could continue to demolish Strachey, as he himself thought that he
was destroying his four characters. Thus, he did not consult primary
sources; he ran together incidents separated by years or months to make
one event, for style and effect; and he did not hesitate to invent conversations because he thought there was circumstantial evidence to justify
them. So, why bother with him? The main reason is that a very large
number of people has read and continues to read his book. It may even
be that the 1996 film *Carrington* will have renewed or aroused interest,
as many people claim to find the portrayal of him more dominating than
that of Dora Carrington herself.

If not from Strachey, then for many, knowledge may have come from
reading Mrs Cecil Woodham-Smith's biography of Florence Nightingale which was first published in 1950. There had been nineteen or
so before this, all in the shadow of Sir Edward Cook's life. (Dr Baly
says that she read twenty-four before beginning on her own research.)
Woodham-Smith has been reprinted nine times in hardback and three
times in paperback. It was written in difficult circumstances in the
immediate post-1945 years – for example, over 10,000 of the Nightingale papers in the British Library had been sent to Wales for safe keeping
during the War, and she found herself working in cramped conditions in
Aberystwyth. It, in turn, has been assessed critically by Dr Monica Baly,
though she points out in a letter that Mrs Woodham-Smith did not
claim to be the authoritative biographer of FN, and did her most
concentrated work on the Crimean War itself – leading to her book, *The
Reason Why*. But her Nightingale biography may well be much the most
read because it concentrates on telling the story of the whole life, while
other treatises concentrate on specific thematic approaches.

In view of these inadequacies in the most accessible accounts of her, it is necessary to say something about Florence Nightingale's achievement up to the foundation of the Training School, which itself came from her work at Scutari and before.

Remarkable though she was, she could not have followed her chosen path if she had not been a well-born lady with many social connections. Her father, from a background of reasonable means, inherited much more money and changed his surname to fit with the inheritance – he even added heraldic details to a coat of arms, for which he had no permission from the College of Heralds. His house at Embley Park near Romsey in Hampshire was substantially enlarged to make it into a launching pad from which to achieve good marriages for his two daughters. For example, the main ground-floor rooms were given French windows to open onto a terrace, so providing ample space for conversation, display and the forming of liaisons. There is a considerable amount of Jane Austen's Mr and Mrs Bennett about the Nightingale parents – the studious father, with a splendid library into which to retreat, and a mother almost entirely preoccupied with the social round that would bring advantageous marriages. Governesses did not survive and William Edward Nightingale undertook to educate his daughters in a fascinatingly idiosyncratic way that was much more effective with Florence than with the elder daughter, Parthenope. From his tuition, Florence acquired considerable knowledge of mathematics, architecture, techniques of building and other practicalities, as well as familiarity with art and literature. He also imbued her with his Unitarianism, which provided a background for the development of her own eclectic religious views. This altogether unusual education for a young woman in the 1830s and 40s indisputably helped to give her a sense of authority when the time came, and she was able to challenge and confront military and technical men on their own ground. One thing became completely clear, that she was to have no long-term interest in the marriageable men she came to know. However, to feel 'called' by God to some undefined service to humanity, whilst seated under a tree in Embley Park, was a strange phenomenon in mid-19th century Protestant England.

In 1847, whilst on holiday in Rome, she had come to know Sidney Herbert and his wife and their extended circle of friends in high places. Herbert (the half-brother of the Earl of Pembroke), and particularly Mrs Herbert, were themselves interested in nursing and in the care of convalescents. In 1853 Florence Nightingale made her first major move into her chosen world; she took up the post of Superintendent of The Institution for the Care of Sick Gentlewomen in Distressed Circumstances in No 1 Chandos Street, but soon in Harley Street, a position that could go only to a gentlewoman herself. (When matters concerning FN's religious opinions have been discussed in the course of writing this book, it has been pointed out that, whatever else she was, she was a luke-warm member of the Church of England – at Harley Street, her room had a separate entrance so that no one could notice that she did not go to church. The fact that she received Communion from Benjamin Jowett, Master of Balliol College Oxford, proves nothing very much – his own views were so unorthodox that he came near to being charged with heresy before the University Vice-Chancellor.)

The Herberts watched FN's progress. In 1852, Sidney Herbert had become Secretary at War. (Modern readers can be confused by his title because there was also a Secretary of State *for* War, the Duke of Newcastle. Herbert was, in our terms, the junior Minister, the Minister of State.) As such he found himself responsible for the treatment of the sick and wounded when war with Russia led to the Crimean campaign in 1854.

Faced by the famous reports on the awful conditions at Scutari in *The Times* newspaper by Thomas Chenery (such reports from a modern war-field would most certainly be censored now), Herbert asked Miss Nightingale formally, in the name of the Government, to go out to take over the former military barracks on the other side of the Bosphorus from Constantinople, to take charge of nursing the sick and wounded shipped back there from the Crimea. In itself a truly extraordinary proposal, there was no one else in England to whom it could have been acceptably addressed. By coincidence she had accepted already an invitation to take a small group of nurses there, on her own initiative and using her own money. The story of her work in Scutari has been written about often enough. Against obstinacy, obfuscation, incompetence beyond belief and the long-standing contempt of the officers for the ordinary soldiers, she battled to be given plenary power, and got it only towards the end of the War. On March 16th 1856, a dispatch 'establishing her position in terms far beyond anything of which she had ever dreamed, reached the Crimea.'[6] A recent discovery of seventy letters written by Major Francis Beckford Ward, Royal Artillery, from the Crimean battlefield to his parents, gives further evidence of the hostility to FN from the military command. 'Miss Nightingale is here again, and I understand that she threatens to pay a visit to my hospital again during the present week.' The manuscript specialist at Phillips the auctioneers in London commented at the time of their sale that 'She was seen not as a saint but as an interfering pain in the neck.'[7] She herself wrote to Elizabeth Herbert in 1855: 'The real grievance against us is that we are independent of promotion and therefore of the displeasure of our Chiefs . . . we are superior to them in influence and in the chance of being heard at home. It is an anomolous position. But so is war, to us English, anomolous.'[8]

What had taken FN to her post as Superintendent of Sick Gentlewomen in 1853? It needs to be emphasised that there were very few opportunities, once marriage was rejected, for a well-to-do young woman in Protestant mid-Victorian England to fulfil herself and to maintain her social position. It has already been noticed that she was briefly attracted to Catholicism; if she had been converted she might have found her place as the foundress of a new Institute of Congregation. A good deal in her thinking and ideas on dedicated organisation nevertheless came from her friendship with Henry Edward (later Cardinal) Manning who was to be instrumental in arranging that a party of nuns from Deptford went to join her at Scutari.

Once she began to perceive her calling to nursing, which perhaps began when she was 17 or 18 and from which her family failed to deflect her, she embarked on visits to the sick, shewing from the outset her considerable analytical powers and her dedicated unsentimentality in her reflections on them. Her determination was to discern the necessary principles of good nursing, which she linked right from the beginning with character formation, efficient management, hygiene and sanitation. Everything else was a means to these ends – for example, she was to insist that her nurses should go to chapel and attend prayers, but also reminded readers of *Notes on Nursing* that 'Patients, Sir, will not stop dying while we are in church.'[9] The admiration, and indeed adoration that she later inspired was often accompanied by a distaste for her gift for manipulation and occasional ruthlessness, even to those near to her. Dominant achievers are not necessarily likeable. She used her social position to enable her to talk with authority to those in authority. As one General said of Field Marshal Montgomery: 'It's not likeable Generals that we need, it's Generals who win battles.' Florence Nightingale did not aim to be loved by all – that would have greatly reduced her effectiveness. But the 'Lady with the Lamp' is not an invented myth. She was loved by thousands of soldiers. At Scutari, she personally assisted at operations, tended the most serious cases and sat with dying men. She may be compared with some of the great commanders in history, well-briefed and knowing the terrain; and it has been remarked already, the Army was her enduring love.

It is often said that she 'invented nursing' as both a secularised and properly organised profession. This claim needs careful scrutiny and considerable modification, not least because a later view developed that she was not interested in nursing as such, and an even later view – one still current – that she actually hindered the development of nursing. She did not involve herself in nursing back in England as she had done out in Scutari. She wrote about it, famously, but her mind was concentrated far more on the planning, organisation and good management of hospitals as a whole. Certainly, on her return she was much more preoccupied with these than with what to do with the money that was being collected in her honour. In 1860 she had views on nursing, but no clearly worked-out syllabus of training. Whilst she was still in Scutari, she had written to her friend, Mrs Bracebridge, in answer to a question about how she might wish the Fund then being raised to be used. 'If I had a plan it would be to take the poorest and least organised hospital in London and *put myself there and see what I could do*, not touching the Fund perhaps for years, *till experience had shown* how the Fund might best be available . . . (The) Fund will be invaluable as the occasion arises.'[10]

There were many parallels to her work, sometimes minimised by Florence Nightingale herself. A central purpose in most medieval religious Orders had been to nurse the sick and give alms to the poor. This was particularly the case with the abbeys and convents of nuns, whose history has never been examined in the detail given to the study of the male monastic Orders. But all monastic life ceased in England with the Reformation and from the 16th century onwards the institutional care of the sick and the needy depended on secular philanthropy, a sense of obligation towards the less fortunate amongst some of the more wealthy lay people, which showed itself in the foundation of almshouses and 'hospitals' for the sick, the elderly and lepers. By the earlier part of the 19th century, from the Evangelical side of the Church of England, from Nonconformity, and from the devotionalism of the Oxford Movement came some new move towards organising nursing as part of a religious life.

Elizabeth Fry, a Quaker, chiefly remembered for her work in prison visiting and for prison reform, established an Institute of Nursing in 1840. Choosing young women from respectable but lowly families, she taught them to read and write, clothed them well but plainly, gained for them some limited practical training at Guy's Hospital, based mainly on observation, and found work for them in private nursing.[11] This was a small-scale achievement; by 1857 only ninety such nurses had been trained and the teaching was of a very limited kind.

On a somewhat larger scale there were developments in the Church of England. The essence of the Oxford Movement, whose beginning is usually put at 1833 with John Keble's Assize Sermon in Oxford, was its claim that it was reactivating the Catholicism of the Church of England. Therefore, it should come as no surprise that, just as there were moves to establish Anglican monasteries and convents, so there were moves to create religious communities to care for the sick, the poor and the dying. In 1845, the Park Village Community was founded under the guidance of Dr Pusey (along with Keble and Newman, one of the luminaries of the Movement). The women, who took the title of Sisters of Mercy, received no hospital training. Three years later, a similar group with the same name was started in Devonport by Miss Priscilla Sellon. The two groups merged in 1866; eight of their number, described as Sellonites, were to work with FN at Scutari. More importantly, in 1848, St John's House was set up by a group of eminent clergy and doctors as 'a training institution for nurses in hospitals, families and the poor'.[12] It was the best organised, although strictly hierarchical, of the pre-Nightingale movements. It introduced the notion of training probationers (but for an undefined period) who were expected to perform domestic duties in exchange for free board and lodging. Then there were socially superior women who could come in without training, and Sisters who, whilst carrying responsibility, were apparently expected to pay for the privilege.[13] (The revived use of the appellation 'Sister' has a conventual connotation.) The minimum age of entry was 18, but most were between 20 and 40. The House acquired a good reputation and was made responsible for the nursing in King's College Hospital from 1856. A separate group, the All Saints Sisterhood, based on All Saints Margaret Street, took over the nursing and training at University College Hospital in 1862. The Orders remained distinct and have survived to the present day. In a recent conversation, in March 1997, Dr Baly emphasised her ever-strengthening desire to rescue the reputations of many of the ordinary secular pre-Nightingale nurses. Her researches have ranged beyond FN, the School and St Thomas's Hospital, and she is well-placed to take up FN's own point, when she wrote,

> I have always believed, since I knew hospitals at all, and I believe it more and more every day I live, that, with all their faults and short-comings, which are easily learnt and more easily declaimed against, our great English hospitals are places in which more is done for the relief and care of human misery, or, rather, of that large branch of it arising from disease, than in any other places in the world. Also that their faults are not essential to them, but that they may, by God's blessing on the patient endeavours of many years, be very much modified.[14]

Outside the hospital world, there was also much to do in the work-houses created by the Poor Law Reform Act of 1834. This Act, seen by Whig reformers as one of their greatest achievements, abolished all previous ways of looking after the unemployed, the aged, the poor and the needy and impelled all of them into the newly created workhouses, in which men and women were segregated. These were regarded by many as purely evil, by others as at at best a necessary evil. There was certainly room for merciful works. The experiences of a number of dedicated women – for example Miss Twining and Miss Power Cobbe – became telling evidence for the commission set up by *The Lancet* in 1865 to look into the state of workhouse infirmaries. The immediate cause was the death in December of 1864 in Holborn Workhouse of Timothy Daly, a pauper. The appalling circumstances of his death enabled FN to write to the President of the Poor Law Board to urge the improvement of nursing in workhouse infirmaries. She was able to refer him to what was going to be done in the Liverpool Workhouse Infirmary with a staff of trained nurses and a matron from the Nightingale Training School. Dr Baly has pointed out in conversation that FN, later in life, regretted that she had not done more for Poor Law nursing, but has added in a private letter her own opinion that 'FN probably did more for Poor Law nursing than she did for general hospitals.'

Many more such examples of activity quite separate from the Training School could be recorded, most by religious foundations. FN, from her own experience, became critical of their inadequate standards of training, not least in matters concerning cleanliness and hygiene; many individual nurses won her admiration, but their institutions did not. Without doubt she was sceptical about some of their motives, suspecting that they were more interested in the spiritual than the physical well-being of their patients. She was determined that her trained nurses would keep their minds on the job and not proselytise. Her nurses were to attend prayers and chapel, but as part of their personal character formation. Their views were not to be obtruded on patients. The suspicion that Catholics might be more prone to attempt to convert may be one element, an unjustified one and perhaps not the only one, in the anti-Catholic attitudes that ran through the history of the Training School until the 1960s.

She worked in harmony and deepening friendship with Mother Clare Moore, the Superior of the House of the Sisters of Mercy in Bermondsey, who had responded to the appeal of her diocesan Ordinary, Bishop Grant, taking with her four nuns from the House to go to Scutari. Indeed, Mother Clare remained a spiritual adviser to FN for some years after the War. But FN found it difficult to work with another woman of equally strong character to herself, the Reverend Mother Frances Bridgeman, an Irish Sister of Mercy from Kinsale.

FN arrived at the War in company with Mary Stanley (the sister of Dr Stanley, at that time a Canon of Canterbury, later to become Dean of Westminster), whose mission had not been communicated to FN, resulting in any number of personality clashes and tensions. Mary Stanley had kept secret from Sidney Herbert her intention to become a Catholic. Likewise, Mother Bridgeman, according to Mrs Woodham-Smith, made it abundantly clear that she intended a spiritual as well as a medical mission. The resulting problems, not least the rumours reaching England that FN's purposes were dominated by Catholicism and neo-Catholicism, certainly confirmed her in her determination to steer clear of denominational religion. On the other hand, it also convinced her of the value of organised obedience and of discipline, and this strengthened her belief that organisation should not depend for its existence on one person. She intended that the Training School, if and when eventually it came to be established, would be based on principles and not on personalities. Strive as she might, the fact is that the personalities of strong men and women, and not only her own, have permeated its history.

To record her work after she returned from the War in 1856 is to trace the extension of her ideas and practice about nursing, and the increasing, though uneven, clarification of her thinking about it. Without any doubt her first preoccupation after the War was not with the Fund and the possiblity of a Training School but with the health and welfare of soldiers in the Army. (The origins and the early history of the Fund and the Fund Council will be dealt with in Chapter Two.) This led her to give much advice about the design of the proposed new Royal Victoria Hospital at Netley, on Southampton Water. Here she put forward her strongly held views about the pavilion plan, which puts every ward, of around thirty beds, into separate buildings linked to the rest of the hospital only by a through corridor. On this she was over-ruled by senior military staff, to the great disadvantage of future patients. Her views on the necessity for good ventilation, fresh air and cleanliness were more noticed. Hardly had she suffered the disappointment about design – and there was nothing that she cared more passionately about because the rest would follow from it – than she was brought in, at a time of acute ill-health, to help with what proved to be seemingly interminable preparatory work, initiated by her greatest admirer, the Queen, to establish a Royal Commission on the Health of the Army. 'No-one can feel for the Army as I do,' she wrote in a private note.[15] The Commission received its Royal Warrant to begin in May 1857. Her greatest contribution no doubt was *Notes on Matters Affecting the Health, Efficiency and Hospital Administration of the British Army*, 830 octavo pages in all, which she produced in 1858. This was followed by a second volume of *Subsidiary Notes – The Introduction of Female Nursing into Military Hospitals in Peace and War*. The writing of these documents perhaps did more than anything else to clarify her ideas on the training of nurses.

In such circumstances, and with many family problems to deal with, the matter of using the Fund to create a Training School was indeed far from being at the front of her mind. Furthermore, whilst still involved in all this, she was persuaded to turn her attention to the health of the Army in India, producing her *Suggestions in Regard to Sanitary Works Required for the Improvement of Indian Stations*. Her connection with India, which she never visited, continued over many years, bringing for her, as was so often the case, frustration, disappointment and, in the end, only partial success. The battle of a solitary woman against obstructive bureaucracy is one of the main themes of her life. Disappointments, however, did not prevent the growth of the legend about her.

In these years, then, she was much more concerned with the design, the building and the detailed layout of hospitals than with nursing and the training of nurses. Her life was not neatly compartmented. She did not always undertake one task at a time, and the queue of people seeking admission for her advice covered many different fields. At the same time, she was writing copiously in an attempt to work out and clarify a distinctive religious position of her own.

So busy was she with all these other matters that the question of what to do with the money that had been raised in her honour continued to be put to the back of her mind. Not only was she preoccupied with the Army, but also with all her writing, and so she continued to postpone thinking about the School. At a point of impatient exhaustion she indicated in a letter to her uncle, Samuel Smith, that the money might as well be deflected straight to St Thomas's Hospital in London, though, indeed, at this time – 1857/58 – she was not firmly committed to that hospital at all and entertained ideas of settling the School at the Middlesex, or The Royal Free, or University College Hospital. The reasons for her final choice are more complicated than once thought.

The School did open in 1860, but only one year later she had become heavily involved in and distracted by working with William Rathbone's projects for Liverpool. He was one of the merchant princes of the city, who two years previously had established the beginnings of District Nursing. At first he relied on a Mrs Robinson, trained by St John's House, but when it became clear that there was no one else equipped to work with her, he asked FN for help. As a result of this, the Royal Liverpool Infirmary opened a Training School and Home for Nurses that made his scheme workable for a time.

Then came a further involvement, again with William Rathbone, to improve workhouse nursing. On May 16th 1865, twelve nurses and a matron – Nightingale Nurses trained in the Nightingale School – went to the Liverpool Workhouse Infirmary. Achievement here turned into frustration and failure on a larger scale in London when her efforts to help were accepted but not incorporated in the way that she wanted in the Metropolitan Poor Act of 1867.

Just when she thought that the multitude of demands on her was lessening, and when more system was brought into her affairs by the appointment of Henry Bonham Carter as Secretary of the Nightingale Fund, the outbreak of war between Prussia and France, in June 1870, plunged her into new activity. In July The National Society for Aid to the Sick and Wounded was founded, soon to be called The British Red

Cross Aid Society, and FN was pressed to give up all other work and take control. It was a reminder of how much the general public saw her as the only dominant figure in nursing. For example, contributions that came in as a response to many varied appeals were, time and again, addressed to her personally. 'Every man and woman in the world seems to have come into it with the express purpose of writing to me. Would I could go to the seat of War instead of all this writing, writing, writing.'[16] In common with public opinion generally, her sympathies began by being for Prussia and then changed to France. The Crown Princess of Prussia – Queen Victoria's eldest daughter – was an enthusiastic student of *Notes on Nursing*, and continuously in correspondence with FN. Her reputation stood high in Germany – the Grand Duchess of Baden said that 'I love and respect her more than anyone in the world.'

In a world of word processors and calculators, and before that, of typewriters and adding machines, one must be reminded of the time when work was a laborious matter with pen and ink and personally collected and tabulated statistics. In the years after 1867, driven by her own outrage and shock arising from the work she undertook, Florence Nightingale found herself more and more involved in the assembling and collation of medical statistics – she said that she found them the most interesting of all reading. Peggy Nuttall, writing in the Fellowship *Journal* for January 1984, No. 110, said that on the very day in June 1860 when *The Times* carried its advertisement inviting would-be nurses to apply to Mrs Wardroper, the Matron of St Thomas's, for entry to a Training School soon to be established in FN's name, FN herself was working with her friend, Dr William Farr, compiler of statistics for the Registrar General, to plan the programme for the International Statistical Congress to be held in London that summer. FN's interest in statistics certainly had flowered during the Crimean War. In 1857, William Farr had already sent her the volumes of the *Statistical Society Journal* dealing with hospital statistics. In November 1858 he joined with others in proposing her as the first woman Fellow of the Statistical Society. At first she was reluctant to enter this male domain, but she was accepted in January 1859. Her paper on *Hospital Statistics* was presented to the international congress of 1860 and played an important part in the beginnings of an international standardisation of medical data. She was happy to be called a 'passionate statistician'. In *Notes Towards a History of Teaching Statistics* (1986), John Bibby quotes Karl Pearson: 'Her statistics were more than a study, they were indeed her religion. To understand God's thoughts, she held we must study statistics, for these are the measure of his purpose . . . They were the cipher by which we may read the thoughts of God.' Bibby also quotes one of FN's letters in which she says: 'Statistics compiled by meteorologists show that storms can be foreseen. When a ship goes down in an "unforeseen" gale, do we say "How could God permit such a dreadful calamity? The devil must have done it." No. We say "Study the signs of approaching gales and you will not be lost." '[17]

She was to use statistics in her arguments about the siting of the new St Thomas's Hospital, but her skills were developed by her involvement at King's College Hospital. The immediate cause here was an outbreak of puerperal fever in the lying-in wards, which brought her to realise that there was no collected, analysed, reliable information about mortality in childbirth. Using an ever-extended network of informants first in this country and then throughout the world she was enabled to shew, amongst other things, that women were much more at risk in hospital than in their homes, no matter how squalid those were – a startling conclusion. The resulting information was so overwhelming that it had to be put forward in more concentrated form by her friend, Dr Sutherland, in *Introductory Notes on Lying-in Institutions*, in 1871. Just as she had insisted that nursing was a calling that educated women could follow, so she pressed the same case for midwifery.

The years went by, largely taken up with further involvement in and frequent frustration with major initiatives already begun. For example, in 1887, she was asked to send Nightingale Nurses to serve in the follow-up to the campaign in Sudan after General Gordon's murder in 1885. In 1891, an International Conference on Hygiene and Demography held in London contained a section on the progress of Indian Sanitation, entirely due to her insistence. In 1893, at an Exhibition of Women's Work in Chicago, a paper was read from her, dedicated to Princess Christian, a daughter of Queen Victoria who had become particularly involved in much philanthropic work including nursing. The paper was received in awe. At this time FN was, nevertheless, in substantial disagreement with the Princess over a National Register of Nurses. FN held that simply to enter names on a list neither indicated a grading of quality nor charted subsequent training and development, or lack of it. To the end, she stood for nursing as a way of life for dedicated people – more or less a life-time's career; marriage would mean resignation.

Behind and beyond all these activities, enormously important as they were, lay a work already referred to, the capturing of the quintessence of her experience and wisdom in *Florence Nightingale's Notes on Nursing: What it is and What it is Not*. The first version, a short piece of writing that asked for comment and critical appraisal, came out early in 1860. The second edition, revised and enlarged, came out later the same year, a third in 1861 and a major revision and extension in 1869. She took matters into further detail in 1875, but this never appeared in print because of sharp exchanges and disagreements with Dr Sutherland, of the Board of Health and the Sanitary Commission. She regarded the Notes as her 'little book', hoping by keeping it small to ensure a large circulation.

The result of over 12,000 letters and many long preliminary essays, the *Notes* set out her principles of nursing in a distinctive and highly readable style. The first fundamental principle is that nurses are to care for patients and not for diseases. Then she is firm that people are composed of biological, psychological, social and spiritual elements, so making herself the first to advocate and press home a holistic approach. This has endeared her to the nursing world in the United States, where she has a huge following – these days caught up into the feminist movement.

Florence Nightingale required nothing of anyone else that she had not done herself. Her serious, indeed dangerously serious illness in Scutari had given her the experience of being a patient. From all this came the insistence that the nurses trained in her School ideally should develop a capacity to understand the minds and outlooks as well as the workings of the bodies of those they nursed – an aim that took decades to achieve, and is still being pursued. In all things she was a pragmatist, developing ideas out of experience, and accepting the necessity to compromise on the way, however reluctantly, and sometimes most reluctantly.

She did not see nursing as something to be done only in the event of illness or injury; it was concerned as much with health promotion and rehabilitation as with restoration.[18] Nursing was a 'calling'. She may have adhered to no particular religious creed, and indeed feared lest nurses should attempt to proselytise, but she was convinced that the principles of Natural Law could be perceived by an intelligent person and used to help people improve their health and existence. Nursing was more than an occupation, and was not something that could be put aside even for a short time. Like it or not, the clear analogy with religious Orders is inescapable; to take up nursing was the equivalent of a religious vow. Nursing was an art and required vision and idealism, making it among the most exalted vocations. But in the Chicago paper, she also investigated the concept of nursing as a science, demanding formal education including a grasp of statistics, logic and the laws of health and health practice. In the same paper, she also warned that 'Nursing cannot be taught by lecturers or by books alone although these are valuable accessories if used as such: otherwise what is in the book stays in the book.'[19] Nursing is distinct: doctor and nurse are equal but different. Florence Nightingale's insistence on the education of nurses was part of her belief in the value of educating women in general, but all her life she required theory to be put into practice.

On some crucially important matters she was wrong-headed and turned her face against the evidence. This was particularly true of her refusal to accept the germ theory of infection, despite a growing body of research. From this grew a series of attitudes about the training of nurses and their relationship to doctors that held up desirable development. She alienated people whose support was needed. She knew so much about the practicalities of administration and nursing and had saved so many lives, but she never had a systematic education in medical science and was ambivalent about this when it came to the curriculum in her own School. Later Superintendents had to put these matters right.

The time came when she had to admit that her original intention to base nursing on young women from the tradesmen's and labouring world had failed, and that it was necessary to bring in those of means and education – the 'Specials'. These, not all of whom necessarily paid, could train other nurses and deal with doctors and members of hospital Boards as equals. Sir Joshua Jebb, a member of the Nightingale Fund Committee, was certain that if nursing reform were to succeed it would have to be imposed from the top. It would be 'backed up by [such nurses] having been originally in a higher position than the ordinary run of nurses.'[20]

The Training School, founded under her name and with the money from the Fund, was visited by her only once, in 1881, but the listing of her commitments and activities should shew why. Its direction was in the hands of Mrs Wardroper, the Fund having established that the Matron of St Thomas's should 'ex officio' be the Superintendent of the

School. It is easy to gain the impression that the choice of Mrs Wardroper was made quickly and easily, whereas in fact her appointment, like much else to do with the beginnings of the School, was complicated. Once the School was established, FN's interest was real but uneven; her major intervention came when it was made clear that change was necessary. This led to the decision in March, 1872, to appoint someone who, it was hoped, would be truly in charge whilst Mrs Wardroper remained officially so. The title chosen then was Home Sister, which was by no means descriptive of the duties entailed – what we would call a 'job description' would have made her 'Mistress of the Probationers', or in modern usage, 'Director of Nursing Education and Training'. She was to be resident in the School, to be the personal tutor of every nurse and to supervise all aspects of education and training with particular reference to character formation. FN did heed Jowett's remonstrance in 1882, that she herself should not think of taking up permanent residence within the school. Knowing what one does about her, one can look with alarm on what might have happened if she had.

By 1887, the following hospitals, institutions and organisations had matrons or superintendents who had been trained in the Nightingale School: The Westminster Hospital, St Mary's Paddington, the Marylebone Infirmary, the Highgate Infirmary, the Metropolitan and National Nursing Association, the North London District Association, the Cumberland Infirmary, the Edinburgh Royal Infirmary, the Huntingdon County Hospital, the Leeds Infirmary, the Lincoln County Hospital, the Royal Infirmary and the Workhouse Infirmary and the Southern Infirmary (all in Liverpool), the Royal Victoria Hospital at Netley, the Royal Hospital for Incurables at Putney, and the Salisbury Infirmary. Parties of nurses under a Nightingale-trained superintendent had gone to the United States of America, Sydney, Montreal, India, Sri Lanka, Germany and Sweden. Training schools modelled on the Nightingale School and supervised by Nightingale Superintendents were established in Edinburgh and in three major London hospitals.[21]

A study of the history of the Royal County Hospital in Winchester shows that this list is by no means comprehensive. The first two Matrons of this new hospital, which was built by the distinguished Victorian-Gothic architect, William Butterfield, to the expressed designs of FN, having already been appointed, were each sent to the Nightingale School for further proper training. It was always FN's intention that Nightingale nurses should be so enthused that they could 'Go out and teach all nations.' Indeed it has been said more than once that it was often the best who fled the nest.

From the time that FN returned from the Crimea she held a unique position in people's minds. William Rathbone, the wealthy Liverpool Unitarian merchant and ship-owner, said that 'In any matter of nursing, Miss Nightingale is my Pope and I believe in her infallibility' – an interesting statement from a Unitarian.[22] She became one of those eminent Victorians who, by living a long life, emerged at the end, controversy behind her, into serenity. In 1889, Benjamin Jowett who was by then Vice-Chancellor of Oxford University as well as Master of Balliol, wrote to her:

> There was a great deal of romantic feeling about you years ago when you came home from the Crimea. (I really believe that you might have been a Duchess if you had played your cards better.) And now you work on in silence, and nobody knows how many lives are saved by your nurses in hospitals (you have introduced a new era in nursing); how many thousand soldiers who would have fallen victim to bad air, bad water, bad drainage and ventilation, are now alive owing to your forethought and diligence; how many natives of India (they might be counted probably by hundreds of thousands) have been preserved by the energy of a sick lady who can scarcely rise from her bed. The world does not know all this, or think about it. But I know it and often think about it, and I want you to, so that . . . you may see what a blessed life yours is and has been. I think that the romance too . . . did a great deal of good. Like Dr Pusey you are a Myth in your own lifetime. Do you know that there are thousands of girls . . . named after you?[23]

After this brief survey of FN's life and achievements, there remain some aspects of her personality which continue to stir speculation and controversy. When Freudian psychology was popularised, and indeed all the fashion, speculation began about FN's sexuality. As a young woman she had formed a passionate attachment to Selina Bracebridge, whom she had come to know in 1847 through mutual friends. This passion seems to have worried FN greatly. Mrs Woodham–Smith gives extensive evidence of how besotted FN was and how guilty she felt. It led her to the hard conclusion that she would have to foreswear love. 'Oh God, no more love. No more marriage O God.'[24]

As far as can be ascertained, she never felt love which included a strong sexual desire for any man, although she was much attracted by Richard Monckton Milnes. Though she refused to marry him (she could not have known, but he came to possess one of the largest porno-graphic libraries in Europe), she was furious when he married someone else. Her intimate friendship with Benjamin Jowett was conducted very largely by letter. In later life, her letters to close friends and associates contain emotional endearments of a kind that would not normally be used today. As she grew older she seems to have seen herself as a mother-figure to new generations of her nurses. All of this made good copy for the likes of Lytton Strachey, who said that whereas in her ear-lier days she had written 'with the vindictive relish of a Swift, she now spent long hours composing sympathetic Addresses to Probationers, whom she petted and wept over in turn.' Reading these Addresses is certainly an embarrassing experience; they are blush-making. But why Strachey picked on her emotionalism, with its sexual undertow, is a little puzzling, because the Bloomsbury way of looking at things was all for self-expression and against repression, and stressed the importance of personal friendship, including an easy acceptance of homosexuality and lesbianism.

Victorian men normally addressed each other by surname, and yet in their letters could display much emotion and affection. Those who were capable wrote memorable poems on the death of those close to them. The death of Tennyson's dear friend, Arthur Hallam (1811–1833), inspired his poem *In Memoriam*. The death of Arthur Hugh Clough (a cousin of FN's by marriage) in 1861, who played an indispensable and notable part in her life and work, as her secretary and amanuensis, was commemorated by Matthew Arnold in *Thyrsis, a Monody*. Clough, like Herbert, worked to exhaustion point; what is more he had tuberculosis. FN paid for him to go to Italy to recover but he died, aged 42, in Flo-rence, aptly enough. The picture of him that one gets through the Nightingale story, of a sad, somewhat lugubrious and harassed figure, is difficult to fit in with the wit and humour of the man who re-wrote the Ten Commandments ('The Latest Decalogue', published posthu-mously in 1862), satirised the newly rich materialism of the time and mocked the growth of unthinking agnosticism. What FN thought of this side of a man to whom she was personally greatly devoted – 'My love for thee was very great, passing the love of women'[25] – is not recorded. How did she feel about the biting but often misinterpreted

> *Thou shalt not kill; but need'st not strive*
> *Officiously to keep alive.*

Or again,

> *Do not adultery commit;*
> *Advantage rarely comes of it.*

Or what would FN, whose religious faith, though unorthodox, was powerful indeed, have made of his poem 'There is no God' which ends?

> *And almost everyone when age,*
> *Disease, or sorrows strike him,*
> *Inclines to think there is a God,*
> *Or something very like Him.*

In a letter Florence Nightingale addressed Benjamin Jowett as 'my darling Jowett'. Their friendship deepened into what can only be described as devotion, and friends thought that he pressed her to marry him, but this is unproven. Whatever the case, she depended greatly on his advice and devotion. Though she visited him on occasion, substantially it was affection by letter. If he influenced her, equally she influenced him, not least in her encouragement of his efforts to introduce the study of Politics to Oxford, in which she thought that Statistics would play an essential part.[26] The moves failed, and it was not until 1919 that Politics, Philosophy and Economics (PPE – 'Modern Greats') were established as a degree course at Oxford.

To express personal feelings in terms of hyperbole was the custom of the time and of the social milieu in which she lived. Her old friend, Lady Ashburton, wrote of 'the deep joy of communion with my beloved' after spending a day with FN when she was nearly 60, and repeatedly addressed her as 'Guiding Star of My Life'. Miss Pringle, who resigned from her position as the second Superintendent of the School when she became a Catholic, was called 'The Pearl' by FN, and Miss Rachel Williams, 'The Goddess Baby'.[27]

FN found that leadership, power and influence made for loneliness. So perhaps this outflow of affection on paper was some compensation. The loneliness was a price to be paid because there was no other way

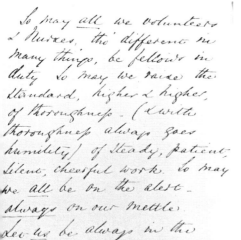

So may all we volunteers & Nurses, tho' different in many things, be fellows in duty. So may we raise the standard, higher & higher, of thoroughness. (& with thoroughness always goes humility) of steady, patient, silent, cheerful work. So may we all be on the alert – always on our mettle. Let us be always in the van of wise & noiseless high training & progress. God bless you all.

Florence Nightingale

May 23/83

13

Left: Florence Nightingale. A bronze cast from the marble bust by Sir John Steell, presented to her by the non-commissioned officers and men of the British Army in 1862.

Right: Mary Crossland, Home Sister, 1875 to 1896, photographed in 1861.

A letter from Florence Nightingale to the probationers, 1883.

St Thomas's Hospital, Surrey Gardens, its home from 1862 to 1871.

Opened by Her Majesty – the new St Thomas's, 1871.

St Thomas's, photographed in 1939, with trams on Westminster Bridge.

St Thomas' rebuilt, 1992.

REGULATIONS

Training of Hospital Nurses under the Nightingale Fund.

1. The Committee of the Nightingale Fund have made arrangements with the authorities of St. Thomas's Hospital for giving a year's training to women desirous of working as Hospital Nurses.

2. Women desirous of receiving this course of training should apply to Mrs. WARDROPER, the Matron, at St. Thomas's Hospital, subject to whose selection they will be received into the Hospital as Probationers. The age considered desirable for Probationers is from 25 to 35; single or widows; a certificate of age and other particular will be required, according to the form printed at the back.

3. The term of the Probationer's training is *a complete year*; it may, however, be extended by the Committee for another quarter, and Probationers will be received on the distinct understanding that they will remain for the required term. They may, however, be allowed to withdraw upon grounds to be approved by the Committee. They will be subject to be discharged at any time by the Matron, in case of misconduct, or should she consider them inefficient or negligent of their duties.

4. The Probationers will be under the authority of the Matron of the Hospital, and will be subject to the rules of the Hospital.

5. They will be lodged in the Hospital, each having a separate bedroom, and will be supplied, at the cost of the Nightingale Fund, with board, including tea and sugar, and washing, and with a certain quantity of outer clothing, of an uniform character, which they will always be required to wear when in the Hospital. They will serve as Assistant-nurses in the wards of the Hospital.

6. They will receive instruction from the Sisters and the Medical Secretary. They will receive at the end of the 1st quarter a sum of £2; at the end of the 2nd quarter £2 10s; at the end of the 3rd quarter £2 10s; at the end of the 4th quarter £3; and if the term be extended, at the end of the 5th quarter £3. This will be in addition to the clothing, costing about £4 4s.

7. At the close of a year, their training will usually be considered complete, *and during the four years next succeeding the completion of their training, they will be required to enter into service as Hospital Nurses in such situations as may from time to time be offered to them by the Committee.* After the expiration of the four years they are expected still to continue in Hospital employment.

8. The names of the Probationers will be entered in a Register in which a record will be kept of their conduct and qualifications. This will be submitted at the end of every month to the Committee of the Nightingale Fund. At the end of a year those whom the Committee find to have passed satisfactorily through the course of instruction and training will be entered in the Register as certified Nurses, and will be recommended for employment accordingly. The Committee have hitherto readily found employment for their certified Nurses in some public Hospital or Infirmary, at salaries usually commencing at £20, with board (including tea and sugar) and washing.

9. Engagements are not to be made except through the Committee, and no engagement is to be put an end to without a quarter's previous notice to the Committee.

10. The Committee will allow a yearly gratuity of £2 to all their certified Nurses, to be paid at the end of every complete year of service succeeding the term of training, up to the third year inclusive, provided that evidence be given at the end of each year that the Nurse has served the whole time satisfactorily. No gratuity will be paid if the Committee have reason to suppose that the Nurse intends to discontinue her employment.

The usual times for admission are the Quarter Days. Applications must be made in person, to Mrs. WARDROPER, *St. Thomas's Hospital, Albert Embankment, Westminster Bridge, London, S.E.*, between 10 and 11 a.m. only, unless by appointment. These Regulations may be obtained by writing to HENRY BONHAM-CARTER, Esq., Secretary to the Nightingale Fund, 91, *Gloucester Terrace, Hyde Park, London, W.*

At the expiration of one month from the date of entry, every Probationer will be required to write a Letter to the following effect :—

TO THE CHAIRMAN OF THE COMMITTEE OF THE NIGHTINGALE FUND.

SIR,

Having now become practically acquainted with the duties required of a Hospital Nurse, I am satisfied that I shall be able and willing, on the completion of my year's training, to enter into service in a Public Hospital or Infirmary, and I engage, in accordance with the annexed Regulations of the Nightingale Fund and in return for the advantages bestowed upon me, to continue in such service for the space of at least four years, in whatever situations the Committee shall think suitable to my abilities, it being my intention from henceforth to devote myself to Hospital employment. I further agree not to enter into any engagement except through the Committee, and not to leave any situation without having given due notice to the Committee.

10/1871.

I am, SIR, &c. &c.

Nightingale School Fund Regulations for Training, 1871.

Sister Adelaide, Lady Acland (née Ovans) in her Ward bedsitting room, 1896.

Dr Theodore Acland with (seated from left) Sister Florence (Lady Riddell), Sister Christian, Sister George, and Sister Arthur, 1898.

Elizabeth Ward staff, pre 1900: Sister, Day Nurse, Night Nurse, three probationers.

Seymour Ward, 1907: Sister, Miss Ram, probationer H I G Piper. Note the Doulton tile nursery rhyme pictures in this children's Ward.

Beatrice Ward, 1904.

Miss Gordon, Matron, Miss Haig Brown, Home Sister, with a group of nurses, c. 1900.

Sisters and nurses dismounting from buses at St Paul's for Florence Nightingale's memorial service, 20 August, 1910.

Miss Hamilton, Matron, and Ward Sisters, 1912–1913.

that she could have done her work. She organised and she commanded. Delegation was under strict control. If she were disappointed in someone, this was made very clear, and nothing shows her in a worse light than in her dealings with Sidney Herbert when he was seriously, indeed mortally, ill; only much later after his death did remorse set in.

The other area of FN's life which has given rise to continual speculation is her chronic invalidism. This began in 1861, and from then until 1868, she was bed-ridden with spinal pain so severe that she was unable to change position, and which was eventually only relieved by opium injections. An article in *The Times* on 18th January 1996 took the matter up. The writer, Dr James Le Fanu, observed: 'It is a great misfortune to be afflicted by some malady for which neither doctors nor their panoply of sophisticated tests can find a cause. Sooner or later it will be made clear that, as they can find nothing wrong, the symptoms must be psychosomatic or a manifestion of hypochrondriasis. But what if this verdict is wrong?' He went on to remind the reader that FN's reputation has always been scarred by the slur that her personal life was the antithesis of the virtues she promoted in public. 'Her aims may have been loving and humanitarian, her administrative gifts exceptional, her writings a masterpiece of lucidity and common sense, but her personal relationships were cold and her attitude to others tyrannical.' Dr Le Fanu quoted the historian Professor F. B. Smith's remark that her illness could not give sufficient evidence to the doctors of the time to work on, but added, 'Her illness was genuine, the cause of not only great physical distress, but also of a profound melancholia which, together, more than explained the change in her personality.'

In the same article, Dr David Young, formerly principal scientist at the Wellcome Foundation, says that the explanation lies in the severe feverish illness to which she fell victim while in the Crimea. It was called 'Crimean Fever' at the time, but there is little doubt that this was Brucellosis caused by milk contaminated with the Brucella bacterium which, though rare in Britain, remains an occupational hazard especially for farmers. (Other candidates for FN's illness have been typhoid or typhus.) After the first severe attack, Brucella persists in the body causing invalidity over many years with occasional returns to apparently ordinary health. It attacks the nerves and joints especially of the lower back, leading to severe and at times incapacitating pain. It can also cause symptoms misinterpreted as psychosomatic, including depression, loss of appetite, palpitations and nervous tremors. It is known that

47

she employed a masseuse in the 1860s, and that she was in so much pain that she could not bear conversation. This was not haughty eccentricity, but an effect of a severe illness which, the doctors say, eventually burns itself out. So it did. Dr Young says, 'As her character blossomed in its benevolence, this emaciated woman became a dignified, stout old lady with a large good-humoured face.'

It is fortuitous that this article should have been published as this book began to be written, and it appears that the thesis is receiving general acceptance. Indeed on 19th May 1996, in the *Sunday Telegraph*, Dr Le Fanu returned to the subject in an article prompted by the final closure of the Nightingale School of Nursing. He told of recent cases indicating that Brucellosis can still be a severe illness threatening many working in what he called 'exotic places'. He continued: 'One wonders how many of those intrepid founders of the Empire must have returned to a life of chronic ill-health, whose cause was never identified and for which there was no treatment.' He emphasised that Brucellosis is one of the most incapacitating and painful maladies that can affect people, though it can now be treated by a course of Tetracycline. With a nice flourish Dr Le Fanu concluded: 'It occurs to me, having re-read Lytton Strachey's . . . portrayal . . . and knowing now the scale of the physical distress that dogged her life, that Florence Nightingale's public achievements were not merely extraordinary but superhuman.'

The drugs that she took, one of which was bromide and another laudanum, were indicative of the limited help for problems of depression and tension in her time. She was in no sense unusual in being prescribed these drugs. In taking to her bed, and withdrawing to complete rest, she was accepting the only course prescribed at that time by the doctors, which may have made the illness worse. Some have thought that, nevertheless, she used her illness to a purpose; comparative isolation suited her and gave her a particular power of manipulation.

The house bought for £7,000 in South Street, Mayfair in 1865 became her home and base for the rest of her life. Until then, since her return from the War she had lived in an hotel in London and spent much time in the family homes at Embley and at Lea Hurst in Derbyshire. The forty-five years in South Street, which runs from Farm Street into Park Lane, represent half her life. It was originally number 35 and later renumbered 10. The domestic arrangements have aroused much interest. She paid the same kind of attention to the running of the household as she did, in writing, to the training of nurses or to sending them to far foreign fields. From her room she conducted work of an order which had not been done before – for example in the collation and analysis of medical statistics – engaged in a vast correspondence, all hand-written with a steel-nibbed pen, and received an unending stream of visitors whose credentials and reasons for wanting to see her were most carefully scrutinised before admission was granted. This kind of perfectionism, which ran into every corner of life, is never comfortable for other people, but in her case, never hindered her influence or diminished the number of those who wanted to see her. She made many excursions and visits to her brother-in-law's home, Claydon House in Buckinghamshire (now owned by the National Trust), to which she took parties of nurses, and once in 1890 she travelled to Oxford to visit Jowett in Balliol. Substantially speaking, nevertheless, number 10 South Street was where her life passed.

The debate about FN's character, sparked off by Lytton Strachey, continues. The editors of her Selected Letters, presumably from considerable study and prolonged familiarity, use strong language about her: lack of generosity, vindictiveness, manipulation: 'she used her illness to force other people into action', but she was 'a brilliant reformer' with an 'indefatigable capacity to study, absorb, and relate material to a larger picture.'[28] Come wind, come weather, she was served devotedly first and briefly by Arthur Hugh Clough and then for over forty years by Henry Bonham Carter as Secretary of the Fund Council. Both were relatives, the first by marriage. Bonham Carter is surely the unsung hero. He was the Secretary of the Nightingale Fund from 1861 to 1899 and continued to sit on the Council until four years after her death. Over all these years, he received £50 a year for his work. A letter came from her almost every morning at breakfast, and her messenger awaited his response. After fourteen years of this method, he finally persuaded FN that they might work more efficiently if she would admit him to her room. It is clear that without such an uncomplaining amanuensis, a go-between, a pacifier, and a man thoroughly acquainted with the ways of committees, she would have found her work formidably more difficult. Their letters form a kind of continuous conversation, covering every aspect of her work and interests. He was indispensable.

Queen Victoria's reign lasted another thirty-five years. Her Golden Jubilee in 1887 was paralleled in FN's mind by her own Jubilee; it was fifty years since the first 'calling' under the tree at Embley. Her physical strength persisted after the onset of blindness and increasing forgetfulness, and it is likely that she was not much aware of what was happening around her from 1906 onwards. She died three months after Edward VII, on August 13th 1910. It was he who had created the Order of Merit into which she was admitted in 1907, an Order outside the traditional chivalric world and intended to bestow a special distinction on its limited number of holders. She was the first woman to receive it, though by that time it is doubtful that she realised its significance. When the Badge of the Nightingale Training School was designed in 1925, the colour blue was chosen because it was the colour of the ribbon of the Order of Merit. Her adamant insistence on a quiet funeral prevented burial in Westminster Abbey, so she lies in the family grave at East Wellow, near Romsey.

CHAPTER TWO

The Beginnings of the School

There are unexpected obscurities and difficulties in recounting the first years of the Training School. There is no lack of material, but people were not always as precise or as accurate or as truthful as a historian might wish. One may call to mind Carlyle's railing, in *Past and Present* (1843), against the medieval chronicler who wrote about what interested him rather than what we want to know. Also, it has already been pointed out that the first biographies and accounts of Florence Nightingale and descriptions of the School have come in for major revision only in recent years. In FN's lifetime and later, there was a strong temptation to idealise – and even 'canonise': Mrs Gaskell wrote, for example, that 'she stands perfectly alone, half way between God and His creatures'. There is, furthermore, always a strong human tendency to create traditions which soon become entrenched and unquestioned. Past events are seen to have a simple sense of purpose and continuity that do not bear close examination. One might recall the great Dutch historian Pieter Geyl's dictum that the study of History is one of unending argument.

On 9th November, 1855, a public meeting was held in Willis's Rooms, King's Street, St James's, chaired by the Duke of Cambridge, Queen Victoria's cousin, who had fought gallantly in the Crimean War and was to be Commander in Chief of and a great encumbrance on the British Army for thirty-nine years. In the introduction to a file in the Greater London Record Office, it is recorded that this gathering resolved to:

> inaugurate a public subscription in gratitude for FN's work in the Crimean War. £44,000 was raised, a committee was set up to administer the fund and on March 13th 1860, A.H. Clough wrote on behalf of the Nightingale Fund Council to the President, Treasurer and Governors of St Thomas's Hospital about the possibility of founding a Training School for nurses at the hospital.[1]

It is said that nearly £9,000 was raised from ordinary soldiers, whose admiration, almost adoration of FN was based on harder experience than that of many of their lukewarm officers. Roy Jenkins, in his life of Gladstone, says that he has found it useful when dealing with Victorian money to multiply by 50 to get 1996 values. By this reckoning, the Fund raised £2¼ millions, of which the soldiers contributed nearly half a million.

The original Trust Deed was made on 20th June 1857. In 1860 the Nightingale Fund Council was formed to 'effectuate the objects afore-said', which were 'for the training, sustenance and protection of nurses and hospital attendants.' Its first Chairman was Sidney Herbert, created Lord Herbert of Lea in December 1860. The Secretary was Arthur Hugh Clough, a cousin by marriage of FN. Both died within a very short time, to be replaced by Sir Harry Verney, FN's brother-in-law, as Chairman, and by Henry Bonham Carter as Secretary. Each was to serve for an astonishingly long time, Bonham Carter for fifty-three years. The Minutes of the Council are the most obvious source of information about its activities, though the daily exchange of letters and notes between FN and Bonham Carter, and to a lesser extent Verney, give a more lively and personal sense of what was going on. (A digest of Bonham Carter's own activities as Secretary is in the Notes on Sources.) For many years the Council's main task and preoccupation was to oversee the training of the young women in the School and to conduct relations with the Governors of St Thomas's Hospital. Dr Baly has called attention to the fact that a venture to train women as nurses, to be managed by a woman Matron, never had a woman member of the Council in FN's lifetime. As the years went by, the Council extended its activities, though it will be seen that its resources became stretched as more demands were made on it, so that the Governors of the Hospital became unavoidably the dominant players. By the time that the School entered the period of those Nightingales still alive today, the Fund was mainly concerned to support the further education and training of nurses already qualified. The later history of the Fund Council is described in detail in Dr Baly's doctoral thesis.[2] In 1974 it decided to spend its whole income on post-graduate training. The Fund Council Minutes recorded: 'Such a course would involve giving up the present commitment with St Thomas's Hospital. Miss Nightingale contemplated this as some day possible, nor is the Fund bound either legally or morally to the Hospital. Every hospital has to undertake its own training, and, as things are, St Thomas's does, as we have seen, undertake the major part of the training of its nurses.' (It will be seen in Chapter Four that, very surprisingly, three members of the Council in sub-committee submitted a Report in 1914 that foreshadows all this by sixty years.)

From that time on, the Fund Council has spent its income on financing nurses from any training school who meet the Council's requirements and who wish to undertake post-graduate work. It is particularly concerned to enable them to become nurse tutors and midwife tutors. Lady Bonham-Carter, in a letter of 26th February 1997, wrote to say that 'Unfortunately, the Funds are such that we can currently assist only about forty candidates each year.' In 1995 the Council stated that it was making a special effort to raise money to meet the needs of a 'window of opportunity' for State-enrolled nurses to convert to a full 1st Level Registered Nurse qualification; such courses cost £3000 for each nurse and the Council was seeking sources for further assistance.

In the same letter she was proud to record that her husband's family (Henry Bonham Carter was his grandfather) has been connected with the Fund Council continuously except for a few years after Walter Bonham Carter's death, when the Secretaryship passed to his legal partner. She indicates that the links between the Fund and the Fellowship (started in 1928) have always been slender, though the Council will always look favourably on Nightingales as candidates for financial help; Professor Macleod Clark, the present Director of the Nightingale Institute at King's College, London, is the Fund's professional adviser. Lady Bonham-Carter recalls that Henry Bonham Carter wrote that 'It should be recorded that Miss Nightingale expressed a distinct wish *not* to be tied to St Thomas's.'

The School opened in the old St Thomas's Hospital in the Borough of Southwark, two years before its demolition. The Hospital was to provide board and separate lodging for the probationers – as they were to be called – under the charge of a Sister; the Fund paid the Hospital for this expenditure. It is therefore most likely that the Probationers were lodged within the Hospital, but exactly how or where it is not possible to establish. The Sister in charge had her own bedroom and sitting room, there was a common sitting room furnished with books and pictures and supplies of fresh flowers from Embley Park. The demolition of this Hospital, which had stood on its site for 600 years, was itself the result of much heated argument. The infant School was transferred into temporary accommodation that was highly inconvenient and took time to convert. This was in the former Surrey Zoological Gardens, in Vauxhall – or Kennington, if one wishes; the gardens had put on all kinds of spectacles and shows besides the zoo. The deficiencies were enormous and are described not only in the memories of Mrs Rebecca Strong, one of the early and astonishingly long-lived and distinguished Nightingales (she died in 1941), but also in the history of the Hospital by E.M. McInnes, as well as being recapitulated by Dr Baly.

In a Report to the Fund Council Committee in midsummer 1862, it was said:

> In consequence of the removal of St Thomas's Hospital, the admission of Probationers was suspended for a time. Arrangements, however, have been made for a temporary Hospital at the Surrey Gardens, in connexion with which accommodation has been provided for a reduced number of Probationer-Nurses, viz., ten, under the same regulations as heretofore. The Committee while regretting this diminution in the number under instruction, consider it a matter of congratulation that no interruption should have been caused in the working of a scheme hitherto so successfully carried on in connexion with this Hospital . . . The new temporary Hospital was opened on the 1st October, all vacancies amongst the Probationers having been filled up.

To try to develop the Training School in this accommodation was in itself an horrendous challenge, made no easier (in spite of Sir Joshua Jebb's complacency) by the lack of clarity of purpose in these early years. It seems clear that the Fund, through Henry Bonham Carter, concerned itself with accommodation at Surrey Gardens. In May 1864, a dormitory for day nurses and probationers was to have twenty-five beds. In January 1865 a house – 22 Manor Place, Newington – was rented for a few months to accommodate additional Probationers who were being trained for Liverpool and Manchester. In October 1865, Mrs Wardroper, the Matron of St Thomas's Hospital, and Mr Whitfield, its Resident Medical Officer, were again discussing how to ease the shortage of accommodation for Probationers.

In the meantime, argument raged about where the new Hospital was to be built – there were six alternatives. So bitter were the arguments, that at one point FN considered whether it would not be more sensible to make the School independent and site it separately. In the event, a

Thames-side site in Stangate at the foot of Westminster Bridge was decided on. The victorious party wanted to keep the Hospital within sight of the City. The result was to put a vast new building within a few feet of a stinking river, and open sewer. Luckily the 'Great Stink' during the hot summer of 1858, when the foul Thames made the Houses of Parliament virtually uninhabitable, had concentrated the legislature on the need to do something. The next year was worse and the temperature reached 97°F in the shade, making it impossible to work in Whitehall.[3] But the Metropolitan Board of Works had only just got the Thames Embankment (South) Act passed, which meant the site of the new Hospital was still dramatically unhealthy. Furthermore, there were the London fogs. Coal was the universal fuel, and a city of more than two million people burnt it in every fireplace, while being lit by gas from coal-fuelled gas-works. Every winter brought the 'pea-soupers'. Reference to fog so thick that the Ward Sister could not see from one end of the ward to the other is not infrequent.

In other words, a completely unsuitable site was decided upon. One of the alternatives was Blackheath, away from the river and up on a hill. This was FN's preferred choice, with Southwark used only for Casualty and Administration, while in-patients would be moved to Blackheath by train. But, once she lost the argument and the South Bank site had been chosen, she was vastly more successful in arguing for the design of the new hospital. The pavilion plan, drawn up by Henry Currey in 1865, followed the ideas of the French hospital at Lariboisière, except that the blocks were to be in a continuous line instead of on two sides of a square. It was to take 588 beds and work began in July 1866, though the foundation stone was laid by Queen Victoria on 13th May, 1868. Three years later, the Queen again visited the Hospital on 21st June 1871, to declare it open.

Why was St Thomas's chosen to be home to the School? Mrs Wardroper had been Matron there since 1854 and had established a reputation for thoroughness and reform in management and in trying to recruit a better quality of nurse. She had made no innovation in training. One of her nurses, Mrs Roberts, had gone to Scutari and nursed FN through her critical illness. In this way FN had come to know about Mrs Wardroper and also about Mr Richard Whitfield, the Resident Medical Officer of St Thomas's Hospital. In 1857, FN was ill and the question, indeed the problem of where to site the new Training School was largely decided by other notables. The old hospital in the slums of Southwark was greatly dilapidated and as long ago as 1830 it had been proposed that it should be rebuilt. FN was persuaded by Mr Whitfield to support a rebuilding in the suburbs; as a 'quid pro quo' he undertook to persuade the Governors of St Thomas's to accept a training school of nursing in FN's name. The Governors were firmly in charge of the negotiations, and though the Fund Council was not happy, it realised that something had to be done with the money because time was passing. The complex negotiations are described in detail in Dr Baly's seminal book, *Florence Nightingale and the Nursing Legacy* (1986). She makes it clear that FN agreed to the siting at St Thomas's because she thought that she would get her way about situating the new hospital in the suburbs.[4]

After many concessions and compromises, after opposition from some members of the Fund Council, campaigns (some more open than others), difficult and protracted negotiations between the Fund Council, the Delegated Committee which was to act for it, and the Hospital Authorities, a 'humble beginning' was made. Without doubt, the Hospital management got the best of the deal, and it was to be said often in the following years that the Fund was, in effect, supplying cheap labour to the Hospital through the Probationers, who were handed over to the Sisters and doctors for their training. No new syllabus, no model was devised. The teaching was simply to be ward-based, in charge of Sisters who by definition had received no new training, and possessed no education of the kind that FN herself regarded as essential for those in command.

E.M. McInnes in her history of the hospital claimed that its most special feature was to aim to train nurses for the work of nursing generally – to be sent anywhere.[5] Dr Baly believes that Miss McInnes was wrong in maintaining that this was an idea particular to the new training school, and that it was in fact fairly common practice in other hospitals. Nightingales, when trained, were normally to be taken on to the staff of St Thomas's, but it was a condition of entry to the School that they should go wherever the Council of the Nightingale Fund directed them. Apparently Henry Bonham Carter thought privately that it would not be possible to keep them to the contract, and many did break it. The School was to be under the direction of the Matron, who was thereby in a very powerful position. In later years, FN questioned whether too much power had been given to the Matron, but this system was to last until 1970.

On the 9th July, 1860, the first group of fourteen probationers entered the School; a fifteenth arrived on July 12th. It is not clear whether a new sixteenth entrant arrived on the 30th, or whether this person, Harriet Parker, was merely a replacement for one of the fifteen who had not arrived. Although another probationer, M.A. Tennant, may have been dismissed by 30th July 1860, it may also have been the intention to admit sixteen from the very first. A good deal depends on how diligent Mrs Wardroper was in her record-keeping. The admissions are listed aphabetically and not chronologically, but some puzzles remain. Certainly two more probationers were dismissed in September. Jane Elizabeth Couchman and Fanny Wilde were appointed as Extra Nurses, but according to the Probationers' Record Book, they were considered probationers.[6]

Dr Baly copied the entries from the Red Register for the first ten years in her book *The History of Nursing – The State of the Art*.[7] In the nine-year period when the School was in Surrey Gardens, that is, two years after it opened, 188 were admitted, sixty-two of whom did not complete the training. Of those first entrants, the following did complete the course: Mary Barker, Jane Elizabeth Couchman, Annie Lees, Charlotte Nixon, Harriet Parker, Georgina Pike, Fanny Wilde, Emily Medhurst, Mary Ann Philips, Caroline Stone, Emma Whitlock. Admitted for one year, any of them was allowed officially to leave early if they gave three months' notice. The Minutes of the Council of the Nightingale Fund, usually issued in the December of the year, always list the number of entrants – and failures – registered, but matters were complicated by admissions during a year on a separate register; and probationers were qualifying at different times. There is reference in a number of accounts to Mrs Wardroper's inadequacies in record-keeping. By 1862, the Minutes recorded the positions to which the first probationers went. (By 1861, there was 'surplus money' in the Fund that was diverted into the new scheme for Midwifery Training, which was expensive and soon brought problems.)

Originally, the School possessed considerable independence because, although the Fund Council could withdaw any or all of its nurses from the hospital, little had been drawn from the Fund. This right of withdrawal was never exercised at St Thomas's but it was applied on occasion to Nightingales serving in other hospitals; for example, in the midwifery crisis at King's College Hospital in December 1867. Only the mounting costs of financing the training of its nurses

57

made the Council more dependent on St Thomas's. The original entrants, recruited after great publicity largely conducted by the members of the Fund Council, came in on a paid basis which included board and lodging, small comforts like tea and sugar, washing and free uniform and £10 for the one-year's training. The Council then set wages for the trained Nurses and Sisters – £20 a year with board and lodging for Nurses, £50 for Sisters (or £60 without board and lodging). The Council insisted on the maintenance of these rates when Nightingales took up posts elsewhere. The publicity stressed that this was a life suitable to socially superior young women, though it was respectable women from the lower classes whom FN initially wished to train. Such did not come forward in any great number, unsurprisingly when it is remembered that the places were advertised in *The Times*, not the normal reading of such people. Mr Bracebridge commented that the contract on offer was for the 'servant class, of a kind that FN had with her parlour maid'.[8]

There was, however, an increasing interest from women of private means, who came to be referred to as 'Ladies', as a result of which five – to be known as 'Specials' – were admitted in 1867, and so a dual system was instituted. This had been heralded by Sir Joshua Jebb, a member of the Fund Council (and Surveyor-General of Prisons: he was the architect of the model Pentonville Prison), in his Report to the Council for November 1862.

> Ladies . . . are not excluded; on the contrary where sufficient evidence is shown that they they intend to pursue the calling as a business, and have those qualifications which will fit them to become superintendents, their admission would be considered an advantage and they would readily find employment.

The School was thus caught from an early point in Victorian social distinctions. The socially superior would expect a superior nursing position, namely superintendence, which in itself would require more challenging training. This dilemma was one that the Fund never resolved, and was handed on to 20th-century nursing. The desire was to recruit candidates between 25 and 35. In 1865, FN resisted, fiercely, the proposal to admit much younger girls – and was scathing about admitting older women: 'Do you not find it difficult to teach a woman of near 40 anything like Nursing, if she has not begun before?' she wrote in a letter to the Lady Superintendent of St John's House. Not until 1939 was a woman under 20 admitted.

The ordinary probationers were paid for, while most of the Specials paid for their training. However, there were problems from an early point with both the paid and the paying probationers. Although FN sought to bring in young women from the lower orders and to offer them a profession and a calling, their educational inadequacies often meant that the teaching they received – and in those days they received little – was above their heads. This was a problem not tackled until there was a 'Home Sister'. One of her duties was to 'translate' the lectures into words they could understand. The paying probationers posed rather different problems which FN herself began to take seriously in February 1873. She had come to realise that not only was their tuition scanty, but their upbringing and, apparently, their lack of stamina made them unfit for the rigours of working on the wards. In a letter to Henry Bonham Carter on 1st February 1873, she urges that though they should work exactly as the others at first, after six months they should be relieved of 'all housemaid's work'.

I w'd not relieve them of emptying slops and the like for this is strictly nurse's work. But of the rest I would. The more so because the less physically able who are by no means the less fit for Sisters are actually tired before 9 in the morning – and worn out before their year's training. That the Lady Probationers must be relieved from the first of the afternoons from 2–6 pm I am fully persuaded. And this in spite of the jealousy of the other Probationers.

1. to be exempted from housemaid's work,
2. to be free from 2–6 pm, sh'd be immediately granted . . .

And for those who are to become Sisters (Training) at St Thomas' it is of imperative necessity in order to prepare themselves for it. We intend the Lady Probationers for a different course – we hold out for them a different future – from the others.

And yet we give them no means by wh: to prepare themselves for it.

To read *in* the Ward is physically impossible – even in afternoon. They have, of course, to jump at the least want of the Patients. Else they are unfit to be Nurses. N.B. The Staff Nurses and the Nurse Probationers are so afraid of the Lady Prob'rs not taking their share of the work – the Sisters are so over-tasked & thereby compelled to over-task the ever-willing Lady Prob'rs that these actually get *more* of their share of the work – and of the most menial work.[9]

The fear was that the Ladies would not complete the training, but in her arguing of their case, the long hours and tiring demands made on all the probationers do become emphasised. The reminiscences of early Nightingales as they looked back in 1929 to their first years as nurses on the wards, reinforce the picture of extraordinarily arduous working lives, up to and including those of the Sisters. The length of the main corridor, the steps between floors in each Pavilion, as well as the hours on duty in the ward, must have led to great fatigue.

Training was, to use a later phrase, 'hands on', and it was believed only the lessons learnt from experience would clarify and extend the probationers' knowledge and skills. It is important to reiterate that the School did not open with a written, practical syllabus for training; but by 1880, the course was set out in great detail in the Minutes of the Fund Council's Annual General Meeting of that year. FN, in her first edition of *Notes on Nursing* in 1860, had laid down her ideal, her 'philosophy', but theory and practice, once again, were two very different things. During these early years her mind was preoccupied with many other matters that were more pressing for her than the curriculum in the School. E.M. McInnes observes that 'The move [to Surrey Gardens] may even have been beneficial, enabling the School to pass through the experimental stages while the hospital was very restricted in the number of its patients, so that when at last the buildings in Lambeth were ready, there was an organised body of nurses ready to take over.'[10] This is putting it optimistically.

All entrants had to be able to read and write, and because directions on medicine bottles were given in Latin, they had to learn at least the necessary Latin abbreviations. The progress of these first probationers was monitored, but not always very efficiently. If approved at the year end, they became the first entrants on a Register of Certified Nurses and the Fund Council took responsibility for posting them – in groups, as we know, and not singly. It soon found itself inundated with requests for its nurses, and began to lay down conditions for posting them. It became, in due course and not intentionally, an important regulatory body.

Applications to enter the School began to come from outside, from established Matrons in already established hospitals, as for example

Winchester, not far from the family home in Embley Park. This is worth a digression. FN had been much involved in 1863–1864 in the decision to leave the old hospital in the centre of that city and in the detailed design of the new one, executed by William Butterfield. Her preoccupation, well-nigh obsession, with space and light has caused problems in hospitals built to her requirements. The ceilings of the Butterfield building in Winchester have had to be lowered twice to conserve heat. Her father was, reluctantly, present at some of the planning meetings, although the driving force was Sir William Heathcote of Hursley Park. When the new hospital in Winchester was being built in 1867 the Governors sent its first Matron, Mrs Freeman, to the Nightingale School at Surrey Gardens, and all her nurses subsequently underwent the same training. Mrs Carpenter Turner, the historian of the Winchester hospital (granted the title of Royal from its opening day in 1868), points out that its fame derived from the fact that over many years all its nurses were Nightingales who believed (as many still do) that they had received the best possible training.[11]

One of the Nightingales who went back to Winchester as pioneers with Mrs Freeman was Rebecca Strong, whose name runs through the history of Nightingales. She entered the School in 1867, and has recorded, memorably, what conditions were like at that time. From Winchester, where she was sent with five others, she soon moved to Netley. In 1874, she was appointed Matron of the Royal Infirmary at Dundee, where, in partnership with a sympathetic superintendent, she began to introduce Nightingale principles. Five years later, she went to Glasgow Royal Infirmary, where her determination to bring in change led to trouble with the managers and her resignation. Intent on putting her ideas into practice, she opened a small private nursing home in Glasgow in 1885, and so impressed Sir William McEwan, 'the greatest surgical genius of his generation', that he advocated in many public lectures the establishment of a Preliminary Training School and the recognition of nursing as a distinct profession.[12] Mrs Strong was reappointed Matron of Glasgow Infirmary in 1891, where 'she inaugurated a scheme of education in nursing which has been the foundation of all such schemes ever since.' A tribute to her in the Fellowship *Journal* in 1939, indicates the nature of the training in detail, with many quotations that could have come straight from FN. For example: 'If I find a nurse untidy in her person and keeping an untidy room I lose confidence in her as a nurse.' She retired from Glasgow in 1927 and continued most actively for many years, being appointed OBE in 1939. She lived to be 101.

FN had both a straightforward, achievable notion of training, which is the one most often referred to, and a more profound one that stemmed directly from her religious thinking. This latter was never achieved in everyday practice, but as long as she was able, she kept her ideals in front of her Nightingales by her messages and letters to them. The straightforward side is summed up: 'Training is to teach not only what is to be done, but how to do it. The physician or surgeon orders what is to be done. Training has to teach the nurse how to do it to his order; and to teach, not only how to do it but *why* such and such a thing is done.' The more profound side is summoned up by the quotation below.

To obey *is* to understand orders, and to understand orders really is to obey. A nurse does not know how to do what she is told without such 'training' as enables her to understand what she is told; or without such moral and disciplinary 'training' as enables her to give her whole self to obey.

Training is to teach the nurse how God makes health, and how He makes disease. Training is to teach the nurse to know her business, that is, to observe exactly in such stupendous issues as life and death, health and disease . . . True loyalty to orders cannot be without the independent sense or energy of responsibility, which alone secures real trustworthiness.

These quotations are to be found in Rob van der Peet's *The Nightingale Model of Nursing*.[13] He maintains that 'the former concept of training is related to a concept of nursing being ancillary to medicine, the latter concept corresponds to FN's concept of sanitary nursing and . . . to the service to God through the service to mankind.' One can readily see that the first concept was easier to put into action, though the charge hangs over Mrs Wardroper that she 'simplified' it to the point that Probationers often saw themselves as cheap labour. The second would be difficult to realise in any system of training nurses, because it is a theological concept; FN hoped that her nurses would be a step further on the way to becoming 'perfect as our Father in Heaven is perfect.' R Nash, in *Florence Nightingale to her Nurses*, states that she had in mind 'the conception . . . of a moral government of the world in which science, activity, and religion were one.'[14] In conversation, Dr Baly emphasised that it was impossible truly to understand FN's views on nursing without a diligent study of her *Suggestions For Thought* (1859), privately printed in three volumes and directed, interestingly, to the Artisans of England. She overestimated the reading capacity of the artisans at that time – such schooling as some of them had came from crowded elementary schools run by the three main religious communions, Non-Conformist, Anglican and Catholic. Only with the passing of the Education Act of 1870 was the whole child population required to go to school at the age of 5, though how long they stayed there was a different matter. The *Suggestions* rest on the proposition that God helps those who help themselves. Do not pray to God for protection against cholera. Go out, improve the water supply and clean the drains. The steady advance of Science would bring Utopia, though FN did not follow this tenet logically and unequivocally.

To return to FN's straightforward notions of nursing: the requirements for Nightingales drawn up by her are widely known, but they merit repetition. They came entirely and precisely from her own experience.

You are required to be:

SOBER
HONEST
TRUTHFUL
TRUSTWORTHY
PUNCTUAL
QUIET AND ORDERLY
CLEANLY AND NEAT

You are expected to become skilful:

1. In the dressing of blisters, burns, sores, wounds, and in applying fermentations, poultices and minor dressings.

2. In the application of leeches, externally and internally.

3. In the administration of enemas for men and women.

4. In the management of trusses, and appliances in uterine complaints.

5. In the best method of friction to the body and extremities.

6. In the management of helpless patients, i.e., moving, chang-

ing, personal cleanliness, feeding, cleaning, keeping warm or cool, preventing and dressing bed sores, managing position of.

7. In bandaging, making bandages, and rollers, lining of splints etc.

8. In making the beds of the patients, and removal of sheets whilst patient is in bed.

9. You are required to attend at operations.

10. To be competent to cook gruel, arrowroot, egg flip, puddings, drinks, for the sick.

11. To understand ventilation, keeping the ward fresh by night as well as by day; you are to be careful that great cleanliness is observed in all the utensils; those used for the secretions as well as those required for cooking.

12. To make strict observation of the sick in the following particulars: The state of secretions, expectoration, pulse, skin, appetite; intelligence, as delirium or stupor; breathing, sleep, state of wounds, eruptions, formation of matter, effect of diet or of stimulants, and of medicines.

13. And to learn the management of convalescents.

The number of probationers fluctuated during the remaining years at Surrey Gardens. Exacting criteria both for entry and during training were laid down, but the evidence is – for example that of the much-quoted Mrs Strong – that conditions were cramped, primitive and highly inconvenient. These were not resolvable until the move to the new hospital which was designed to accommodate forty probationers. In 1865, Henry Bonham Carter attempted to analyse the position: 'there were great difficulties because probationers were selected to fill vacancies some of whom are considered to have completed their training though they have not.' It is suggested that Mrs Wardroper, faced with drop-out, filled vacancies as they occurred, which must have made the administration of the course very difficult. There is a much-voiced criticism, referred to above, that the probationers of this time could be seen as unpaid labour, presenting a further reason for keeping numbers up. These were the years when FN's attention was largely elsewhere and it was only at the end of the decade that she came to realise that all was not well. What emerges as perhaps more disturbing than the quality of selection, or the length of persistence and, therefore, of drop-out, is the fact that so many of them were ill, often very seriously, during their time there. Without any doubt, the unhealthiness of the site and deficiencies of the building must have played their part. Mrs Wardroper and Mr Whitfield were themselves ill during these years.

The overall picture of the Surrey Garden years is not happy. Dr Baly has the uncomfortable statistics, and based on them she is entitled to observe that the Nightingale School achieved very little in its first ten years. Against this, a wide knowledge of how famous institutions have begun, shews that their early years are generally tentative, with mistakes and fluctuations. We are concerned with the story of this School over 136 years. Dr Baly shews that a) out of 126 'survivors' from this period, 12 were dismissed from their first post – 2 for insobriety; b) a further 24 resigned and 'left the service'; c) after 10 years of the scheme, there were probably not more than 50 Nightingales in active hospital work.[15] Dr Baly's conclusion that the early years of the School were 'a missed opportunity' has to be accepted.

She gives the first timetable for the probationers under the Nightingale Fund: the day began at 6am with breakfast at 6.30, then onto the wards at 7am. There they stayed until dinner at 1pm, returning at 2pm. From 3.30 to 5pm they were to take exercise, returning for tea and then onto the wards at 6pm. They were to be in their dormitory by 8.30, though supper was at 9pm. Bed was at 10pm. Those on night duty rose at 9pm, tea at 9.30, then onto the wards at 10pm. They returned to their dormitory at 6am, had breakfast at 6.30, then back to the wards at 7am. They were to be back in their dormitory at 10am, with exercise from 11am to 1pm. Dinner was at 1pm and bed at 2pm. During the week prayers were to be read in the wards at 8am and in the dormitory at 9.45pm. They were expected to attend the Parish Church at 11am on Sunday.[16] This is a regime, like so much else in FN's thinking, that came out of army practice. It is often put that Nightingales are no longer aware of their early history and the demands that were made on those young women, and perhaps it is salutary that they should be.

What is usually seen as a cut-and-dried system was set up as a 'humble experiment' in 1860 to meet the needs of the time. In time it was adjusted to deal with the intrigues of the 1870s and the ambitions of the ladies in the 1880s. But because it was associated with the name of FN, this experiment, with its rules, came to be regarded as Tablets handed down from Sinai.

Writing clairvoyantly in the Fellowship *Journal* in 1983 and not knowing then what is known now about the organisation and purposes of the new Nightingale Institute, Dr Baly said,

... the inheritors of this scheme have torn themselves apart as to whether nursing is a profession, a calling or a 'manual craft'; whether there should be more than one standard of entry and whether all should be trained in the same mould and whether this training should be given on the job, in the classroom or in an institution of higher education.[17]

Against her bleak view of the early days, Dr Baly does concede that 'For better or worse the Fund succeeded in carving out an empire for nursing, the matron was supreme in nursing matters and nurses became accountable to nurses . . . it also gave a career structure.'[18]

FN had two foundation principles: 'That Nurses should have their technical training in hospitals specially organised for the purpose. That they should live in special homes that were fit to form their moral life and discipline.' Later generations of Nightingales have seen themselves as a group apart, and no doubt have felt that this status goes back to the beginnings, but in fact FN herself was at best chary of anything like a special pride: 'I see you say that the nursing at St Thomas's is as good as and probably supercedes that of other hospitals. I don't think you should invite comparisons.' On another occasion in 1895 she wrote: 'This is grievous – the public will take them for the crème de la crème – and they are not even skim milk.' Two years later, she wrote: 'The probationers are loud and nasty.'[19]

The doctors certainly were resentful because they feared encroachment into their male preserve. John Fleet South, the Senior Consulting Surgeon at St Thomas's and, what is more, the President of the Royal College of Surgeons, wrote to the Hospital Treasurer that: 'the intention . . . however carefully concealed, is to change entirely the whole nursing establishment of the house and to place it in the hands of persons who will never be content until *they* become the executive of the hospital.'

In 1857, he published a short book, *Facts Relating to Hospital Nurses*, to defend the existing system. In much quoted words, he wrote that: 'as regards the nurses or ward maids, these are in much the same position as housemaids, and require little teaching beyond that of poultice making . . . the enforcement of cleanliness and attention to the patients' wants.'[20]

The idea of a residential Home pre-dated the first women's colleges attached to Cambridge and Oxford (Girton 1869, Newnham 1871,

Lady Margaret Hall 1878, Somerville 1879). It emphasised the sense of separateness, not least when one looks at what FN and Mrs Wardroper aimed to do – to provide single cubicles, pleasant furniture, a place for rest and recuperation (Mrs Wardroper thought that to provide so many flowers sent by FN was risking over-indulgence), good food and regularised clothing. The brown uniform with white apron and cap may have been the beginning of standardised Nurses' uniform. As the years went by and the gradations of promotion were established, these were symbolised by differences in uniform. Over the decades, these became formalised and stylised in great detail. For those who wore them, it was a comprehensible world; for those outside, it could be perplexing, not least because many changes were made over time: student nurse, staff nurse, charge nurse, sister, senior sister, matron – all with great changes in terminology in recent years. It is amusing to find an article on 'Nursing Uniforms, Medals etc.' in *The Queen, The Lady's Newspaper* for the 1st February 1890:

> It is not because it is least that this hospital is left unillustrated, but because it is so terribly behind-hand in the matter of uniforms. The very earliest training school is cursed by too great conservatism, and thus its probationers have to work in a clumsy and unbecoming uniform consisting of rough grey linsey dresses, new caps, and brown holland aprons . . . until St Thomas's Committee have the sense to alter this ugly inappropriate dress they must in this matter, take a back place. The staff nurses wear a sensible enough blue and white washing gown and the sisters wear dark blue serge and caps tying under the chin.

The requirement of the unmarried life, a pattern followed by other schools of nursing, must have been a trial for many, but it was maintained until 1962, when the first Nightingale in training was permitted to get married.

There was a clear intention that the School and the Nightingales should be non-sectarian in the sense of a refusal to be tied to one form of the Christian religion. Compulsory attendance at the Parish Church was more a matter of disciplinary form than an act of worship. One must remember the strength of feeling, the fervour that led to so much public disagreement and the parting of friends. Matters concerning religion provoked more intensity of discussion and disagreement in mid-Victorian England amongst the educated classes than at any other time since the Reformation, with the possible exception of the Civil War period. It is difficult to recapture how informed English public opinion looked on with bated breath in 1845 as Newman made his painful journey from the Church of England to the Catholic Church – and only six years later, Henry Edward Manning, a rising star who might well have been Archbishop of Canterbury, followed him. As has been noted, Miss Nightingale knew Manning and had had many conversations with him, deciding, after all, not to 'submit'. When she began to run the Home for Distressed Gentlewomen, FN had resisted the idea that it should be solely a Church of England establishment. The particular difficulty for Catholics as nurses in training was that, until the Second Vatican Council in 1963, they were forbidden to take part in undenominational services or prayers; this gave them an air of separateness that FN and senior nurses did not want. Knowing the Catholic Church as she did, she had a further fear of proselytising. Mrs Wardroper's first successor as Matron, Miss Pringle, resigned in 1889, after less than two years in office, on becoming a Catholic. Even in 1957, when one eminent Nightingale came for her first interview, she was told by a Sister: 'You know that you will never be able to hold a position of responsibility or become a Ward Sister because you are a Catholic.' In fact, the first Catholic Ward Sister was Rosemary Starkey who began to train in 1946, but was allowed to work at first only out at the rural outpost at Hydestyle for some years before moving to St Thomas's itself.

The discussion about 'the Catholic matter' sways backwards and forwards – was her conversion to Rome really the only reason for Miss Pringle's departure? But it is possible to detect an anti-Catholic sentiment, which is difficult to explain, running through the history of the School until recent times. Miss Nuttall, in conversation, recalled a Miss Collins, who was advised by her priest not even to bother to apply and who went to the London Hospital instead. She also referred to two nurses of her acquaintanceship, exact contemporaries, one of whom on promotion to Sister, wore the full uniform, while the other – a Catholic – on promotion was differently dressed. Other Nightingales have offered further examples of this bias. It is to be noted from the Fellowship *Journal* that all services in the Chapel were taken by high dignitaries in the Church of England. In this century it became a very Anglican establishment, FN or no FN, far removed from her sentiments. These were displayed vividly in the case of Miss Jones, who had been Superintendent of St John's House, and six of whose nurses were sent to Scutari. In 1856 she became responsible for the nursing service at King's College Hospital, but she provoked FN to total exasperation with any idea that nurses should be connected to religious foundations: 'I look upon this crisis as one of deeper importance than you or even Miss Jones do. I look upon it *that Sisterhoods are from henceforth impossible*', she wrote to her friend, Dr Bowman.

The sense that Nightingales were special became pervasive. As recently as the 12th May 1996, a Nightingale was heard to say: 'After all, we *were* the best, weren't we?' Only in the late 1950s were nurses who had not been Nightingale-trained appointed to be Ward Sisters in St Thomas's, but, pointedly, not allowed to wear the normal Sister's cap. Miss Gullan, it will be shewn, was admitted to the privilege of wearing the Badge in 1935 – it does rather resemble the conferring of an Honorary Degree. The first man to be trained and to be eligible for membership of the Nightingale Fellowship was Leslie Graham, in 1974.

Mrs Wardroper was undoubtedly stern, and strict discipline was the rule for many decades. In a private note to FN about one probationer, she wrote: 'Although I have not the smallest reason to doubt the correctness of her moral character, her manner, none the less, is objectionable and she uses her eyes unpleasantly.'[21] This sounds like what the Army calls 'dumb insolence'. She had been Matron of St Thomas's since 1854, and was to be Superintendent of the School for twenty-seven years, until 1887. Of her successors, only Dame Alicia Lloyd Still came near her tenure – twenty-five years, 1913–1937. Mrs Wardroper was formidable; no doubt she needed to be in her circumstances. When she died in 1892, FN wrote the most important of the obituaries:

> No Mrs Gamp could live in her neighbourhood. Mrs Gamp is extinct for ever . . . At the time of the retirement upwards of 500 nurses had completed the course in the School and entered into service on the Staff of St Thomas's and other Hospitals, and of these over 50 educated gentlewomen were occupying important posts as Matrons or Superintendents of Nurses in Hospitals, Infirmaries or Nursing Institutions – and not only the United Kingdom but also abroad.[22]

Privately, FN's view was not always so complimentary; she had little opinion of Mrs Wardroper's judgement of character. In a letter to Henry Bonham Carter on the 15th October 1872, she wrote: 'she is a real Hospital genius – manages St T's better than anyone or than I could ever have done it, hardly ever makes a mistake. But she does not know and never will know one woman from another.'[23] Mrs Wardroper was also accused by FN of being inconceivably indiscreet, prevaricating, insincere and secretive. She chose to ignore Mr Whitfield's drunken habits and what would be called these days his sexual harassment of the nurses.

The three Matrons who followed Mrs Wardroper had trained under her and, therefore, continued her patterns. Consolidation came after the pioneering years, but as the century went by, the School, far from pioneering, fell behind other training schools in significant ways.

FN's own influence on the School fluctuated, not least because of her many other commitments. The evidence from her published letters is that she was well-informed about all the gossip, had no hesitation in interfering if the circumstances justified it, and exercised considerable control from a distance. Her method was epistolary management, a mixture of the soundest advice and shrewdest diagnosis with homilies of a quasi-mystical kind, and not a little malicious meddling. The death of her father, in January 1874, brought her some very demanding family responsibilities. Even so, it is said that she required to approve the appointment of each Ward Sister, and received them in South Street. Dame Alicia Lloyd Still, when plain Miss Lloyd Still, received her 'Charge' as Sister 'direct from Florence Nightingale in her home in South Sreet, together with a medical text book and a posy of flowers. There is a tradition that she was the last Sister to be so honoured.'[24]

The daily routine of Probationers in those early years is well-documented: working under supervision in the wards, attending lectures from doctors and receiving instruction from the Sisters – who were not themselves, in the first years, trained Nightingales. Instruction took place in extraordinary circumstances in the Surrey Zoological Gardens years. So stretched were the conditions that the kitchen was used as an operating theatre. F.G. Parsons (the first historian of the Hospital since 1819) reported that the former Giraffe House was used as the cholera ward while the Elephant House became the dissecting room.[25] At the completion of a satisfactory year, whatever that might have meant, they were under contract to the Fund and required to go in groups wherever directed. A detailed report on every probationer's progress was attempted – and later kept – with the whole course summed up in a few sentences. In the top right-hand corner of each Nurse's Record Sheet there was a special section with the heading 'Moral Character During Probation – First dereliction causes dismissal'. The three sub-headings were Sobriety, Honesty and Truthfulness.

Not all FN's original principles were achieved, then or later, but one that was of first importance to her, the position of the Lady Superintendent, was firmly linked 'ex officio' to the post of the Matron of the Hospital 'who is herself the best nurse in the hospital, the example and leader in all that she wishes her nurses to be, in all that training is to make her nurses.' This arrangement endured until the office of Matron itself ended in 1970. But, in the Autumn of 1881, an article highly critical of the Fund and its administration appeared in *The Queen* magazine. A particular point was made of the despotic power of the Matron. By then, FN herself was questioning this. 'My views are exceedingly altered as to the supremacy of the Matron. It did very well for me whose fault is subserviency and civility. It does ill for Matrons whose fault is the love of power and a lawlessness towards medical and other authorities.' One may stand back somewhat amazed at the second sentence. In 1894 she wrote, 'I am not so sure that the nursing ought to be so entirely in the Matron's hands now. We have no dominance over her now. We have recommended people lately who ought not to be within a mile of the hospital.'[26]

In the Surrey Gardens period, requests for nurses to be sent out to posts of responsibility were met wherever possible, like William Rathbone's request for help in Liverpool. The most dramatic of these was the Colonial Secretary's urgent desire that some Nightingales should be sent to Sydney Hospital in New South Wales. FN felt that this should be done, even though the nurses could be ill-afforded, because Australians had contributed so generously to the Fund. So Miss Lucy Osburn, aged 29, went in December 1867 with five nurses to take up a three-year contract, only to find a situation most unacceptable to their training and thinking, according to an article in the *Nursing Times* in 1960.

Miss Osburn had not been trained to sit passively and accept such conditions. She was sharp of tongue and as efficient and tireless as Miss Nightingale herself, by whom she was backed to the last barricade. Miss Nightingale wrote an 18 page letter to the Chairman of a Royal Commission to investigate conditions of Sydney Hospital; it was not long before Miss Osburn was given complete control of the administration of the hospital, including cooks and cleaners, and was freed from interference in her control of the nursing. This step, together with the placing of the finances and administration of the hospital on a firm basis and the founding of the Faculty of Medicine at Sydney University, brought Australia to the forefront of the medical advances of the time.[27]

Writing privately in 1997 Dr Baly indicates that there has been a good deal of research about this episode in Australia, and in fact the Osburn enterprise was regarded as a failure by FN, who dismissed all the nurses except one. Miss Osburn's masterful and difficult manner was linked to her 'High Church leanings', and this did not help either with the Australians or with FN.

FN was a 'child of her time' – as most people are. She had a strong sense of the superiority of the English which she shared with almost the entire population. There was an English duty to send nurse-missionaries to other parts of the world, but she had no idea of admitting non-Europeans to be trained in the School. Mary Seacole, a black Jamaican nurse, was excluded; so were two Japanese nurses in the 1880s, despite the firm support of the British Ambassador to Japan. At the end of the century Caribbeans asking to be trained in the School were told that it would be better for British nurses to go from the School to the Caribbean to train nurses there. Prejudice against Catholics (which, it must be said, was so often on the grounds that they were 'foreign' – for example, Irish) was not the only one.

Although this mission to Australia was unique during the Surrey Gardens years, the School, barely established, already faced such demands that it was stretched to its limits. And it had other problems too. In 1860, the Fund Council had delegated power to a sub-committee in the matter of admissions. This was perhaps not vigilant enough in checking the qualification and suitability of applicants, the first of whom do not seem to have been from the higher respectable classes – so provision was made for remedial education. The probationers were allocated to Ward Sisters whose supervisory practice varied; checking against FN's famous list of requirements was unsystematic. Mrs Wardroper was a formidable woman, but she was not a nurse and never claimed to be one. The personal habits of the probationers were variable and the lack of continuous pastoral care was an element in the number of defections, dismissals and uncompleted courses. There was much that needed attention, but there was much on which to build.

In February 1997, talking about training, Sue Norman, Chief Executive and Registrar of the United Kingdom Central Council for Nursing and Midwifery, used the word 'apprentice'. This made the very apposite point that the first teaching methods in the School, and elsewhere, were analagous to the apprenticeship system in the crafts and industry (except that there was no indenture). This fixed the status of the nurse at a low social point and certainly did not mark her as a professional. Like all apprentices she was cheap labour, provided with clothing, food and lodgings and paid a pittance. On qualification she became, so to speak, a 'journeyman'; and only the Ward Sisters and the Matron (whose salaries were paid by the Fund Council for some considerable time), could be seen as ranking with the 'Masters'. The doctors did not willingly accept any of them, except the Matron, as having comparable rank, though it is clear that even she always had to fight for her place. This book records the long march from apprenticeship to professionalism and the desire for full partnership in the medical world.

CHAPTER THREE

The School in the new St Thomas's

In 1871, the new St Thomas's Hospital was opened by Queen Victoria on its present site, built to the 'pavilion plan' of self-contained blocks, as desired by FN. Writing in 1929 about the new hospital in volume one of the Fellowship *Journal*, Miss G.H. Makins said 'the general appearance of the furniture would now suggest a poor law infirmary of old days rather than an up-to-date hospital' – over-expenditure had left the Governors too poor to do the job properly. 'The walls were still covered by the original unpainted pink cement . . . Many of the bedsteads were the old ones from London Bridge [Southwark] . . . An unpainted deal combined locker and seat stood by each bed, and two white deal tables at the centre completed the ward furniture.' She went on to describe the two large cupboards on either side of the entrance door, one containing 'Sister's sacred store . . . the best linen bandages etc. ', the other for the wines and spirits, 'of which a generous quantity was then kept'. There were two anterooms. One was the Sister's bed-sitting room, in which she lived, with one day off duty in every ten. The other was the kitchen; that on the first floor in each block was used as the dining-room for all the Sisters and nurses of that block. The staff nurses' bedrooms were in the attic floor.

Forty probationers could be accommodated in Block Two, which included the Matron's residence. In the basement were the cellars for coal, beer and wine, the kitchens and the larder. Matron's dining-room, the probationers' dining-room and day room and one of their dormitories were on the ground floor; the rest of their dormitories occupied (along with Matron's other rooms) the first and second floors and the attics. The Fund Council insisted on calling this accommodation the Nurses' Home, and it largely fulfilled FN's desire to have the probationers accommodated as nearly as possible in a unitary setting. As soon as the year's training was over, they became nurses and had to be provided for by the Hospital, and therefore lived in the different blocks. It was always maintained that the heart of the training was on the wards, but as FN wrote:

Ward training is but half training. The other half consists in women being trained in habits of order, cleanliness, regularity and moral discipline ... The whole establishment must be so constructed that the probationers' dining rooms and day rooms, dormitories and the Matron's residence and office must be put together and the probationers under the Matron's immediate hourly direct inspection and control.[1]

The much larger hospital, with its provision for forty probationers, greatly increased Mrs Wardroper's responsibilities, and the burden of work could not be managed simply with help from her son and from an interestingly named Sister Extra, that is a Sister without portfolio. Some people realised that all was not well and alerted FN and Henry Bonham Carter, but it was difficult to know how to tackle the problem, not the least part of which was the character of Mrs Wardroper herself. She had been Matron for a very long time – since 1854 – and did not take kindly to the idea of a deputy. But it was decided in March 1872 to bring Miss Torrance, who had been one of the first Lady Probationers, back from her post in Highgate to take up this role. The decision was softened by a description of duties, drawn up by Bonham Carter for FN, that was reluctantly accepted by Mrs Wardroper. Miss Torrance's duties were:

To take charge under the Matron of the Probationers' Home, of its servants, housekeeping, accounts etc.

To take general charge under the Matron of the Probationers: to see to their preparing notes of lectures, case books, diaries etc. and to verify and correct these previously submitting them to the Matron.

To give such classes whether religious or of general improvement as shall be from time to time arranged.

To read prayers when read in the Home.

To preside at meals, see to carrying out of rules, hours etc.

To undertake all such correspondence concerning the Probationers as the Matron may desire.

To give such superintendence in the wards or in such wards, as the Matron may from time to time appoint.

(The matter of diaries provides a very good illustration of FN's detailed knowledge of what went on during training. In a letter dated August

1881, to Miss Crossland who was then Home Sister, a title explained below, she shews with what thoroughness she had called in and read the diaries. She collates her criticisms, all of which are examples of failures, not only to do things but to give the reasons for which they should have been done – ranging from cleaning the lavatory to taking temperatures, to making beds, to bathing patients in bed. 'Another remark I would make almost universally. No one gives you the *progress* of the *cases*. One cannot make out from anyone's Diary whether the case is going well or ill. Surely for one interested in her cases, this is of the first interest.')[2]

Sisters were known by the name of their wards. Miss Torrance was not in charge of any ward, so she soon became known as Home Sister, that being the base from which she worked. FN did not have a high opinion of the title which, in her view, did not at all indicate what the duties should be, but she did have a high regard for Miss Torrance: 'Altogether I had rather have her opinion upon our women than that of any woman now living.' In a letter to Henry Bonham Carter on 24th June 1871 – before these events had taken place – FN recorded what amounted to a long conversation with Miss Torrance in which the two of them surveyed well nigh the whole nursing scene, not sparing personalities. Miss Torrance had a low opinion of the Sisters, 'always excepting "Sister Accident" (Miss Pringle).' In particular she saw no use for Sister Extra.

The appointment of Miss Torrance on limited terms side-stepped the issues of poor standards of teaching and professional supervision. Mrs Wardroper's preoccupation was with her ultimate authority, which would be signified by who controlled the wards. The title Home Sister carried far more of a pastoral connotation; pastoral it was, but the real intention was to try to create a Director of Studies. Fudging the problem, however, was not helped by the fact that Miss Torrance stayed only for a short time – much to FN's disgust, she left to get married. That four Home Sisters succeeded each other in three years illustrates the tensions, resolved only by the appointment of Miss Crossland in 1875. She was a close friend and disciple of FN and saw it as her Christian duty to persevere in the office. She visited FN frequently and kept her well informed about events in the School. FN took and kept notes of every visit. The problem of providing systematic teaching and supervision was finally solved only in 1914 by the appointment of Miss Gullan as Sister Tutor.

In Volume 4 of the Fellowship *Journal*, 1948, W.A.C. Egan wrote most interestingly about her training as a probationer in 1888/89, when Miss Pringle was Matron and Miss Crossland was still Home Sister. There were thirty-six probationers in a nursing staff of 120. Twelve were 'specials' who were trained for administrative posts; the other twenty-four were 'nurses', paid £10 for their year with a gratuity of £2 at the end of it. The ward duties were the same for all. There is a detailed description of the uniforms worn:

> Probationers: lilac and white striped dresses on weekdays, grey beige (a material, not a colour) on Sundays. Brown holland aprons, with bibs and straps for ward work, but without these for wear in the Home. (Ward aprons could not be worn at mealtimes or off-duty.)
> Staff Nurses: darker shade of grey beige (extra staff, blue and white striped galateas).
> Sisters: navy blue serge, with caps and aprons.

There follows a description of the work and training. There were twelve wards: four male surgical, two male medical and two of each for women; Adelaide (obstetrics and ophthalmic); Victoria (children). The circular wards were: the operating theatres where only the Sister and the staff nurses were trained, block 8 (infectious diseases), Florence and Mary (empty – to accommodate patients of wards being redecorated). 'There were three probationers to each ward, "Duster", "Lavatory" and "Third"; each had her special duties which had to be completed by 10 am when the doctors began their rounds.' At this point, the Sister and staff nurse and the probationers on duty went off, leaving one on duty often in the embarrassing position of being ignorant about patients because she had not heard the night nurse's report. This had led the young Miss Egan to resolve that if ever she were to be night nurse, she would take care that probationers were well instructed. Home Sister held classes on five mornings a week; other than these there was little oral instruction. The doctor to the Home held an oral examination on practical matters at the end of nine months' training, and any probationer who failed was dismissed.

Miss Egan continues by describing life in the wards: 'lit by gas, and, during the night, by oil lamps; throats and eyes were examined by an ophthalmic lamp (oil) and antiseptic dressings were done under the carbolic spray . . . sterilising hardly existed.' Surgeons and nurses at operations had no overalls or masks, only aprons and rolled up sleeves, but, the reader will be delighted to learn, there was very little septic trouble. 'Dr Cullingworth, who performed all his extensive obstetric operations (except Caesarian Sections) in "Adelaide" bathroom, dressed all his wounds with a strip of dry boric lint and a wood wool pad made in the Ward . . .'

Miss Crossland, as we know, was much in touch with FN and received a present of eggs each week, pots of flowers in summer and mince pies for the probationers' supper on Christmas Day. 'One day in every summer, the probationers of the year were invited with Home Sister (to Claydon) and spent a most happy day . . . only a favoured few were interviewed by Miss Nightingale, but all saw her as she stood at an open window to wave a hand as we left for a drive with Lady Verney in the afternoon.'

The article ends by making two points, the first – one that is made so often by Nightingales – that the day was regulated by Big Ben, and the second that Home Sister 'was feared and respected . . . very just she was, but never affectionate.'

The growing demand for the services of Nightingales meant the School kept to its one-year course long after other newer schools adopted a two- or even three-year period of training. Even so it still proved difficult to find suitable recruits. FN protested that 'We can't get the women. The remunerative employment is there, and in plenty. The want is the women fit to take it.' It seems as if the very families from which it was hoped to gain nurses frequently were deterred by what they saw as the unladylike nature of the work, in contrast to the world of the governess. This interpretation sits oddly with the statement in Dr Baly's thesis, that in 1883 over 1,000 applications were received from Ladies, from which Mrs Wardroper selected nineteen, of whom ten survived their training; in her last year twenty-four were selected from 1,455 candidates.[3] Whatever the reason, the position was not satisfactory. One problem is that no one knows whether Mrs Wardroper was telling the truth.

E.M. McInnes, in the course of the work done for the history of St Thomas's Hospital, gathered a large number of notes concerning the content of teaching in the Training School. These came mainly from the Minutes of the meetings of the Fund Council. The most detailed description of the training when it was for one year is that in the Fund Council Report for 1880.

The practical work of the Probationers as Assistant Nurses in the Wards forms the foundations of the training; here they receive definite teaching from the Ward-Sisters and Nurses in Nursing duties, and the Ward-Sisters are required to note weekly, under different heads, upon a printed form ... with a view further to test the progress of the Probationers ... each one is required once a month, to record a detailed account of her day's work, such as nursing, washing helpless Patients, cleansing utensils, ventilation of the Wards etc., and any special instructions given by the Ward-Sister or Nurse. Thus the record affords some indication both of what the Probationer has done, and also of what she has been taught. To the daily practice in the Ward is added attendance on lectures ... At the close of each course, the more advanced Probationers underwent a written examination by each lecturer, who assigned marks to the replies, and on the whole they acquitted themselves in a satisfactory manner.

For all that she was criticised, Mrs Wardroper laid the foundations of what so many have recognised as the heart of much of the Nightingale training, namely the teaching of skills on the wards.

She never lectured to the probationers but she trained them more thoroughly ... than the highly trained matron of the present day, and certainly maintained a far higher standard of discipline in the hospital and wards. In her time, if a probationer had been found 'chatting' to a young medical student or surgeon she would have been dismissed at once.[4]

Such training was seen by some as too exacting. A clergyman is quoted as saying that 'the training at St Thomas's was calculated to crush all enthusiasm and spirit in order to force the character to its ideal without making any allowance for natural bent.' This comment was echoed in conversations with older Nightingales in May 1996, who recalled a rigidity of training that was not concerned with the details of personal development, a view expressed many times and over many years in the answers to the questionnaire. Training, not education, was the rule in the 19th century and for decades beyond. Lady probationers were given a wider scope – two afternoons a week to follow a reading course drawn up by Dr Croft, who succeeded the increasingly lamentable Mr Whitfield as Medical Instructor in 1872. FN tried hard to keep in touch with the probationers, and with them as nurses after their training had finished, usually by inviting them to tea – after which she made notes on them: 'As self-comfortable a jackass (or Joan-ass) as ever I saw.' 'Miserable nurse though an interesting woman and can answer questions.'[5]

E.M. McInnes records that training through lectures was the responsibility of the Medical Instructor while the Home Sister gave 'improvement classes for the benefit of such of the probationers as required such aid.' Other doctors came in to give lectures in their particular fields. From 1874, monthly examinations were instituted, after which probationers were 'catechised and advised' in the presence of Mrs Wardroper and the Home Sister. In 1874, Mr Croft lectured on elementary classifications of medicines, chief poisons and treatment of, use of stomach pump, method of cupping, glossary of medical terms and abbreviations, review of lectures on bones with aid of skeleton (twenty-five lectures in all). Dr Bernays gave four lectures on the constituents of various articles of food, while Dr Peacock (Senior Physician to the Hospital) gave six lectures on the principles of medicine. Each year after that saw an increase in content. In 1883, cookery lessons were instituted for all probationers. In 1884, Mr Croft added five demonstrations including one on bed-making.

And so the lists continue, indicating that the Lady/Special probationers received more detailed teaching. There is a very full account of this in the recollections of S.E. Hampson, who was accepted as a Special Probationer in the Queen's Golden Jubilee Year of 1887, having decided to change careers at the age of 30. She saw Home Sister, Miss Crossland, first. Her interview with Mrs Wardroper was not pleasant; she was told that she was 'a fool' for changing careers. The description of the training emphasises how tedious it could be, with much dusting and scrubbing, fetching and carrying, some of it exceedingly heavy work.

> First, washing the bathroom basins (of a very awkward pattern) and scrubbing the utensils . . . Then carrying round the tray of meals. The mugs were filled with tea, milk or broth, and were of the heaviest crockery, and it was difficult to keep one's footing on the polished floors . . . the lifting of the screens was very exhausting, as they were heavy wooden frames – six feet high at a guess – and were covered with American cloth. After a few weeks of this Junior's work, washing patients and bed-making became privileged promotion.[6]

She gives some horrendous descriptions of operating theatre practices, which make for queasy reading, and recounts that: 'In those days instruments were in charge of a man named Downes, the surgical stores keeper, who appeared at operations and handed instruments, ligatures and sutures . . . the practice survived of a surgeon sending to his ward an old coat for theatre work.' All the hospital authorities treated a new probationer on the assumption that she was a complete fool: 'Their attitude seemed to be a desire to reduce one to tears – then the training was really felt to be started.'

Flora Masson saw the new hospital being built, and then entered it in the summer of 1885. After two months, she was the only survivor of a group of four entrants; 'the others had gone their ways to fresh woods and pastures new.' Even in 1885 buildings and conditions were spartan, though, writing in 1935, she can look back on it all 'with an abiding love.' She describes how responsibilities could come extraordinarily rapidly, by being given temporary Sister's duties, and how the discipline of the School could return the nurse who had been so promoted to the lowliest rank, 'which meant, sometimes, scrubbing the dear old white wooden lockers up one side of the ward.' In her case, real promotion came swiftly. Mrs Wardroper informed her in March 1887 that she was to be Sister of George Ward, a medical ward; she had hoped for a surgical ward, and a vexed Matron said to her in amazement, 'I am offering you the Senior Medical Ward of St Thomas's Hospital. Do you realise what that means?' Miss Masson wrote: 'I did not, then. I think I did, afterwards.'[7]

Miss Pringle, 'the Pearl', became Matron and Superintendent of the School when Mrs Wardroper at last retired in 1887. To many, she represents a remarkable case of 'might have been'. She and Rachel Williams, another Lady Special, were regarded as the ablest young women of the early years. From being a Ward Sister at St Thomas's she was one of a group sent to the Royal Infirmary in Edinburgh in 1872, and after a very turbulent time, became Superintendent of Nursing in 1874. She remained in Edinburgh for fourteen years and was outstandingly successful in the training of nurses and future Matrons. By 1882 there were thirty-eight probationers, classes run by a Home Sister, four separate courses of lectures by doctors, and classes in cookery and needlework. It was a successful and pointedly systematic training school. Therefore FN and Henry Bonham Carter were overjoyed by their success in persuading Miss Pringle to apply for the post of Matron and Superintendent. High hopes were entertained, and it is reasonable to speculate that if she had stayed, she would have introduced into the Nightingale School many of the changes that had to wait another twenty-five years for implementation. But she left St Thomas's in 1889 after converting to Catholicism.

A thread running through this narrative is that of 'anti- Romanism', distinctly puzzling in its occasional vehemence – FN was not a practising Anglican, and we know of her attraction to Rome. 'Why cannot I enter the Catholic Church at once, as the best form of truth I have ever known, and as cutting the Gordian knot I cannot untie?' she had written in 1852. True enough, she did not become a Catholic, but there is no evidence that she was ever anti-Catholic. Dr Baly has asked in conversation, whether the shortness of Miss Pringle's tenure was really due to her conversion, and if not, to what was it due? St Thomas's Hospital, as a medieval religious foundation, could be said to have become unavoidably Anglican at the Reformation; in which case it could be maintained that a Catholic should not be its Matron. There seems to be no evidence of any public move by the Managers to ask Miss Pringle to resign. FN's own letters suggest that Miss Pringle agonised over what to do. FN, and indeed everybody, must have realised what was being lost, and in Presbyterian Edinburgh a tablet was put up in 1920 in the Royal Infirmary Chapel:

In honoured and affectionate memory of Angelique Lucille Pringle, Lady Superintendent of Nurses 1874 to 1887. Departed this life 29th February 1920.

The pupil and friend of Miss Florence Nightingale, Miss Pringle introduced the modern method of hospital nursing and was the Founder of the Training School for nurses in the Royal Infirmary Edinburgh where her work will ever be held in grateful remembrance.

Gentleness. Goodness. Faith.

In 1897, Home Sister began to give a class on massage and special tuition about night duty. Miss Crossland had left in August 1896, and her place had been taken by Miss Haigh Brown. In 1931 she was to publish the *Probationer's Primer* based on her seven years as Home Sister. In 1900 came a major change when the non-paying probationers were required to sign up for three more years after their year's probation.

Lady/paying probationers were to continue for two years, or in very exceptional cases for one year. It was laid down that there were to be no appointments to other hospitals until three years had been served as a nurse at St Thomas's. From 1904, each probationer was required to spend three months on night duty during her first year and, as far as possible, had two months of special duty under the Theatre Sister in her third year. In 1906, the building of a new Nurses' Home in Gassiot House freed accommodation to give every probationer a separate bed-room.

The book produced in 1960 to celebrate the Centenary of the School, *The Nightingale Training School St Thomas' Hospital 1860 – 1960*, has a chapter on the life of a probationer in 1900. To pick out some of the salient points:

1. Her first instructors were the patients themselves, or fellow probationers of slightly longer standing. There were usually three probationers to a ward, working under a Sister and staff nurse. The day lasted from 7 am to 8.30 pm.

2. The morning ward work began with bed-making. The two more senior took a side each, and each pair had fifteen beds to complete in half an hour. Meanwhile, the juniors, called 'Thirds', did various jobs in the middle of the ward. Everything had to be over by 8 am, when Sister was ready for prayers.

3. One of the three probationers brewed tea and had twenty minutes off; the others had two hours off for 'walking exercise' (she who had been on duty in the morning had three hours off in the afternoon).

4. Probationers left the wards at 8.30 pm to go to the Home. There, Home Sister reviewed the day, correcting minor misdemeanours. Only then did they get supper (only one plate was provided and it was used for both courses).

5. Leave for day nurses was one day a month, for night nurses two nights in two months. At the end of the first year probationers had a month's holiday.

6. The distinction between special and ordinary probationers was clear. Only the former could hope to become Sister and they received special lectures in Medicine, Surgery and Chemistry. The system remained that ordinary instruction came from the ward Sisters and Home Sister. All lectures came in off-duty time, and nurses on night duty were called up in the day for them.

In 1910, rather late in the day, a Preliminary Training School was established to provide a seven-week course of instruction in elementary hygiene, anatomy and physiology, bandaging, splint-padding, bed-making and invalid cookery. Only the appointment of a Sister Tutor in 1914 brought an over-all, consistent and systematized training scheme into operation – which is another way of emphasising that the School had fallen behind in comparison with other major training schools, and had only now caught up.

It is difficult to escape the strong impression that right through to the appointment of Alicia Lloyd Still as Matron in 1913, the training of probationers had a considerable amount of 'ad hoc-ery' about it, and that the quality of different elements varied enormously. Rebecca Strong started a training school at the Glasgow Royal Hospital in 1893, much disapproved by FN; not even her dear friend Eva Lückes could persuade her of its advantages. Rebecca Strong, an early Nightingale, illustrates well the point made that the enterprising and innovative had to get away to fulfil themselves.

Alicia Lloyd Still herself, having been a Sister for seven years at St Thomas's, went to be Matron of the Brompton Hospital in 1904, where she was able to introduce far-reaching changes in training in the light of new developments in the treatment of disease; for example, in her case, of tuberculosis. In 1909, she went to be Matron of the Middlesex Hospital. Ideas and practices from these two periods in high office were brought back to St Thomas's and to the School. The origins of the Preliminary Training School went back to her experiences and conversations at the Brompton Hospital and visits paid to Guy's Hospital. She began the practice of examining each candidate in the PTS at the end of her training. The memoir of her by Lucy Seymer puts it discreetly, saying that when she 'came as Superintendent she felt that much more remained to be accomplished in improving the training as a whole.'

Dr Baly mounts a severe critique of the years to 1913 in chapter ten of her book.[8] It ranges from pointing out that the doctors rarely made an accurate assessment of the intelligence and stages of achievement of the probationers, so that their lectures sometimes were too elementary and at others too difficult (it was one of the duties of Home Sister to try to remedy this problem), to a general view that the very foundation of the whole training, namely direct experience and teaching in the wards, was only too often inadequate. Ward Sisters rarely had time enough and frequently were not good as teachers.

Hanging over all these years is the nature of FN's influence and contribution. On the one hand, there is the ample evidence of her continued interest and concern, which included a good deal of intriguing and plotting but which also involved a close scrutiny of the Report Books, the Red Registers with their fourteen headings, and the diaries and case notes. (The Red Registers were the compilations of the checklists kept by each Ward Sister of the performance of each probationer.) On the other hand, there were the strengths and weaknesses of her views on what nursing itself was about. The comment that she saw God as the great sanitary engineer in the sky indicates her preoccupation with cleanliness, drains, system and order through which fresh air should circulate. Into this came her unshakeable view that patients came first and last and were 'honoured guests'. This teaching, handed down through generations, shines through clearly in the answers received to the questionnaire that went out to a very considerable number of Nightingales as this book began to be written.

Nevertheless, one cannot avoid recognising that FN refused in the middle and later years of her life to accept and incorporate into her thinking and into her advice – regarded as magisterial – new developments in medical research and practice in the second half of the 19th century. The usual illustration given of this is her refusal to accept the 'germ theory'. She clung to the 'miasmatic' explanation of infection against ever-increasing evidence, although, as Rob van der Peet, in *The Nightingale Model of Nursing*, points out, what it was that was passed in or via a miasma – a harmful influence in the environment – was never precisely explained.[9] Her beliefs underpinned her insistence on the good planning of hospitals, with excellent ventilation; the proper placement and size of windows; the detailed instructions about washing, damp-dusting, scrubbing and polishing. The environment was always central to her view of health. In *Nursing of the Sick*, written in 1893, she defined disease as 'Nature's way of getting rid of the effects of conditions which have interfered with health', a clear expression of a decidedly idiosyncratic view.[10]

Rob van der Peet cites her fierce opposition to quarantine not only as another aspect of her rejection of the scientific developments of her time, but also as a reflection of her religious beliefs.

Were 'contagion' a fact, what would be its lesson? To isolate and to fly from the fever and cholera patient, and leave him to die . . .

instead of improving the conditions . . . This is the strictly logical 'lesson' of 'contagion'. If it is not strictly followed, it is only because men are so much better than their God. If 'contagion' were a fact – this being the lesson which it teaches – we cannot escape the conclusion that God is a Spirit of Evil, and not of Love.[11]

He also claims that although she appeared to be addressing all the major elements of the discipline of nursing – the patient, the environment, health and the practice of nursing itself – in fact there were deficiencies in her conceptual model (clearly, not a term that FN would have used). She is criticised for seeing the patient largely as passive when she said: 'half the battle of nursing is to relieve your sick from having to think for themselves at all – least of all for their own nursing.'[12] Her definition of health went beyond the absence of disease towards a state of moral well-being: 'Health is not only to be well, but to use well every power we have to use.'[13] In the Introduction to the *Notes on Nursing* she wrote: 'The same laws of health or of nursing, for they are in reality the same, obtain among the well as among the sick. The breaking of them produces only a less violent consequence among the former than among the latter.'[14]

Her interest in health promotion and home nursing was innovative; here she might be seen as impregnable, but again it was based almost entirely on the sanitary position. 'The work we are speaking of has nothing to do with nursing disease but with maintaining health by removing things which disturb it, which have been summed up in the population in general as "dirt, drink, diet, damp, draughts and drains".' Her definition of disease was distinctly unusual: 'Diseases are, practically speaking, adjectives, not noun substantives.' She saw them not only as *conditions*, which were under people's control, but also as the reactions of Nature (referred to by FN, it would seem, in the Wordsworthian sense) to conditions in which people put themselves (*Notes on Nursing*). Nevertheless, she always maintained it was through disease and suffering that man could come to understand the laws of God. Disease was a challenge set by God to man. The conquest of it was a step nearer to Him. Many people have pondered on such matters; many find them inexplicable. FN did not. One has to read her *Suggestions for Thought*, which an orthodox Christian would find an interesting example of what may happen when an intelligent human being tries to invent a new way of looking at religion. It is a mixture of sharp insight and oddity.[16] Her family had a Unitarian background; she might be better seen as a 'child of the Enlightenment', a Deist, certainly not a Trinitarian Christian; some aphorisms lean towards to predestination but, mainly, the trend is towards a belief in the perfectibility of Man. Everything, so to speak, would get better and better – sanitary science would eventually abolish insanitary sickness, hence the much-quoted saying: 'I look to the day when there will be no more hospitals for the sick.'

Although her three main publications about the fourth element in the model – the practice of nursing – were addressed to different readers and dealt with different aspects of her subject, they are consistent in what they seek to promote. The first version of the *Notes*, published in January 1860, was immediately successful. In two months, 15,000 copies were sold throughout Britain. It remained in print until after Queen Victoria's death in 1901. Victor Skretkowicz, in the informative introduction to his 1992 edition, claims that, even now, it is 'practically global . . . The most recent translation has been into Japanese . . . the culmination of more than a century of international response.'[17]

Notes is essentially pragmatic, humorous, occasionally ironic – for example, in what men expect nurses to be – sometimes metaphorical, sometimes colloquial, but always readable. It is not a text book on nursing and was addressed to a wide audience – from the first version aimed at domestic servants, to the second at professionals, and to the cheaper third version, the first edition of which was given the title *Notes on Nursing for the Labouring Classes*, which came out in 1861. Victor Skretkowicz points out that the 'fullest and most sophisticated text is that of the undiluted second version, the Library Standard edition, and not the third version,' and it is on the second that his edition is based.

It has often been remarked that FN was more interested in the planning and administration of hospitals than in the coherent and up-to-date training of nurses. There indeed lay the strength of her immense achievements in India and other colonial territories. She was a great benefactor to serving soldiers, and it is with them that her heart always lay. However blinkered she was towards the germ theory, it is irrefutable that many of the major killer diseases of the 19th century were linked to bad sanitation. The Prince Consort died of typhoid, so it said on his death certificate signed on 21st December 1861 by his doctor, Jenner – 'Typhoid Fever; duration 21 days' (though a recent biography of the Prince questions again whether this was the case, putting forward an alternative diagnosis of stomach cancer).[18] Whatever the cause, there is no doubting that the drains at Windsor Castle were in a deplorable condition.

> Nothing had been done to improve the drains in connection with the various water closets, sinks etc. within the Castle. The noxious effluvia which escapes from the old drains and numerous cesspools still remaining, is frequently so exceedingly offensive as to render many parts of the Castle almost uninhabitable.

So wrote the Lord Chamberlain in 1862, a month or so after the Prince's death. According to Christopher Hibbert, in his book *The Court at Windsor*, from which the Lord Chamberlain's comment is taken, the Queen herself had suffered from typhoid fever many years before, and in the earlier years of their marriage, the Prince had insisted on a substantial series of changes to drainage and sanitation in Buckingham Palace. The Prince of Wales, later Edward VII, almost died of the same fever in December 1871, giving Alfred Austin, journalist, versifier and, later, Poet Laureate, the reason to write the following memorable lines:

> *Across the wires the electric message came:*
> *'He is no better, he is much the same.'*

To typhoid, add typhus and cholera; to bad ventilation and over-crowding, attribute much tuberculosis. B. Seebohm Rowntree in his study of the poor in York, *Poverty: A Study of Town Life* (1901) lists – and it is a very long list – the diseases that had caused grave illness or death there in the previous year, and anyone could see that bad sanitation and over-crowding were the chief factors. One remembers Disraeli's weary comment on what seemed to be the government's preoccupation with sanitary legislation: 'Sanitas sanitatum, omnia sanitas'. Even if FN would not make a connection between bad sanitation and germs, between environment and biology, it is beyond doubt there would have been less illness and mortality had sanitation been better and had her views on this had been fully heeded.

As an ironical corrective to all this talk of sanitation it is, however, worth noticing a Report on the Sanitary State of St Thomas's Hospital in 1878 claimed that the new buildings were far from hygienic. It was an extremely expensive hospital to run, yet even so windows were difficult to open, shutes for soiled linen were not used, buckets were without lids, chamber pots were left under beds and hidden by the pinned-down quilts. Conditions were worst for the night staff, usually fewer in number. In 1880, thirty-nine probationers were recruited (of whom fourteen were Specials). There was a drop-out of sixteen, the main reason for which was ill-health. Bonham Carter and Croft issued a memorandum for probationers containing seventeen instructions concerning preventative measures and self-care.[19]

FN had begun in the 1850s with her determination to establish nursing as its own self-respecting way of life, not as ancillary to the doctors. This self-respect would come from personal discipline, self-sacrifice, adherence to method, obedience (not blind), immense attention to detail; cleanliness indeed came next to Godliness, and Godliness was central to her thinking. 'Is it possible that we who live among the sick and the dying can be satisfied not to make friends with God each night?'[20] It is interesting, but no doubt not very fruitful, to ponder on how far her devotees through the generations have accepted or would accept her central axiom that nursing is Christ-centered: 'The future Sister must be not of the governing but of the Saviour turn of mind . . .[21] You cannot help being missionaries, if you would. There are missionaries for evil as well as for good. Can you help choosing?'[22] Here is a longer passage on this theme from 1883.

We here below cannot judge the motives which bring you into the work: Let us all have the benefit of the opinion that some high resolve or pure actuated us. But how, when we become Nurses, do we keep that high resolve, that pure motive ever in view? – are we proud to be Nurses? – to be called *Nurse*? . . . Remember, the Nurse is wanted most by the most helpless and often most disagreeable cases; in one sense there is no credit in nursing pleasant patients . . . One word more: Year by year our numbers increase. We are becoming a large band. See that we are banded together by mutual good will . . . Thank God there are numerous other training schools in existence. Let us give them the right hand of fellowship. Wherever we see thorough work, let us feel those are our Sisters . . . Let *us* be always in the van of wise and noiseless high training and progress.

Perhaps the greatest controversy to overshadow FN's later years concerned the move to create a national register of nurses. The prime instigator at first was Mrs Bedford Fenwick, who devoted all her time from 1887 to promoting this cause, buying the *Nursing Record* in 1893 to be a chief means of making the matter known through an increasing readership. She thought that the case was self-evident; it would lead to the establishment of a national standard of nursing dependent on agreed principles of assessment, and enable Matrons and other medical officials to appoint with confidence across the national field. In 1887, the British Nurses' Association was formed

> to unite all qualified British nurses in membership of a recognised profession, to provide for their registration on terms satisfactory to surgeons and physicians as evidence of their having received systematic training, and to associate them for mutual help and protection and for advancement in every way of their professional work.

It followed that just as nurses could be admitted to, so their names could be taken off the register for misconduct. The campaign hoped to receive parliamentary approval, and its failure is usually attributed to the opposition of the Nightingale faction. The Association thenceforward settled for trying to achieve a Royal Charter, and through this to establish a legal register.

In the light of all this, it is interesting to read the comments of S.E. Hampson, a Nightingale, writing much later, for the 1935 Fellowship *Journal*. She had been a probationer at St Thomas's in 1887. She judged that the training was 'lopsided', and that there was 'a feeling of injustice which caused nurses to fight for a systematized and recognised training . . . examination and registration . . . (which was) resisted at St Thomas's.'

Why was there such opposition from FN and her supporters to such an apparently reasonable movement? One element in her attack was simply to analyse and fairly easily to find faults and mistakes in much of the BNA's compilations. More importantly, there was a fear that national standards, achieved through national examinations, would lead to lowest common denominator qualifications, and diminish the case that had been put forward by FN and the Fund Council since the earliest years. They saw the training of nurses as a moral matter, and that the only proper assessment would come from observation by dedicated people rather than impersonal examinations, in public places, that could not possibly arrive at judgements about character suitability and development. She wrote in 1888 to Nightingales: 'This is the "day" of

Examinations in the turn that Education – Elementary, the Higher Education, Professional Education – seems taking. And it is a great stop which has substituted this which used to be called "interest". Let us never allow it to encroach upon what cannot be tested by examinations.'[23]

That same year, Henry Bonham Carter encapsulated FN's and the Fund Council's views in a booklet called *Is a General Register for Nurses Desirable?* FN also opposed the BNA's campaign to establish a three-year training programme for probationers. Ironically, this was itself established in the Nightingale School a few years later, though by then FN was no longer capable of understanding what was going on. In our own time, there has been a move away from dry impersonal examinations towards personal assessments, often confidential, as a more complex and participatory way of arriving at conclusions about achievements. In today's jargon, it is about getting away from product to process. Now, as in the 1890s, the arguments are hotly debated in nursing, and indeed in education generally.

The case advanced by the BNA continued to provoke fierce confrontations. In 1893, Princess Christian of Schleswig Holstein, one of Queen Victoria's daughters, accepted the Presidency of the BNA and the Queen gave it permission to add 'Royal' to its title. The Privy Council followed quickly by granting the RBNA a Royal Charter. In 1895 – astonishingly enough – it resolved that a Register was 'inexpedient in principle, injurious to the best interests of nurses and of doubtful benefit.' Mrs Bedford Fenwick retaliated by founding the Matrons' Council, and then felt the cause greatly boosted by the Midwives Act of 1902, requiring that no midwife should practise professionally unless under the direction of a doctor or certified by the Central Midwives Board. So the story continued. Private Members' Bills were presented to Parliament in 1903 and 1904, and failed, but a Select Committee on Registration was set up, recommending in favour of State Registration in 1905. This did not diminish the arguments, which went on until halted by the outbreak of war in 1914. The battle was won finally in 1919.

One feels that in resisting registration FN was searching for a deeper answer, looking into more profound issues, and that she was not simply obstructive. FN and Bonham Carter could not believe that nursing standards and the personal moral development of nurses would be improved by national standardisation. They never surrendered their view of nursing as a 'calling', a path to God. To them, national systems were utilitarian, but 'the spirit of the time' was going against them. Dr Baly points out that from that point onwards, the Fund Council kept itself 'out of the fray of nursing politics, except for the occasional anti-registrationist shot . . . The Nightingale system went on as before.'[24]

In fact, as the 19th century wore on, the relationship between training and practice in the case of both nurses and doctors became less clear. The situation was exacerbated by the increase in scientific knowledge. Arguments about the proportion of time to be given to practice and to theory have continued right up to the present day.

One indisputable achievement of FN and the Council was to establish the role and the rule of the Matron and to bring into our hospitals this often formidable figure whose ward rounds were like Visitations from on High. Nevertheless, her role as Superintendent in the Nightingale School enabled her to be guarantor of the professional separateness of nursing and a great defence against doctors – they might terrify nurses but they never terrified Matrons.

In the latter part of FN's life there were two Matron/Superintendents, Miss Gordon (1889 to 1902) and Miss Hamilton (1902 to 1913). Personal information and public assessment of their achievements is hard to come by. S.E. Hampson, writing in the Fellowship *Journal* of 1935, says: 'After Miss Pringle's resignation Miss Gordon came from Leeds . . . She was a most striking personality. Her chief characteristic, to my mind, was her large-minded benevolence, giving her the considered judgment of a man. Although often ill and in pain, she faced life with amazing courage.' L.F.P., writing in the following year, certainly emphasises continuity, that is lack of change, from the days of Mrs Wardroper and underlines that Miss Gordon made no structural alteration in the organisation of the School. There is some reference to improvements in nurses' conditions in the hospital, and to new courses of lectures, and to some alterations in posts and responsibilities. She also continued Miss Pringle's work in caring for the ward-maids: 'Her time as Matron may, therefore, be said to mark the end of the definitely "pioneer" stage of the School, and to coincide with that improvement and consolidation of the training to which she contributed so much.' This is bland enough, but these tributes were written many years after Miss Gordon's time as Matron.

Her successor, Miss Hamilton, had entered the Training School in 1886. Only two years later she became a Ward Sister – an illustration of the privilege of the Specials – and in 1892 became Matron in Carlisle Infirmary. After two years she returned to London as Matron of the Victoria Hospital for Children. In 1899, she became Matron of University College Hospital, and in 1902 achieved her life's ambition by returning to St Thomas's. This is a fast-track career. In 1913 she resigned because of failing health and retired, 'seeing only her oldest friends, and those even at long intervals'. The picture given of her is that of 'a very vivid attractive figure with a ready wit and sharp tongue, which carried its shafts all the better for a slight Irish accent.' But then her earlier accessibility turned to a reserve 'which made it less easy than of yore to appeal to the old sense of humour.' In the comparatively grand style in which the Matron lived, she 'surrounded herself with objects of art, such as fine furniture and china, for which she had a remarkable flair.'

Apart from the general management of the School, Miss Hamilton's tenure was marked by two major decisions and one major event. Firstly, she appointed Miss D.S. Coode to be Home Sister in 1903. She concentrated on improving the quality and the quantity of the teaching, in order to diminish what she regarded as a great handicap in her own training: namely, that she had learnt more from patients than from anyone else. F.T. Redl wrote that 'with the advent of Miss Coode to the Nightingale Home a new era began for the probationers. Three days spent under her supervision before coming into the wards were of an unspeakable benefit.'[25] Miss Coode was clearly a rising star, already much loved as well as respected, but her health deteriorated and she resigned in 1910. Undoubtedly, she would otherwise have been appointed to run what was the newly established Preliminary Training School, which was Miss Hamilton's second major decision. In her stead, the Hon. Gertrude Best was given the position. Her stay was short, and when Miss Alicia Lloyd Still became Matron and Superintendent in 1913 she specially requested Miss Coode to return as Sister in charge of the PTS. The major event was the completion in 1906 of Gassiot House as a new Home for nurses and probationers, which gave the latter individual rooms for the first time. However, except for Miss Hamilton's establishment of the Preliminary Training School, there is nothing to dispel the feeling that, as long as FN lived, the School did not change in its fundamentals.

CHAPTER FOUR

Dame Alicia Lloyd Still and the Tradition

Alicia Lloyd Still was Matron and Superintendent for twenty-four years. It is said that her long tenure of office, in which she became unchallengeable, convinced the Fund Council that, so far as possible, no appointment as Matron and Superintendent would ever be made that was likely to last as long. None of her successors served for more then ten years. Much has been written about her and there are those alive who knew her. One Nightingale, in writing about her training from 1928 to 1931, commented in passing that a main reason for wishing to enter the School was: 'My aunt was trained at St Thomas's and started her training the same day as Miss Lloyd Still who announced that one day she would be Matron of St Thomas's. They remained friends for the rest of their lives.'

She made three crucial decisions in her first year or so in office: the first to persuade Miss Coode to take charge of preliminary training, the second, in July 1914, to appoint Miss M. A. Gullan to the new post, with a new title, of Sister Tutor, and the third to establish the practice of examining each candidate in the PTS as the course finished. Miss Lloyd Still thus consolidated changes that went back to the turn of the century, but which might have been transient except for her determination. It had become clear to the Fund Council that, given a more or less constant wastage rate of 40 per cent of those entering as probationers before her time, it was important to increase the attractiveness of the Nightingale training, to ensure the continuance of its ethos, and to reinforce the links with the Hospital. The prestige and the experience that she had already acquired put her in an unchallengeable position. The Hospital accepted the full financial responsibility for the PTS, and by the summer of 1914 Miss Lloyd Still and the new Sister Tutor had worked out an integrated comprehensive syllabus of training.

In the light of all this, it comes as a surprise to read that in March 1914 a sub-committee of the Fund Council, consisting of W. Minet, A. W. West and D. F. Pennant, was appointed 'to prepare a scheme for a post-

94

graduate course of instruction for nurses.' Writing from the knowledge that one has of the schemes and programmes in the 1980s and 1990s to enhance the training of nurses and to achieve a recognisable academic status that could lead to an all-graduate profession, this report makes astonishing reading. It begins by asserting that FN's first idea was to establish a School for the *scientific* training of nurses. It continues with the interesting comment that the first contract of arrangements with St Thomas's and the Fund Council was contained 'in an agreement which, by some mischance, no longer exists.' Therefore, the writers reconstructed it: '. . . the only guide we have as to what the agreement was . . . is what we find existing today'. There had been a move from one year's training to three; the Fund Council was financially responsible only for the first year, and the Hospital for the ensuing years. They had found that they were not spending the whole of their income on the Nightingale Home (where probationers lived) 'in connection with the Hospital'. The writers had undertaken to investigate how the surplus money might best be spent. 'Let us therefore consider whether there be anything wanting in the existing training of nurses which the Fund at our disposal might enable us to supply.' They continued that 'nursing has become a science' and that therefore many would see it as a profession and look forward to attaining to the higher positions it offered. These were now seen to demand qualifications 'other than and beyond a knowledge of skilled nursing'. These are listed, and in modern terms, one would say that they encompassed a comprehensive training in management. Such had not been attempted before and many promoted nurses had said that it was in this field 'that they find themselves painfully lacking'. The Report proclaimed that this was an absolutely new field and 'were the Nightingale Fund to enter it, it would be doing what Miss Nightingale herself would have approved, by once again making her Fund the pioneer in what is now the great want in the training of nurses.' It is wisely pointed out that major innovations required an experimental beginning, for which the money was available. Were this to happen, the sub-committee said it would involve giving up the connection with the Hospital, though this would be a sad occasion. Where was such an experiment to be tried? 'We think we have found exactly what is needed at the King's College for Women . . . shortly to remove to a new building, which will include a hostel where students can live.' This College was a branch of London University, the Principal of which had received the idea most sympathetically.

Roughly our proposals are as follows:

1. To offer to nurses, who have attained a certificate in some recognised training school after not less then three years' training, a year's further course at King's College.

2. The fees . . . will be paid by us, as also a sum to provide board and lodging, with a further sum as an indemnity for the salary the scholar would otherwise be earning during the year of her course.

Further proposals were that this course should be open to all nurses (qualified) up to 35 years of age. The Council would select candidates, and success in the examinations would confer the title of Nightingale Scholar. This plan had received enthusiastic support from a whole range of influential people. 'The proposal is experimental, we are committed to nothing – should it succeed we can enlarge it, should it fail we can leave it, and turn in some wiser direction.' The tantalising phrase is 'post-graduate course'. Was this a loose use of words? Was it implying that the three years' course in any training school leading to a certificate was in fact to be seen as the equivalent of a university degree? One presumes that Dame Alicia was informed of this thinking and read the Report. The document's last paragraph said that '. . . the idea is new in this country, but it is not new in the United States, where the scheme is in practice at Columbia College, and we have had the advantage of consulting a lady occupying a high post here who has passed through that course.' To recapitulate: a professional qualification in hospital management, open to older women, taken out of any connection with St Thomas's and based in King's College, London University – these points foreshadow much of the Nightingale Institute eighty years later.

All this never happened because on 28th June 1914, the Archduke Franz Ferdinand was murdered in Sarajevo. There followed 'the Time of the Breaking of Nations'. The War made an immediate impact, the scheme was shelved and its ideas only brought to the forefront of thinking about nurse education in the 1980s.

As early as 3rd September, 123 men and one officer were brought back wounded from France to St Thomas's, and the number of casualties from the Western Front increased rapidly as the months went by. How to continue training as the War progressed became the biggest problem the School had ever faced.

Three-quarters of a million men from the United Kingdom of Great Britain and Ireland were killed in the War, and one and a half million wounded, many permanently weakened. Certain battles stamped their names on the nation's memory from that day to this: the Somme, Ypres, Passchendaele. On 22nd April 1915, the Germans used gas warfare for the first time on unprotected troops, and a new form of training had to be introduced to deal with this.

The War was not over by Christmas 1914 as had been the easy, jolly expectation in August. As the casualty lists increased and the generals became more and more bewildered about what methods of war would succeed, many field hospitals were set up in northern France – the cross-Channel steamers were kept busy taking families, relations and friends out to visit the injured, in spite of U-boat threats. The same boats brought the more seriously injured, the shell-shocked and the convalescent back to this country. In January 1916, the Military Service Act began to introduce conscription, and the War enfolded the whole population in one way or another.

Among the thousands of nurses who volunteered to serve with the Forces were many Nightingales. They were transferred into one of the three Army Nursing Reserve Corps, Queen Alexandra's Imperial Military Nursing Reserve, the Territorial Force Nursing Service and the Voluntary Aid Detachments – between them, they absorbed 50,000 as military nurses. Miss Lloyd Still herself, according to Lucy Seymer, 'donned the grey uniform and scarlet-lined cape of a Territorial Matron and found herself doubling this role with that of being the civilian Matron and Superintendent of the Training School . . . scarlet-edged uniforms and white Army caps [filled] the familiar corridors and VADs were seen at every turn.'[1]

The Hospital (and all its buildings) was created 'the 5th London (City of London) General Hospital', and wooden ward huts were put up between the pavilions to meet the new crises. G. C. Quentrall, writing for the Fellowship *Journal* about the Hospital from 1914 to 1919, remembered that not only were more and more wards taken over for the military wounded but 'huts were erected in all the quadrangles . . . Our Matron became Principal Matron . . . Thus we who had remained at home had the incalculable boon of "doing our bit" in our own beloved hospital under our own beloved Matron.' There was bombing first by Zeppelin airships and then by conventional aircraft. On one occasion, a bomb fell into the river near Westminster Bridge causing flooding in basements in the Hospital, and on another shrapnel penetrated one of the huts. This was the extent of direct damage. County Hall, opposite

St Thomas's, was being built, and when it was sufficiently safe for occupation, it was used as a refuge. The greatly increased military presence reduced the number of civilian wards, resulting in more patients in each and so adding to the work-load, making the life of the available probationers much more exhausting.

The work of training future Nightingales went on unchecked, though in new circumstances. In 1915, the PTS was extended from eight to nine weeks and it was provided that students should spend some time in the wards, two or three hours daily, in the last fortnight. In 1917, a weekly gymnastic class was set up and made available to those probationers who wished it. A number of new elements had to be added to the integrated syllabus of training put into place just before the War began. The first of these was how to deal with the results of gas warfare. This course was kept in being in the years after the War, in case another war brought the threat of gas to the whole population. Probationers were taught about the tear gas group, the lung irritant group, the blistering gas group, the sneezing gas group and the prussic acid gas group.

A second element was to bring in to the training of probationers the work of the Massage School, which had been started in 1911 under Miss Minnie Randell, Sister Ophthalmic. During the War it was concerned with helping the wounded and the exhausted to return to active physical life – which meant, only too often, a return to the Western Front. Students were able to take the examinations of the Incorporated Society of Trained Masseuses. Others were given new training in dealing with fractured limbs under the supervision of the Physico-therapeutic Department.

A third area where new training was required was venereal disease. This increased greatly in war-time circumstances, so much so that a Royal Commission was set up in 1916 to investigate the most efficient ways of treatment, and in 1917, a new department was created in the Hospital. Lydia Ward was the base for this, with a separate discreet entrance. One must remember that most recruits, first as Volunteers and then under Conscription, came from simple backgrounds, and were, in many respects, sexually innocent. The treatment continued to be provided after the War, and has not ceased. No doubt its scope has been extended.

The memories recorded in the Fellowship *Journals* stress the overcrowding and the temporary hutments, which were not bomb-proof, so that they had to be evacuated as soon as the sirens sounded: 'Can any probationer today imagine what the main corridor outside the Nightingale Home door must have looked like with some sixty patients from A Hut crowded there and a busy array of nurses, VADs and orderlies attending to the men, distributing cocoa etc., while Sister A was trying to reassure some particularly nervous patient?'[2] These circumstances and conditions were to be quite over-shadowed by the events of the Second World War, but E.M. Vezey believed strongly that the '5th' was a proud off-shoot of the Nightingale School.

In 1916, in the middle of these toils and troubles, Alicia Lloyd Still played a major part in establishing the Royal College of Nursing. In the same year, she initiated the Nightingale Medals, endowed by Mrs Minet, a Nightingale, and designed by Countess Fedora Gleichen. Three in number, Gold, Silver and Bronze, they were intended to reward probationers for all-round achievement – 70 per cent of marks for 'ward reports and general conduct'. In order to be awarded the much-coveted Gold Medal, candidates were also required to gain a minimum 60 per cent in written examinations. At the same time Sisters, in supervising the work of their students, were given the task of using the new system of ward charts, which were also to be incorporated into the practices of the new Royal College.

Seymer prints one memorandum from the Matron concerning the Ward Chart: *Written Confidential Reports from Sisters on Senior and Junior Staff Nurses.*

Matron will be grateful if, when writing Reports on their Staff Nurses (Senior and Junior), they will bear in mind the following qualifications, with the understanding that the said Reports largely influence the subsequent position and responsibility that may be entrusted to a Nurse. Will the Sisters also remember that the details as to moral and professional qualifications may be in some instances difficult to report upon in Junior Nurses, developing only *with responsibility*, by which the Sisters are asked to test them during their training.

MORAL QUALIFICATIONS – Temper; Tact; Judgment; Zeal; Energy; Self-reliance; Reliability; Common Sense; Punctuality; Influence for Good generally, and conscientious outlook on all details of work and training. Is she, or will she be, fitted for an administrative position, or for private work etc?

PROFESSIONAL QUALIFICATIONS – General professional

ability; Administrative capacity; Power of initiative and observation; Power of organisation; Ability to instruct and train Probationers and Junior Nurses.

Please note any special merits or defects; Length of service in Ward – Day or Night; Responsibility as to Hospital property and Economy; Working with loyalty to those in authority.[3]

This could have been written by FN herself.

When the War ended in November 1918, there was a slow return to normality. One hundred and fourteen Nightingales had served abroad. One CBE, one OBE, 30 RRCs (Royal Red Cross medals, one of which was awarded to Miss Lloyd Still), two Bars to RRC, three Military Medals and many other honours were gained. The military hospital was decommissioned in 1919, but only in 1921 were all the wards in the pavilions brought back into use. A generous gesture was made by the Fund Council, never well-off, in offering ex-VADs admission to the School as 'Specials' without having to pay for themselves. The War left the Nightingale School facing financial problems and the Fund Council made over a sum of £2100 to help.

The death in June 1923 of Miss Ram, Home Sister since 1910, was felt acutely. Miss Harley took her place. Miss Gullan, the first Sister Tutor, was to remain in office until 1935, a major pillar of strength and continuity. In 1920, she brought out her book on *The Theory and Practice of Nursing*. It ran into many editions. Dedicated to Dame Alicia 'without whose inspiration and untiring efforts to further the education of nurses these pages would never have been written', it became 'the Bible' for generations of probationers, the definitive guide to the training and practice of nursing before the coming of antibiotics. Not many text books have a valid life of perhaps forty years. The twenty-five chapters cover, with five appendices, the whole range of training. In her Foreword, Sister Gullan writes

Probationers may find these summaries somewhat obscure in meaning, as they are intended to be elucidated and amplified in class. Even then only a more or less superficial grasp of the subject will be gained during the first year, but illumination will come by the light of a growing experience. The chapters follow a progressive sequence, and repetition is avoided.

She goes on to recommend systematic revision every three or six months, making personal notes or illustrations from everyday experience. It is pointed out that many scientific terms are used that may seem unnecessary in training, but that they are used in order to become meaningful in the following years of the nurse's life. In a succinct dictum, no doubt to be put in quotation marks followed by the injunction 'Discuss', Miss Nuttall, a Nightingale and former Editor of the *Nursing Times*, said that 'Nursing came to an end with the introduction of antibiotics'. In other words this text book's use began to diminish as the nature of nursing began to change.

In 1922, a new Sister Tutor section of The Royal College of Nursing was founded and Miss Gullan became its first Chairman. She was not a Nightingale herself and in 1925, when the Nightingale School Badge was instituted, the Council bestowed it on her 'deeming that she truly won a place among the members . . . and her position as a Nightingale Nurse.' The Appreciation of her when she retired in 1935 is written in the enthusiastic prose that is the hallmark of the Fellowship *Journal*; qualities and virtues are listed, but it is difficult to see through them to the real person. 'An inquiring mind keeps her interested and interesting. She has read widely, has a sound knowledge of languages.' It is quite pleasing, and comforting to be told that 'her knowledge of men and affairs is outstanding.' Certainly she was greatly valued, and the Sister Tutor Section commissioned a hand-wrought silver rose bowl, bearing her name, and to be awarded annually 'for excellence of work shewn at the Student Nurses' Exhibition', with names inscribed each time.

The years 1919 to 1939 had certain characteristics that impinged on hospitals and nursing as much as on everything else. After a very brief economic boom, 1919 to 1921, a pattern of decline and unrest set in, with short-lived periods of apparent recovery. The greatest scar of all was the General Strike of 1926, which saw the probationers stitching buttons and stripes to the uniforms of Special Constables recruited to keep order. M.C Routh, writing in Volume Two of the Fellowship *Journal*, saw the strike as 'an opportunity for the School to take its part in helping the country at a time of difficulty.'[4]

In 1929 came the world slump sparked off by the Wall Street Crash of 29th October. Unemployment was intractably high already and continued to rise alarmingly; by June 1931, it stood at 2,700,000. Recovery came slowly in the 1930s, and was clearly discernible by

1937, the year of Alicia Lloyd Still's retirement.

In August 1921, Sir Eric Geddes, lately Minister of Transport, had been appointed to chair a Committee to recommend a deflationary policy. The many cuts proposed across the whole of national life were immediately dubbed 'the Geddes axe'. Vast savings were to be made, and the Government, though aghast, accepted them, with some reductions. The Ministry of Health's budget was cut by £2½ millions; even teachers' salaries were cut by 10 per cent. Men returning from the War wanted jobs, and so the economic liberation of women that had been dictated by the War was largely ended. The general practice of these two decades was that if a woman in a job got married, she gave it up. In many cases, for example in teaching, this was contractual.

FN may have paved the way, but the War hastened the move towards seeing nursing as an acceptable occupation for well-to-do young ladies. There is quite a literature of socially superior young women going off to France to nurse, memorably recalled by Vera Brittain in *The Testament of Youth*. Her writings and those of many others also shew how bitter was the sense of let-down they experienced when the War was over and their services no longer required. They seemed as marginal to society as they had been in 1913. Nursing and teaching were the only main career paths for women – and now were subject to the marriage bar. There was also a lurking fear that there would be encroachment into FN's fundamental principle 'that a woman, herself trained in nursing, must be at the head of every Nursing staff and must have full charge of the training and discipline of the staff' – the wording of a resolution passed in 1912 at the International Council of Nurses and re-emphasised at Geneva in 1927 and 1931.[5]

The inter-war years were grey, not only economically and socially, but also medically. No 'great leaps forward' were made at this time; the next War was to be the forcing-house for dramatic changes. Therefore, one records modest advances. In 1928, tannic acid treatment for burns was first introduced, and became part of the training for probationers. In 1930, the introduction of 'Pinkies' – named from their uniform – whose duty it was to polish all furniture and brass and clean sinks and baths, was intended to give more time to probationers to 'do their sides' and clean utensils in the sluice 'as in the old tradition'.[6] The same year saw the provision of a mock ward in the PTS with three beds and one cot, 'arranged on the plan of the real wards even to its "lavatory"'.[7] There were some improvements, already noted, in buildings; for example, the provision of a new dining hall (Shepherd Hall), and new class and lecture rooms.

It is important to recall that hospitals were self-funding – they were called 'Voluntary', dependent largely on voluntary contributions, including some from grateful patients, and on such investments as some of them had. Fund-raising was a permanent preoccupation, and as the years went by it was increasingly clear that this was a completely inadequate way of financing the hospital system. The Ministry of Health's chief duty was, narrowly, to administer the limited National Health Service introduced by Lloyd George in 1909; it was not directly concerned with the running of hospitals.

The poor and unbalanced diet of so much of the population gave a new significance to the training of probationers in dietetics. In each ward, the Sister was as much in control of diet and feeding as of everything else. Each sent daily to the kitchens a list of what food was required for her patients, and it was brought up and served to them. The probationers similarly were catered for, and later as qualified nurses were watched over in an intensely maternalistic institution; those on Night Duty were served breakfast in bed. It is important to stress the autonomy of each ward and each ward Sister. Wards were identical in planning and equipment, and everything to do with their maintenance was the responsibility of the Sister. Promotion to Sister was a very significant occasion, decided upon, as were most things, in Matron's Office, and announced; there was no process of consultation. The inter-war years saw the system at its height, and its strength was such that it functioned with great success in the calamities and dispersals of the Second War.

The very first answer, chronologically speaking, to the questionnaire sent out before beginning to write this book was received from Kathleen Annie Sharwood Burke (née Smith) whose years of training were from 1925 to 1931. She already had a university diploma in agriculture and entered the School when she was 21.

I went to the Wembley Exhibition – I thought I'd like nursing as I had to earn my living. No idea why I chose St Thomas's. I found the first year very hard indeed. We worked long hours – at the end of my first year improvements were made – a half day a week added to a day off a month . . . My second, third and fourth years I loved. We were over-worked and under-paid, but the patients always came first.

This last phrase is an early appearance in the questionnaires of what grew into a major theme, usually, it has to be said, accompanied by a lament for present-day deterioration in standards.

> I'm not at all sure I like what happens now and if I were ever very ill I would prefer to be cared for by one of my contemporaries to what I hear about nursing, or lack of it now.

May one be forgiven for mentioning that the writer was 92 at the time of answering? The next earliest reply, covering the years 1925 to 1929, noted that

> We started with the 'Big Push' – the bed-pan round – for six months. At that point those who were no good disappeared and we went on to watch Sisters doing dressings. After a few months we were allowed actually to do simple dressings.

Then came Miss Evelyn Joan Bocock, known to one and all as 'Poppy', training from 1927 to 1931.

> The Hospital radiated outstanding courtesy. We were welcomed warmly on arrival and Matron herself in her first talk to us reminded us that we should act as hostesses on her behalf . . . Unlike in any other hospitals in those days, ward maids and daily women did the cleaning. We were only responsible for the cleanliness and order of the patients' lockers, and the mackintoshes on which they lay. We had to know and report every morning and evening on the progress of our patients and we always had to accord them the dignity of their name (Mr, Mrs, Miss). Christian names were only for children. The porters and orderlies were called by their surnames, and we were to them Nurse or Sister. There was a very friendly relationship between all staff, consultants, doctors (taken in hand by the ward sisters). At a staff party in World War Two the head Pinkie was addressed by a reporter from the *Evening Standard*. R: Things are sadly changed Mrs M. Head Pinkie: Not at all young man. The company is the same.

More than one correspondent emphasised that fraternisation, as against a friendly relationship, with the male students was strictly forbidden.

Another description of life as a Nightingale from 1928 to 1931 is so characteristic that it is worth quoting at length.

Sister PTS impressed upon us that we were being given a concentrated training so that we would be able to cope whatever happened once we left . . . The Nightingale Home was part of the main hospital buildings but completely independent . . . After breakfast we assembled and as Big Ben started to strike 8.00 am we marched off to our wards. We spent two months in each ward and had three hours off in each twelve-hour day which ran from 8.00 am to 8.00 pm. We had half a day off a week and one day off a month. I was paid £20 for the first year, £25 for the second and £35 for the third. We got two weeks' holiday a year and two weeks' sick leave free. All other days off due to illness had to be made up before we could take our final exams. At the end of the day we went from the ward to the Chapel prayers and then to supper.

After one year I became a Staff Nurse and eligible for night duty, which ran for a stretch of three months at a time with two nights off at the end. There was a special Block for night nurses and you were shut in at midday and not allowed out. There were lectures in the morning during off duty hours and you went even when you were on night duty. One lecturer asked Sister Tutor *who chaperoned us* to make sure she put the night duty nurses at the back as he didn't like lecturing to a row of zombies in the front.

There were hospital exams after three years (and after all sick leave had been made up). SRN exams were held only once a year so that if you missed them you had to come back, as I did.

Albert Ward (Men's Surgical) was the last ward to have a coal-fired stove in the kitchen. During the day the ward maid kept the fire going. At night we had to do it. The first thing we did on coming on duty was to put on lots of kettles to heat so that there would be hot water when needed. Albert Ward was also the last in the hospital to serve porridge at 6 am.

A number of Nightingales, on completing their training, went on to missionary work, mainly in the Empire. Whatever FN's fears had been about institutional religion, it is clear that Chapel played an important part in their formation, much more than simply the required observances. These had settled into conventional Anglicanism and 'deviation' to the Evangelical was as much frowned upon as that towards the Scarlet Woman of Rome.

Whilst I was in the Nightingale Home (1928 to 1933), a number of probationers came to my room and sitting on cushions on the floor had a time of realistic Christian fellowship and prayer on Sunday evenings after ward duty . . . Three of us asked the Matron for advice [on how to develop this]. She graciously consulted Sir Arthur Stanley [the Treasurer] and the Chaplain who under no circumstances would allow us to meet in any sitting room but suggested that we could meet in Chapel at 6.15 am on Saturday mornings. So all through my training and long afterwards the meetings continued with the singing of hymns with the organ, taking turns to read from the Bible and lead the prayers when we remembered patients in the wards, and St Thomas's nurses and doctors working abroad as missionaries.

When the College of Nursing was established in 1916, it had been expected that it would become the registering body, ignoring other nurses' groups. This hope was quashed by the passing of the Nurses' Act 1919, which embraced all existing bodies in the setting up of a General Nursing Council for England and Wales, on which sat some practising nurses. One of its first tasks was to study nurses' salaries and conditions of work and to draw up a Nurses' Charter. This called for better and coordinated training, better salaries, better accommodation, a 48-hour week and a pension scheme. A Department of Education within the Council was put in place to develop advanced, that is postbasic, education for nurses.

Miss Lloyd Still was prominent in all these discussions. She was a nominated member of the first General Nursing Council which met in 1920 and held office until 1923. From then onwards until her retirement, she was elected and re-elected by the Registered Nurses themselves. She was a member of the Council of the College from 1920 to 1938 and the Vice-President from 1938 to 1944. (She had been made a member of the Nursing Board of Queen Alexandra's Imperial Military Nursing Service in 1917, an appointment she accepted joyfully because it was within the FN tradition. From then onwards, each year some Nightingales joined the Army.) The catalogue of honours dates from these years: RRC (First Class) 1917; CBE 1917; Lady of Grace of the Order of St John of Jerusalem 1922. In 1924, she was one of the first members of London University's Advisory Committee to plan a diploma in nursing, which was awarded from 1926. In 1927, Miss Hillyers and Miss Bowes were the first Nightingales to receive it.

In 1919, Miss Lloyd Still was elected first President of the Association of Hospital Matrons, and held the post until her retirement. She became as well-known abroad as at home and amongst the many invitations and honours she received, she regarded her greatest achievement to be the founding of the Florence Nightingale International Foundation in 1933. She was unanimously elected President, and re-elected in 1935 and 1937. In 1933, she was elected International President of the International Congress of Nurses, an office she held until retirement; at the first Congress in Paris, she was awarded the Florence Nightingale Red Cross Medal, and honoured in France with the Medaille d'Honneur de l'Assistance Publique. In 1934 she was made a Dame of the Order of the British Empire, and she was and is referred to colloquially as 'the Dame'. This catalogue of recognition almost parallels that of FN herself.

In 1925, the Nightingale Badge was designed and struck, to be given to all on qualification. It was to be held for life and was meant to be returned on death lest it fell into the wrong hands. Nightingales have been met who have averred that they will do no such thing. The Badge was worn on the uniform during work, and it has been pointed out by one Nightingale that FN would never have approved of such a practice; it was likely to cut or scratch. The final definitive ruling about the Badge was given in 1986.

The decision made by the Council is as follows: The Badges issued before 1970 should be returned on the death of the recipient: as in previous years. On occasion, a close relative has requested that they might retain the Badge or hand it on to a later qualified Nightingale related to them. This has been allowed as the Badge remains in safe keeping and it should be returned on the death of the new holder. It would seem appropriate to house the returned Badges in the security of the Museum when it is built . . . It is requested that Badges awarded since 1970 should still be returned on the death of the holder in the same way to safeguard the security of the Badge.

In 1928 The Nightingale Fellowship was established to embrace all qualified Nightingales. Its first Commemoration Service was held on 12th May 1929, with a dinner and first AGM on the following day. Here it was decided to inaugurate and publish the Fellowship *Journal* during the same year. In her first Letter Miss Lloyd Still wrote

> It has been said that we are late in forming our Fellowship. To that criticism we must submit. But it must be remembered that during those terrible years of the Great War there was no question of division of labour or of interest. The War absorbed our entire energies. Then came the inevitable aftermath of clearing away the old, of drawing up and developing new schemes.

She continues by bringing all her readers up to date on developments in the School – a refurbished Home; two additional storeys built over it, with a lift; extra bedrooms in Gassiot House to accommodate staff and students taking post-graduate courses; a beautiful new dining-room for Sisters and Staff Nurses; new classrooms in the School. She writes very much as either the Principal of a major girls' boarding school or the head of a College might do. Nightingales are referred to as 'Children' and the School is their 'Alma Mater'. In what must have been one of her last appearances before retirement, at the Presentation of the Nightingale Medals in November 1937, she said: 'You all know perfectly well that it is not my happiness to speak. You also know that in this room, so filled with the atmosphere of the past, it is difficult. But I will ask you to "play the game" now and always. Just play a strictly square Nightingale game, here and in the world, wherever you go.'

M.C. Routh, writing about the School from 1919 to 1935, takes the list of extensions and buildings and changes further. In 1924, Miss Coode, so associated with the PTS, became Assistant Matron, resigning in 1933. She had been a Sister of the Nightingale School from 1903, first as Home Sister. There is increasing reference to Miss Hillyers, first in 1927, then awarded a Rockefeller Travelling Fellowship to study nursing education and administration in the USA in 1930, and becoming Assistant Matron in 1933. She was on her way to succeeding Dame Alicia in 1937.

The last and certainly the most splendid building in these two decades was Riddell House, opened by Queen Mary on 14th October 1937. The description of it makes it palatial: six storeys high, with basement, built round a central court, and the glass skylight at the bottom of the court acting as the roof of the swimming pool. There was a nurses' recreation room, running almost the whole length of the frontage, complete with Broadwood grand piano. There were sitting-rooms for the PTS Sister and the PTS Charge Nurse and for visitors. The library was fitted with study alcoves. Another sitting-room had another grand piano. All the sitting-rooms were filled with pieces of antique furniture and other works of art, given by Lady Riddell, the widow of Lord Riddell once a Governor of the Hospital, herself a Nightingale. The rest of the building had well-equipped and comfortable study bedrooms, small kitchens and so on. The other main purpose of the House was to provide new living quarters for the PTS. The House accommodated – one might say enshrined – an exhibition that contained part of FN's South Street House, recently demolished by the London County Council.

In this record of development and achievement at St Thomas's and in the School, it is important to place the *The Lancet* Commission on Nursing. In spite of all that has been described so far, there was, nationally, a 'shortage of candidates, trained and untrained, for nursing the sick.' The Commission was asked for proposals that would make nursing 'more attractive to women suitable for this necessary work.' Its impressive membership, chaired by the Earl of Crawford and Balcarres, was exhorted to 'restore the popularity of nursing amongst educated girls.' It was realised its Report would be controversial, and so it defended itself by making it clear that all their information came from the hospitals themselves, whose statistics were unimpeachable. The Commission summed up the cause of the shortage of candidates as:

1. The gap between school-leaving age and that at which a girl may enter the nursing profession.
2. The long working hours.
3. The low salaries and poor prospects offered to those who had trained successfully.
4. Conditions for admission and service.
5. Professional education.

These headings are self-evident, but the last needs some explanation. It was felt that the training of combined practical and theoretical work was very heavy, and that parents might not wish their daughters to go through it. It was suggested that some of the theoretical work might be done before entry into training, and that before the final State Examinations, candidates should be given time off duty. The Report also advocated a wider recognition by every approved training school of time spent in other approved training schools. This is the first of many Reports on Nursing that will be discussed, and the question can be asked now, as it will be about later Reports: what happened next? Dr Baly said 'the message of *The Lancet* Commission was that, because of an economic slump, and then the Second World War, nursing was able to live on borrowed time.'[8]

Continuing unemployment and the bitterness left by the General Strike led the Trades Union Congress in 1937 to try to assume the leadership and coordination of all whom it regarded as 'Workers'. Six Unions affiliated to the TUC sought Nurses' membership (the three best known being The National Union of County Officers, The National Union of Public Employees, and The Mental Hospital and Institutional Workers' Union); their membership was overwhelmingly male. The College of Nursing resisted affiliation and indeed membership. Its case was that 'The Trades Union looks on the nurse as an overworked, underpaid worker who must be helped out of her present position. We regard the young nurse as being educated to professional life, with freedom to deal with the sick as living beings, whilst working under reasonable conditions.'

The College went further in distancing itself, and saw the Unions as enemies which were 'in deadly earnest and are out all the time for youth. They strive to influence the young nurses even in the PTS. No training school should think itself immune from the propaganda.' The College went on to exhort its members that it was the true spirit of nursing that was endangered. 'It needs such careful protection and fostering, and is rather a tender plant. Planted in this place by Florence Nightingale, and nurtured so wonderfully by our present Matron, we must do our utmost to protect and encourage it.'

By the time Dame Alicia left office in 1937, she had put in place, with help from her closest colleagues, the plans for dealing with casualties in another world war that could be seen to be looming. In that same year the Prime Minister, Stanley Baldwin, said that 'The bomber will always get through.' All preparations assumed the likelihood of overwhelming air attacks, with enormous numbers of wounded and dead.

The era ended symbolically if not chronologically withDame Alicia's retirement. There can be no doubt that she was an outstanding woman of her time but it is as difficult with her as with other prominent

Left: Mrs Sarah E Wardroper,
Matron, 1854–1887.

Right: Nurse Mary Barker; hers
was the first name on the first list
of Nightingale Nurses in 1860.

Miss Angelique L Pringle,
Matron, 1887–1889.

South Wing Operating Theatre, c.1900.

Nightingale Home dining room, c. 1900.

Convalescent soldiers from Hut E, on the Terrace, 1914–1918.

Shepherd Memorial Dining Hall for nurses, c. 1930.

PRELIMINARY TRAINING SCHOOL, ST. THOMAS'S HOSPITAL.

No. 1 CLASS.

Monday.

6.30	Calling Bell
7.30	Breakfast
8. 0	Prayers
	Housework
9.15	Rooms
10. 0	Lunch
10.30	Cookery Demonstration
1. 0	Dinner
2. 0	Physiology Lecture
3—6	Off Duty
6. 0	Notes and Study, etc.
8.45	Supper
9.15	Prayers
10.30	Lights Out

Tuesday.

9.15	Bandage Making
10.15	Lunch
10.45	Cookery Practice
2. 0	Nursing Lecture
3—6	Off Duty

Wednesday.

9.30	Chemistry of Food Lecture
10.30	Lunch
11—1	Bandaging and Practical Nursing
2. 0	Hygiene Lecture
3—6	Off Duty

Thursday.

9.30	Physiology Lecture
10.30	Lunch
11—1	Off Duty
2. 0	Ambulance Lecture
3—5	Cookery Practice

Friday.

9.15	Splint Padding
10.15	Lunch
11—12.45	Class, Test Paper, etc.
2. 0	Hygiene Lecture
3—6	Off Duty

Saturday.

9.30	Nursing Lecture
10.30	Lunch
11—1	Practical Nursing and Bandaging
2. 0	Extra Cleaning
3—6	Off Duty

Sunday.

8.40	Breakfast
9—10	Housework
10.30	Chapel
12—1	Lecture
1.30—7.30	Off Duty
8.45	Supper

Hours not otherwise specified same as Monday.

S. & K. La. 500, 3-36.

Preliminary Training School time table, 1937.

Miss E J Bocock (Poppy) on the roof of the South Wing during a smallpox scare, 1930s.

Matron's Office corridor, 1926.

Bomb damage, September, 1940.

Treasurer's House (Block 1) from Westminster Bridge Road, 9 September, 1940.

(*Top left*) Miss Marion A Gullan, Sister Tutor, 1914–1935. (*Top right*) Miss Dorothy S Coode, Home Sister 1903–1910, Sister of Preliminary Training School 1914–1924, Assistant Matron, 1925–1933. (*Bottom left*) Miss Marion E Gould, Sister Tutor, 1939–1954. (*Bottom right*) Miss Rosmond A Hone, Principal Sister Tutor, 1955–1972.

Nurses arriving by coach, 1949.

Riddell House library, 1954. (*Nursing Mirror*)

Preliminary Training School, Manor House Godalming, 1960.

Miss Gamlen, Sister, Preliminary Training School, Manor House, 1960.

Nightingales to arrive at any proper sense of what she was like, apart from her professional achievements. Historians searching for measured appreciation can find more than one way between the adulatory and the 'sneer' school of Lytton Strachey. Lucy Seymer knew her well, and in her Memoir of May 1953 took on the challenge of trying to portray her. Dame Alicia was five foot ten in height, with long and extremely thick wiry hair, always untidy. She rather enjoyed the story that her hair was the only thing that she had not mastered. Her solicitude for all her probationers and nurses was legendary, and she had a near perfect memory, and an eye for every detail. Though a very public figure, she was difficult to know and not easily approachable. The probationers never knew her and held her in awe. The Sisters were treated as true friends. One is quoted: 'She will always be the most inspiring woman I have ever met or can meet.' Seymer herself says that: 'In the latter part of her life she got on less well with men than with women . . . they often put her down as obstructive or uncooperative.' She wrote little, perhaps because her handwriting was nearly indecipherable. She wrote no text book, and very few articles. She was unimpressive as a public speaker, 'being unfortunately handicapped by a weak voice and poor delivery.' This aside, so many things said about her have a ring of FN: the duties of being a 'hostess' in the ward, or indeed anywhere in the hospital were indelibly impressed on the most junior probationer. 'We were always made to treat the patients as *guests*', one probationer is quoted as saying. She lived in some style, with a personal maid, and was most generous and hospitable. Her house and furnishings were thought to be in excellent taste: 'I do always feel that if Dame Alicia hadn't been a marvellous Matron, she would have a brilliant interior decorator,' said someone to Lucy Seymer. Others thought that she could equally have made her mark in politics. In religion she was markedly Anglo-Catholic, and markedly anti-'Roman'.

Institutions have a habit of creating legends, enhanced by the passage of time. The devotional and uncritical prose of the Fellowship *Journal* and of Lucy Seymer is fine as far as it goes, but without taking things too far, it is also useful to see Dame Alicia through other eyes. There is an interesting novel, not entirely well-written, called *A Bride for St Thomas* by Cynthia Nolan.[9] It recounts the experiences of a young Australian woman, widely travelled in the United States, and already with some training, who applied for entry in the 1930s. She had been told that 'Barts' and 'The London' had a waiting list for over a year, St

Mary's and Guy's for two terms; both required matriculation or the passing of an entrance examination. St Thomas's alone offered her an interview. (She repeats the well-known adage: 'Barts for money. The London for hard work. St Mary's for sport. Guy's for flirts. And St Thomas's for ladies.' There is a variant: 'Barts for workers, Guy's for flirts, Tommy's for snobs.')

One is given a picture of Dame Alicia, formidable certainly, dismissive of the girl's experience, totally proprietorial about the Hospital and the School, preoccupied with obedience and observance of detail, emphatic about her approachability when she was not, genuinely attempting to be friendly but in fact being frightening to a young woman – her height, voice and vocabulary are vividly portrayed. The teaching of a probationer is sharply scrutinised by the writer and critically questioned; it was didactic, averse to enquiry or argument, preoccupied with conformity and 'right practice'. There was an unremitting emphasis on doing menial tasks in the correct way, on bending to discipline – a sense of being 'broken in', and the frequent analogy with the Army is made. Pride in being a Nightingale was instilled all along the way. Dame Alicia is recorded – remember it is a novel – as saying:

At St Thomas's we keep no waiting list for entrants. I don't desire such a thing, it would be incompatible with the system on which I run this hospital – like the Army, my dear child. Does the Army keep a waiting list? It would be ridiculous. So I see every girl individually and I don't mind what recommendations she has, if she is not the right type she will not be admitted to the Florence Nightingale Training School . . . A girl came in here just now – I knew at once. I said to her, 'My dear child, it would not be kind, it would not be fair to you, to take you here. You would never feel comfortable with the other girls, never.' You see? A different background, a different tradition. 'Run along, my girl,' I advised her, 'and join one of the County Council hospitals. They would be pleased to have you.' [Miss Nolan was accepted.] 'And now, run along, child. But remember, any time during your training if you are in trouble, come to me, that is what I am here for. Now run along, and get on with the job. You are an extraordinarily lucky gel, I must say again, to be taking your training in the Nightingale School.'

Nightingales from these years will confirm, modify or reject this picture, given feelingly by the writer. One, in answering the questionnaire, writes: 'Dame Alicia was reluctant to accept me, being an only child, in case my parents needed me.' Another writes that 'Matron and Sisters were held in the greatest respect, almost in fear.' The sense of discipline and decorum comes through all the answers of this period. 'Social activities out of hospital were virtually impossible. Doors were locked at 10 pm, and late passes only occasionally allowed. In mufti when off duty and going out, hats were to be worn.' Those who had been at boarding school found the discipline and routines, as well as the social milieu, easier to absorb. Another writer brings out the best side of Dame Alicia's refusal to pay attention to external qualifications and her reliance on her own intuitive judgement with her story of how she was accepted on personal interview with very little by way of formal education, 'as a late developer'. She was also one of the last 'Lady Probationers', whose father paid £60 for the training, in spite of her lack of qualifications. So, in 1936 the 'dual entry system' ended.

What else comes from this handful of answers from Nightingales in Dame Alicia's last years? There was a strong belief, not usually seen as tenable, in the transference of skills that dominated the training. So, for example, perfection in sweeping and cleaning would lead to good care of patients and proper efficiency in theatre. Another answer to the questionnaire says:

Looking back now, there was no planned training scheme. If one were 'helpful' in a certain ward, one could stay for three – four months. I spent four months in my third year in Lilian Ward and asked to do my last night duty in that Ward. I had no out-patient or casualty experience. I learnt everything from the Ward Sisters.

The same writer takes up a theme that runs through many answers, not only for these years, a lament for the passing of what had been personal and continuous devotion to patients. She comments that when she herself was recently in hospital for over three weeks,

Not once did a Manager pay a visit to the Ward to see how we were getting on. This situation would not have arisen in my day and this is why I am fearful for the future. And perhaps one day Caps will come back and Christian names on duty will be forbidden.

This chapter rightly began, and rightly ends, with Dame Alicia. Her funeral service took place in the Hospital Chapel and she was buried in 'Brookwood Cemetery in the ground set aside for Nightingale Nurses which she herself had acquired for the Hospital.'[10] Not only did she preserve and hand on what she had received – literally, if one remembers – from FN, but greatly added to and enhanced it. Through her, the Idea, the Tradition was perpetuated. One could even say that she invented much of it. The idea of 'patients as honoured guests' has come up time and again in conversation, sometimes amusingly as when a consultant chastised one nurse with the reproach: 'too many honoured guests in this ward, nurse'. Alex Attewell, the Curator of the Nightingale Museum, recalls discussing with Miss Hone where this phrase originated. They realised that they could not trace it to FN herself and came to feel that it was Dame Alicia's interpretation of FN that prompted it – 'or rather, plain Dame Alicia.'

Since writing about the death of Dame Alicia Lloyd Still and her burial in Brookwood Cemetery, Roisin Tierney, in April 1997, has investigated the present position. A confusing picture emerged. St Thomas's Hospital purchased a plot in 1890; Dame Alicia purchased a plot for six further graves in 1919 for Nightingales. In 1950 Miss Smyth paid a sum of money for the maintenance of Dame Alicia's grave 'for ever hereafter', but the state of the plot generally and of individual graves was much in need of attention. Roisin Tierney writes that 'the last burial that I could find was in 1969, that of Katherine Newman. The graves themselves are almost all in need of attention from a stonemason. Some inscriptions are totally illegible, one headstone is leaning at an angle and a cross is lying on top of one grave. The surrounding kerb stones are largely overgrown and some are either in bits or have disappeared.'

There is a certain kind of unity in the story, so far, from 1860. It has been shewn that the history and development of the School was uneven. Its pioneering was overtaken, and FN's obstinate refusal to accept much medical advance seriously held back necessary developments in the training of nurses. The contract signed by the Fund Council with the Hospital disadvantaged it, and as the original Fund capital diminished, the Managers of the Hospital were the final authority; they appointed the Matron who was 'ex officio' Superintendent of the School. The introduction of Lady Specials was an acknowledgement of the unreality of the original idea for recruiting probationers only from the lower orders, and set the tone of the School. The foundation was laid for the notion that Nightingales were a superior body. Recollections and memoirs have shewn that the training was never as scrupulously carried out as laid down in theory, but there is an abiding sense of induction into humility, service and the unwavering belief that a training that began with a rigid insistence on the perfect carrying out of the most lowly tasks would fit women for positions that truly put them in authority and required total self-confidence. It was a pyramidical society, rigid with rules, based firmly on the central importance of the ward and the assiduous devotion to the welfare of the patients within it – those 'honoured guests'. Respect for the living carried over into respect for the dead, and nothing has been more moving than to be told of how 'the last Offices' were always performed, and that the dead were accompanied from the ward to the formal handing over to the mortuary porters by the nurses concerned, who then bade them farewell.

This was a closed, controlling society, but it knew and cared for all its ancillary workers. It took young women – never under 20 – and initiated them into a way of life of which so great a number has remained proud, and the Badge symbolises this. It is clear that this personalised Training School flagged in the years after Mrs Wardroper and was not so much revived as recreated by Dame Alicia. Her successor had been only two years in office when the Second World War began, and it will be seen how well the structure held in those times without parallel.

CHAPTER FIVE

Dispersal and Survival in the Second World War

In 1934 the British Government abandoned the 'ten-year rule' on which foreign policy had been based for the previous nine years, namely that war was not to be expected for ten years. In 1935, the Home Office brought out the first circulars concerning air-raid precautions; it was commonly assumed – looking at the massive rearmament of Germany under Hitler and the methods used by the Italians in attacking Abyssinia – that a war could come suddenly, and wipe out hundreds, indeed thousands of civilians in their own homes through aerial bombardment and gas attacks. Winston Churchill recorded that he was conscious of the new atmosphere when he returned to England from a holiday in 1936. In March of that year, the *New Statesman* wrote: 'We cannot too explicitly state our view that without a profound modification in the Nazi regime there can be no peace in Europe, but only a terrified waiting for war.' Rearmament had begun, not very well organised and still dividing public opinion. The main defence of the Munich Agreement made with Germany at the end of September 1938 – unless one believed Chamberlain's assertion that it meant 'Peace in our time' – was that it provided the indispensable extra months necessary to put the country on a war footing. Certainly, the meagre anti-aircraft defences erected round important targets – the author remembers two machine-guns put up to defend a large power station in Yorkshire – would support the case for inadequacy in 1938. One solitary First World War anti-aircraft gun was erected on Westminster Bridge to guard the Houses of Parliament and St Thomas's Hospital; it was kept polished by a rather bemused soldier.

By September 1939, detailed plans had been drawn up for St Thomas's – Hospital and School – in the event of war. The first proposal, thankfully abandoned, would have taken them to Brighton. Then came the plan for the whole of London and the surrounding area to be divided, when emergency came, into ten sectors radiating from a common centre. St Thomas's was Sector VIII. Sector I covered Essex, the base hospital being at Epping. Sector II was controlled from The London Hospital, with its base at Arlesey in Bedfordshire and the advanced base at South Mimms. In Sector III, Bart's and The Royal Free shared Arlesey, with the advanced base at Barnet. Sector IV was University College Hospital and Charing Cross Hospital, also sharing Arlesey as base. Sector V was the Middlesex Hospital, sharing Arlesey. Sector VI was St Mary's, linked to Basingstoke as was Sector VII, St George's and Westminster, with the advanced base at Staines. Sector IX was King's College Hospital with its base at Epsom. Sector X was Guy's with its base at Pembury. Sector VIII extended beyond Haslemere well into Surrey and Hampshire. The base hospital was to be at Basingstoke with an advanced base at Brookwood Mental Hospital.

A serious shortage of nurses was envisaged and appeals were put out by the Central Emergency Committee, whose spokeswoman was Miss Coode (Home Sister in Gassiot House), for nurses to come back from retirement or to volunteer to nurse as war work. The Fellowship *Journal* for 1939 contains a photograph of Miss Coode, Mrs Dudgeon, Miss Redl (Office Sister) and Miss Quentrall (Home Sister in Riddell House) 'who have been welcomed back on duty'.

Everyone knows that Armageddon did not arrive, so far as this country was concerned, in September 1939. The period from that month until the following May has come to be referred to as the 'Phoney War'. After the first excitement came boredom; evacuated people began to drift back home. By April 1940, the Prime Minister assured Parliament that Hitler 'had missed the 'bus'. Even so, the British Expeditionary Force in France had hospitals and needed nurses. Volume III of the Fellowship *Journal* contains articles by Nightingales such as: *Life on an Ambulance Train in France*. Two Nightingales found themselves billeted in a brothel 'fed and cared for by "Madame" of the yellow hair and fondant pink and mauve blouses, waited on and chatted to by "Giselle" who alternately looked like one of the knitting women in the French Revolution or the snappiest Parisienne, according to mood.' They talk about 'our daily life in this very extraordinary war'. Another Nightingale writes 'on active service', though censorship blacked out any means of knowing where; yet another wrote from a hospital ship. The same Volume has many other letters from *Somewhere in France*: 'There are several Nightingales here . . . Miss Harvey is looking after us all this afternoon . . . Florence Nightingale's lamp (a bicycle one) shines brightly on the table before us.' There are others from *Somewhere in England*. One, very detailed, from Miss Daisy Bridges tells:

> This Unit (No –, General Hospital) consists of 80 nurses . . . We represent between us some 70 different training schools . . . We are experiencing the difficulties of inactivity at a time when more than ever before we long to be up and doing . . . We are likely to remain here as long as there continues to be inactivity on the western front, but our hospital equipment is ready and packed, and we shall move at very short notice if and when the need arises.

The need arose somewhat differently from what was expected. In April 1940, the German forces began a series of offensives that culminated in the defeat of France. Paris was occupied on 14th June. At 6 pm on Friday 10th May, Churchill had been summoned to Buckingham Palace, where he accepted the King's commission to form a government. The 'Phoney War' was over. The *Journal* contains far more information than can be used here about the resulting calamities; for example, a very long article called *Three Army Sisters Leave France*, a representative story of what happened to so many. A contribution to the *Journal* entitled *Life in a Casualty Clearing Station* ends by describing embarkation on a hospital ship on which Miss Theodora Turner was working (Matron 1955 to 1965), 'and so safely back to England, though we heard poor old Boulogne getting it very hotly again when we were well out in the Channel.' Nightingales certainly kept the Editor of the *Journal* well-informed of their lives and experiences, many of them extremely harrowing.

St Thomas's itself, Hospital and School, having carried out evacuation procedures in the months after September 1939, returned home in mistaken optimism. The first bomb fell on St Thomas's on 9th September 1940, seriously damaging Gassiot House. An article by K.G. Douglas, later Matron of St Mary's Paddington, describes 'the first direct hit'. There was no hysteria amongst the patients or staff: in the rubble, dust and broken glass 'the Night Nurse produced clean, fresh blankets in which to wrap all the patients to keep them warm and to prevent the glass hurting them.' The kitchen of Adelaide Ward had not been damaged, the kettle was put on the Aga, tea was made. 'They all said it was the best cup of tea they had ever tasted, and soon they began singing.'

The second bomb came on Friday, 13th September, destroying Jericho (the Night Nurses' Dormitory) and the greater part of Hut E (male

VD Clinic). The third attack, which caused the greatest damage and disruption, happened on 15th September. 'It made a direct hit on the main corridor immediately south of the Central Hall, penetrating to the basement and causing the collapse of the Medical Out-patients' Block and Sitting Room of College House; it wrecked the kitchen, the canteen, the Dispensary and Administrative Block, putting all the essential services of the Hospital out of action.'[1] The first two bombs caused slight injuries only. The third killed two House Surgeons and a nurse; a nurse at the First Aid Post died later and three members of staff were seriously injured.

The questionnaires answered and sent in by Nightingales who were being trained in these years fill out the story of the war years in fascinating detail. Germany's attack on Russia enabled the Matron, Miss Hillyers, writing at Christmas 1941, to remind Nightingales of their Foundress and that the Crimea was once more a battlefield. She recalled them to *Notes on Nursing*, 'the most practical and inspiring handbook ever written . . . We have had to face the destruction of our beloved Nightingale Home, but its spirit lives on in our probationers, who are now able to spend six months of their first year in a country home, set in beautiful surroundings, working daily in the wards of our new hospital.'

In 1939, the PTS had first gone to Horton Mental Hospital in Epsom under Miss Celia Allen, but then found its 'permanent' home in what was clearly a delightful country house at Shamley Green near Guildford, and stayed there until August 1944. The idyllic surroundings made their mark: 'to ears accustomed to the bustle of Westminster Bridge and hawkers' cries in Paris Street it must seem strangely quiet', wrote Miss Allen in 1940.[2] V.D. Cotton described a meticulous resumption of the London routine: lectures, practicals, test papers, 'feverish swotting up of notes, and finishing off of bandages and splints', leading up to the final examination; and, all the time, the old insistence on perfect housework. Matron, that is Miss Hillyers, came on the last day 'when she broke the glad news that we were all going on to the Nightingale Home.' There follows some rather gushing prose, reminiscent of Angela Brazil, about 'the rioting and celebrations . . . including the crazy party where we waded through plates of biscuits and glasses of cider.' Miss Allen wrote an amusing description of life there.

The nurses sleep several in a room – the largest holds six beds and the excellent meals are served on long trestle tables in the dining room. Mr and Mrs Loyd have one sitting room in the house, in which they have no respite from our noise . . . The butler and his wife, the housekeeper, the housemaids and the boy are joined in the conspiracy of helpfulness . . . Hounds are often out and it is excellent country for riding.[3]

In 1944, the owners, Mr and the Hon. Mrs Loyd, wanted the house returned to their own use. What might have been a major crisis was avoided by accepting an invitation by The Royal Infirmary, Edinburgh, to transfer the PTS there, where it stayed until March 1945, when it was transferred to the complex at the Manor House near Godalming. The link with Edinburgh had a particular value because of the connection with Miss Pringle, and led to the singularly generous gesture of sending some of their own nurses to St Thomas's to allow Nightingales a rest period. The connection did not end in 1945. For example, in 1962 Miss Muriel Cullen became Deputy and not long afterwards Lady Superintendent of Nurses and Chief Nursing Officer there. One Nightingale writes:

In November 1944 I was a member of the first of three Sets to undertake PTS in Edinburgh. We either slept at Riddell House the night before journeying North, or met at King's Cross in the morning. Home Sister saw us onto the train in reserved carriages which were locked, and we were put in charge of the guard . . . At Edinburgh we were met by Miss Allen (the Lady Superintendent) and so to the Royal. Miss Allen impressed upon us the fact that we were guests and must be a credit to St Thomas's. The first night somebody flooded the bathroom. We all turned to and cleared up the mess, and the Set was bonded. The Set system was of great value to us as we travelled around from hospital to hospital. In all our trials and tribulations the Set were always together. Miss Allen reported that we were 'dull but worthy' – she may have been right. We never did anything spectacular.

The Nightingale Home to which the largest contingent went was at Park Prewett Mental Hospital, Basingstoke, shared with Sectors VI and VII. Wartime expediency brought a reduction in the age of entry from 20 to 19 and the PTS course was extended from eight to ten weeks. Examinations, which had been suspended during the 'phoney war', were reinstated, and all the recollected memories and all the printed literature tell the same story of training continuing, whatever the circumstances.

Lucilla Andrews in her book *No Time for Romance*, which she calls 'an autobiographical account of a few moments in British and personal history', describes how a 'late vocation' took her from the VADs in 1940 to the Nightingale School in September 1941, influenced by her admiration for a Nightingale with whom she had been working (none other than Miss Theodora Turner, who was to be Matron and Superintendent from 1955 to 1965).[4] Miss Turner advised her to 'just write to the Matron of St Thomas's'. It is interesting that one of her friends told her that 'you haven't a hope in hell of being accepted. It's the most difficult hospital in the country to get into' – this, in the middle of the vicissitudes of War. She was exhorted to 'enjoy yourself amongst all the toffee noses.' Matron, that is, Miss Hillyers, who interviewed her in a scrupulously clean and elegant office in the midst of chaos and bomb damage, said, 'Naturally, St Thomas's has to be careful only to accept the right type, Lucilla.' One former Nightingale told her that nothing would persuade her 'to endure that training again. Four years of sheer slavery.' Another told her that she would not last three months. She was accepted, and describes her training in the PTS at Shamley Green. Sister PTS told her that 'Once you get in the wards, nurse, before you have had time to draw breath your training will be over. And please remember you will work IN and not ON the wards.' After PTS, she went on, as an accepted probationer, to Park Prewett. Other hospitals had wards and departments there, but more than any of them, St Thomas's kept to itself.

> My set, as Nightingale Pros (only St Thomas's first-year students were Pros), worked under Nightingale Sisters, were taught by a Nightingale Sister Tutor, and lived together in the care of a Nightingale Home Sister ... The only personal contact I ever had with non-Nightingale nurses was in the long queues at the serving-counters in the dining room.

All our received information underlines these features of continuity maintained in the most extraordinary circumstances, of routines and practices sustained, and the sense of exclusiveness. Chapels were established; wards were, as far as possible, replicas of STH – with flowers as usual. The names of Sisters resound with their old titles, and Matron visited all her establishments regularly and frequently, driven in a car with strictly rationed petrol. In 1943, she was no longer provided with a driver and was frequently utterly exhausted by her work. Other nurses were greatly encouraged to take up cycling. Particularly in wartime, the importance of the Set is stressed. Here friendships and companionship helped to make many of the privations bearable. There is a general agreement that not only were they 'watched over' – that one expects, knowing the history of the School – but they were well fed. Mind you, hats had to be worn at all times when off duty in 'mufti'. Lucilla Andrews also recollected the unpleasant side of living in a former lunatic asylum – the protected windows, the huge brass locks and heavy keys on all the doors, the low beds (so patients would not injure themselves falling out) and the impossibility of converting everything to convenient use.

In 1941 the Nightingale Home was moved to a large house called Winkworth Hill, south of Godalming, near to what had become in effect St Thomas's Hospital at Hydestile. Here it was possible to build a teaching block, and for the fifty probationers in residence to work in the hospital wards, taken there by special bus. (Miss Hillyers, in her Presidential Address, said that it opened with the installation of twenty-one probationers and that 'Every Nightingale should go and visit it and they will feel refreshed and comforted.') As it was a distance from the hospital, 'the necessity has arisen for an outdoor uniform for Probationers. It is a plain dark blue coat and hat, and a picture of a Probationer in it will appear in the *Journal* [this at a time of stringent clothes rationing for everyone else]. It has also been considered advisable that Miss Smyth (Assistant Matron) should wear a different uniform to distinguish her from the other Sisters working under her charge at Godalming.'[5]

> The first set to occupy Winkworth Hill was the last set which lived in the Nightingale Home under the old regime, and each Nurse was determined to do her utmost to lay the traditional foundations of the new Nightingale Home . . . When Matron pays her frequent visits to the Hospital she always comes to Winkworth Hill, and often spends a night with us.[6]

Home Sister kept up the tradition of giving breakfast in bed to first-year probationers (Black Belt) on their days off – 'an elegant breakfast tray'.

Affection for the real St Thomas's always ran high, and it was counted a privilege to be sent back to work there. Two articles in the Fellowship *Journal*, by D.V. Hanitsch and A.L. Beale (this is the famous Sister Annie Beale) describe a joyous return just in time for further bombing in May 1941.

When one reads of bombing and destruction, of dispersal and evacuation, and of the immense logistical difficulties of keeping Hospital and School operative in such circumstances, it is with some amazement that one comes across the text of an Address to a conference by Miss Coode in November 1941, about 'The reconstruction we hope is going to take place in nursing conditions after the war. We want to get ready for it and to begin now.' This is not the only instance of confident forward planning, when the War was going so badly, to confound an historian – the Beveridge Report and the Green Paper on Education are two major instances. It seems impossible that anyone thinking rationally at that time could assume Victory – stalemate or worse might have been expected – and yet plans were being made to create a National Health Service as well as a system of secondary school education for everyone, and here is Miss Coode outlining her ideas for a complete reorganisation of nursing and the training of nurses. She anticipates the Block System: 'In this scheme the nurse takes her PTS course, then goes to the wards, is later withdrawn for theoretical instruction, and again back to the wards until her training is finished.' Or alternatively, she suggests the Experimental School: 'The nurse would have very careful and comprehensive instruction in theory and practice, she would pay for her training, and would get her instruction irrespective of the nursing needs of a particular hospital.' At the same conference another paper stressed that there was an existing problem in the shortage of nurses, that it went back well before the War, and would have to be tackled when the War ended – numbers, quality of entrant and training. Indomitable optimism.

An article in the *Journal* by the Hospitaller, that is, the Chaplain, Mr Schofield, fills in the picture with a reminder that the real hospital in London had not been abandoned. Two wards (Arthur and Nuffield) were still in use, and religious services were held in the temporary Chapel in Riddell House. The basement was also fully used for a number of purposes and the Out-Patients' Department continued to be extremely busy. At Hydestile in 1942, 'we now have things going as near the old ways as circumstances permit.' He continues:

On one evening I go to Winkworth Hill to take a Study Group for the Probationers, stay the night there and celebrate in their Chapel next morning. Just lately, the three miles on a bicycle have been far from tedious. The snow-covered countryside is pretty on Christmas cards only . . . Of course, wartime necessities, such as the division of the Hospital, the constant moving of nurses between one and another of our centres, makes the Hospitaller's work harder.[7]

Miss Hillyers had taken over as Matron and Superintendent in 1937, and she supervised not only the consequences of bombing but the extraordinarily complex arrangements required to run Sector VIII. For what surely was the most heroic achievement she was later made OBE, not exactly the most generous award. It is known that, as Sister PTS, she had been Dame Alicia's favourite candidate to succeed her, but she was of a very different character, quieter, less forceful, certainly not proprietorial. If one is allowed to make a completely superficial comment, her photograph shews her as a delightful and rather shy woman.

The answers to our questionnaires from those Nightingales who were trained in the War years emphasise how continuity was maintained even though each of them records frequent moves within the Sector. To give two examples, Miss Dorothea Hone was one of the first Set of the War, entering on 23rd September 1939. Her PTS was at Shamley Green near Guildford. She went to the Carol Service at St Thomas's and stayed in the Hospital for some months: 'We lived in the basement because of the bombing . . . We were dispersed to the various Sector Hospitals and our longest stay was at Park Prewett Mental Hospital outside Basingstoke . . . missing lectures through bombing, we pooled our day's work, hence helped to train each other.' Miss Muriel Cullen records that she also did the PTS at Shamley Green, and then: 'Pyrford Orthopaedic; Nightingale Home, Winkworth Hill, Hascombe; Villa I, Park Prewett, Basingstoke; Hill House, Chertsey; Hydestile, Surrey.' She was in fact a student at Pyrford, where nurses and Sisters from St Thomas's went when War began. 'They influenced me to change my original plan to train at The Middlesex and to apply to St Thomas's. I was much impressed by their efficiency and approach to patient care.' Miss Cullen's further comments fill in a remarkable picture of training in the War.

Because of the War and the dispersal of the Nightingale students throughout the Sector, our training programme was disrupted. It is astonishing that we were able to cover the practical and theoretical syllabus whilst moving from hospital to hospital. My programme: 7 weeks PTS: 7 weeks Orthopaedics: 10 weeks Men's Medical, Basingstoke: 6 weeks Women's Surgical, Basingstoke: 6 weeks Orthopaedics, Pyrford: 6 weeks Women's Surgical and Ophthalmic, Hydestile: 6 weeks Medical and Surgical, Hydestile: 6 weeks Gynaecology, Hydestile – end of first year as Probationer, first year practical nursing examination taken.

Second Year – 'on the staff', known as Staff Nurse. Experience in Medical, Surgical, Gynaecological and Children's Wards at Hydestile, both Day and Night Duty. Lectures in Anatomy, Physiology, Surgery and Medicine including Pharmacology, given during Ward time Day or Night duty.

Third Year – 9 months in London, then Botley's Park, Chertsey – Theatre and Acute Wards, Casualty Clearing Station during D-Day: lectures and examinations fitted in.

My training was excellent. Despite the disruption, we learnt to be adaptable.

Every questionnaire that was answered contained valuable information and often marvellously fresh comments bringing particular situations alive. To generalise: the probationers were mainly 20-plus on entry; a few were older and one Nightingale, who has tape-recorded her experiences, was only 19 when she applied. She was told by Dame Alicia to go away and work in a smaller hospital – where in her opinion the girl would receive no training in nursing but would become acclimatized to an atmosphere – and then report back, and she was accepted before she was 20. Almost always, they came from homes ranging from the reasonably well-to-do to the wealthy.

Quite a few of those trained were titled, for example Lady Brigid Guinness who married the grandson of the Kaiser and did not finish her training; Sir Alexander Cadogan's daughter, Gillian; the Hon. Anne Baring, Lady Elizabeth Montagu and Princess Lieven, and they made splendid nurses and with no 'side'.

Many had medical connections; many more had some claim on the School. The average educational qualification was School Certificate, though it was thought desirable that Matriculation Standard should have been reached. (Some, though a minority, had been to Public Schools; otherwise, to Grammar/High Schools – one must remember that these are the years before the implementation of the 1944 Education Act, when most pupils left Elementary Schools at 14, the more intelligent or fortunate entering Grammar Schools at 11 or 13 to take the School Certificate Examination at 15 or 16.) Dame Alicia preferred Matriculation, though this had lost its original meaning – which was that one was entered on to the roll, *matricula*, of a university and given automatic entry. It had become simply a way to indicate that a particular standard had been reached in groups of specified subjects. Even so, there is always the general sense that it was a privilege to be admitted to the Nightingale School. ('You need to be second cousin to the King to be let in, but it's worth a try, said big brother, and to my surprise I was accepted to start my training': May 1943.)

All our correspondents stress how the training held together, in spite of distances and many interruptions. Almost all commented on how tough the going was, but that in wartime and general austerity, it was accepted. Not all who entered completed the training, by any means.

> Twenty-two of us arrived, little knowing of all the blood and sweat and tears that lay ahead. Ten of us fell by the wayside in the first year, but twelve of us soldiered on and lived to tell the tale.

Food was good, except at Park Prewett. The hierarchy was martinet, yet capable of sympathy and affection when needed. It was a simpler, less sophisticated society than one would find in hospitals now, and there was a fair amount of girlish laughter and innocent fun. There was also simple ignorance. Lucilla Andrews wrote:

> One night near the end of the two months' term: 'Will someone please tell me WHAT that lecture was all about?' 'My God, are you another who didn't catch on? Bloody funny! Don't know what a lesbian or a homosexual is? Gather round, chickies, and aunty will elucidate.'[8]

There is also plenty of evidence of leisure activities such as choirs, orchestras, drama societies and sports. The advice to possess a bicycle

126

was sound, and responses are filled with the recollected joy of exploring the countryside. PTS was followed by three years of training based always on the wards themselves; lectures and revision were fitted in as was best possible, leaving very little time for relaxation. The hospital and the Set they were in were the centre of their lives.

Ward experience increasingly meant dealing with the casualties of war, many horrendous, but also an introduction to new forms of medicine and surgery: sulphonamides by 1942, and by D-Day, the first general use of penicillin.

A memorable lecture to which every nurse was called was one evening at Botley's Park. We were awaiting D-Day casualities. The lecturer was Lady Florey who was working with Sir Alexander Fleming on penicillin. She was the member of the team sent to start using it on patients, and instructed us in its administration. It was given by very large and painful injections.

On the surgical side, there were new ways of dealing with serious fractures (from experience first gained in the Spanish Civil War) and the first attempts at cosmetic surgery to deal with the severely disfigured. There is one contribution that looks back just before these breakthroughs, and incidentally shows how some medical treatments come full-circle.

In my first year (1942) several civilian casualties had amputated limbs from gas gangrene – the introduction of AGGS saved many legs. Recently when hearing of specially reared sterile maggots to treat infected wounds, I recollected the sight of maggots on wounds (1944) of casualties transferred from North Africa (in plaster for transport). These maggots were from sand flies from the desert – the surgeons were *delighted*.

When trained, 'our' nurses went on to a variety of careers and/or marriage. Marriage meant leaving. Almost without exception, they found that to be a Nightingale stood them professionally in good stead immediately, and often when they wished to return to nursing later on.

It may seem invidious, when so many worthwhile contributions have been made, to select some for quotation because of their freshness or their wit. However:

PTS: Breakfast at 7.30. 'Nurses, make your beds before you leave your rooms.' 8 to 9 am clean, polish and dust the whole house. 9 am classroom. Anatomy, Physiology, Nursing Lectures. A hospital bed and a large dummy patient to practise on. 1 pm lunch and, Oh bliss, off duty until 5 pm and then more lectures and writing up notes until 7.30 . . .

'Well, nurse,' said Sister, looking at me over her spectacles, 'you may have come top in the exams, but I doubt if you will ever make a nurse.'

First Nurses' Home after PTS. Admission block, Park Prewett Hospital. Twelve of us lived in a ward with curtained cubicles, designed for the safety of lunatics. Straw pillows, with the bed a few inches off the ground in case you had a fit. Windows which would only open a few inches in case you escaped. A key required to turn on the bath water in case you drowned. Stable doors to the lavatories – head and feet visible in case you tried to commit suicide.

We were issued each week with our food rations – a little bit of butter, sugar etc. We tried to keep them safe by hanging them in bags from the curtain rails. The mice ran up the curtains during the night and ate holes in the bags so that the rations fell on the floor.

It was January. It was very cold. It was tough.

There is no affection for Park Prewett in any recollection. Not only mice but rats took food, and in hot weather fleas appeared in large numbers. It was an unlovely building, in those days quite some miles away from Basingstoke which was only a small market town, though it had the advantage of being on the main railway line to London.

St Thomas's, increasingly referred to as 'The Mother Hospital', never closed. Bombing did not cease in 1940, and 1944 brought the horror of the V1, the 'Doodlebug' flying bomb, and the V2, the rocket that arrived totally without warning. In his book *English History, 1914–1945*, A.J.P. Taylor describes how most people thought that the bombing had ended by the middle of 1944. The explosion of the first 'flying bomb' over London on 13th June came, therefore, as an immense shock, leading to a new evacuation of women and children. Six thousand, one hundred and eighty-four people were killed, nearly all in London. But on 8th September the first rockets (V2s) landed, and it was realised that there was no defence against them. He gives the figures: two thousand, seven hundred and fifty-four people were killed.[9] The V1s and V2s made the whole of south-eastern England a danger zone; indeed it is now generally agreed that morale was nearer collapsing in 1944/45 than at any earlier time in the War. Only the Allied advance into the Netherlands and North Germany ended this menace.

Riddell House was never damaged enough to be out of use, and was lived in by the nurses posted back for short periods from all the Sector hospitals. Its comforts were greatly appreciated.

> I was really happy there. Life seemed to be calmer and we were not constantly browbeaten and hassled, though we had still to complete our chores on time . . . There were free theatre tickets to be had if we had an evening off – not a frequent occurrence but nevertheless an occasional treat . . . [When we were] second year nurses with white belts we were back again in London (after a holiday) . . . In 1944 nurses were never allowed to be idle while patients slept and if, when we were on night duty, we had a number of really ill people needing care, then life was indeed hectic . . . I remember one fateful Sunday morning when a bomb hit a block of flats opposite the Hospital just after everyone had come out of the shelters and gone home for breakfast. It was afternoon before any of us thought of going off duty.

If not in blocks of flats, the Lambeth locals lived in streets of small houses, with a poor standard of living and hygiene. (Many of these were damaged by the bombing.) One Nightingale recollects being issued with a small-tooth comb to deal with head lice and fleas, a practice still current in the early 1960s. Many of the inhabitants were ancillaries in the Hospital. 'One usually found that the (carpenter's) father and sometimes his grandfather had worked as a carpenter in the Hospital,' wrote one contributor. All the hospital workshops that kept life going were destroyed or badly damaged. This world was never to be re-created. One needs also to remember the other Lambeth, the Palace, the London residence of the Archbishop of Canterbury. It lay just across the road, and for many decades, Nightingales had been given free access to its gardens. Matrons, certainly Dame Alicia, were on close social terms with Archbishops, and they, in turn, were the normal preachers at the annual Nightingale service. The Palace was badly damaged by bombing, but was rebuilt; the old Lambeth round the Hospital almost disappeared in the post-War demolition and rebuilding.

All the questionnaires and the *Journal* emphasise the endless improvisation that never failed to meet needs; there is much reference to the use of fish kettles and other kitchen pans to sterilise instruments and equipment. With great regret, it had to be admitted that uniforms must be altered:

> Alas! the Nightingale cap is no longer worn by Probationers. Instead they now wear a neat American type which has been standardised by the Government with a mauve-striped dress, short sleeves and turned-down white collar and a black leather belt. Much as we miss the Nightingale cap this uniform looks very neat. The First Year Staff nurse retains her original dress (mauve stripe) but has a Nightingale cap and mauve belt. The uniforms for Sisters and Charge-Nurses have not changed.

A taped contribution emphasises the determination to keep the elaborate starched Sister's cap, each Sister improvising the equipment to ensure its appearance was maintained.

Just as many shops, after the most intense bombing, put up notices proclaiming 'Business as usual', this same indomitable spirit was to be found at St Thomas's itself (and without doubt in all the other hospitals). When a flying bomb wreaked further heavy damage on 4th July 1944 – a quiet Saturday afternoon – the basement ward, covered in dust, carried on with tea. A few hours later it was realised that the ward was unsafe. The Massage Department, which had been in absolute chaos, was turned into a ward for patients unable to be transferred by convoy to other locations in the Sector. The glass and debris were cleared up and the 'repair squad' got to work and brought back normality with miraculous speed. ('This unhappy event meant that once more Miss Randall had to take her Massage School to Manchester, and Miss Carlisle the Electrical Students to Woking.') A second flying bomb hit the Hospital directly on 15th July, this time causing the most serious and extensive damage including 'much of Mary Ward, Matron's house and the Nightingale Home. The whole of the staircase in Block Two was destroyed, also the corridor between Matron's house and Block Two. The Accountant's, Cashier's and Lady Almoner's clerks offices were rendered quite unusable, while the Nurses' Dining Room, which was being used as a carpenters' shop, suffered a similar fate.'[10]

Out in the Sector, Hydestile obviously became the new St Thomas's. (It closed only in 1968.)

We enjoyed our spells in Hydestile as the atmosphere was far more relaxed than in London. We were allowed to introduce dances, to which the medical staff and medical students were invited. We also had musical evenings as we had a number of gifted musicians among the staff. Our hours of off-duty were always difficult. We had either three hours off in the morning, 10–1, which might include lectures, or 2–5 pm or 5 pm onwards. They were unsocial and difficult to fit in with friends in or outside hospital. There were 1½ days off a week.

We worked three months on night duty at a stretch, having three weeks on night duty and then three nights off. We had three weeks' holiday a year. There was no night duty in one's first year, but we moved from ward to ward every two months, which had to include medical and surgical, male and female wards. Third year included special departments e.g. Out-patients, Casualty, Theatre, Mother-craft.

No nursing procedure was undertaken alone until it had been demonstrated and then supervised. We carried charts and these had to be filled in by the Ward Sister on leaving the ward or department. There was never an excuse for poor treatment or having no under-standing of what one was doing.

There is more detail about Hydestile from another contributor:

A flying bomb stopped over the hospital just as we were reporting round the table to Sister in the middle of the ward. Sister said, 'All nurses under the table, all patients under the beds!' One patient called out plaintively, 'I can't get under the bed.' She was 26 stones and being treated for obesity. The flying bomb glided into Godalming and we had casualties half an hour later. Another flying bomb just missed the hospital.

The other Sector hospitals and staff attracted affection and loyalty. 'One indelible memory is of Miss Bocock – Poppy – whizzing round Botley's Park on a sit-up-and-beg-bicycle, steering with one hand, the other clinging to her Sister's cap to prevent it being airborne.' There is equally affectionate remembrance of Midwifery at Woking, and indeed of Botley's Park.

Writing nostalgically, one Nightingale says:

The discipline which regulated how we acted, what we wore, how we looked, our attention to punctuality is now non-existent. Non-nursing friends could not understand how we tolerated such complete supervision of our lives. Certainly nobody today would put up with it. In a life which probably has had more 'downs' than 'ups', I have always been unfailingly grateful for what my training taught me.

Certain names of Sisters occur often enough in the story – Miss Harley, Miss Bocock, Miss Gould – but none seems to have made a greater impression than Miss Coode, who was the first Sister Tutor from 1914 to 1923 and afterwards continued to serve nursing with great distinction. She was a member of the first elected Council of the General Nursing Council. In 1933, she was elected to the Council of the Royal College of Nursing. From 1935 to 1937 she was President of the College, and then Vice-Chairman of the Council for three years. She became Chairman in 1940. She was one of those who returned to duty as a Nightingale at the outbreak of War, becoming Home Sister in Gassiot House. In 1943 she was appointed OBE.

It has been noted already that the danger from Hitler's 'secret weapons' only diminished and disappeared as the Allied Army under Montgomery advanced through Belgium, the Netherlands and into North Germany during 1944 and the first five months of 1945, but even so, the sense that the War would end in victory became irrefutable. In March 1945 the PTS returned from Edinburgh to Godalming, and the Nightingale Home returned to Riddell House shortly afterwards. Workmen began to move into the main Hospital buildings to clear more and more damage and to begin repairs, so that some work was in hand before the War in Europe ended, on 8th May. (An atomic bomb was dropped on Hiroshima on 6th August and a second on Nagasaki on 9th August. On 2nd September all the Japanese forces capitulated and that became VJ Day.)

The relief from sirens, black-out and bricks is almost unbelievable. Unfortunately it takes longer to remove bricks and replace windows than it did to put them up (or so it seems) . . . It is good to see Casualty and Out-Patient Department entrances unbricked and the steps being used again . . . The bonfires in Paris Street were terrifying, reminding us vividly of our past nights of fires, and every few moments the bangs of squibs exploding seemed to make it even more realistic.[11]

In November 1945, Miss Hillyers was able to announce that the PTS Nurses and the Nightingale Probationers were now living in the same buildings at Manor House, Godalming, and that 'at last we have been able to withdraw our Nurses from Park Prewett Hospital.'[12] The end of the War brought the retirement of most of the key Sisters – 'our shock troops' – and a crop of reminiscences over the years. On 12th May 1945, Miss Hillyers, in her President's Address to the Fellowship, said:

The cease-fire has sounded in Europe and with it your thoughts naturally will be turning to the future of our School and Hospital. It seems, therefore, right that I should tell you myself of my impending retirement in the Autumn. Owing to the War I have already stayed two years longer than my appointed time, according to superannuation arrangements brought in by the Treasurer and the Almoners some years ago. It is considered right to advertise the post and I hope experienced Nightingale nurses will make application. The task of the Matron, though glorious, is a heavy one and maybe a younger woman would be able to bring to it a fresher mind and firmness of purpose to blend the old with the new wisely and resolutely. I am afraid I have only just been able to keep the ship afloat, but I am happy to know that I shall be handing over to my successor the most loyal, efficient and progressive Nursing Staff in the world to support her. I ask you to forgive my many weaknesses and sins of omission, and I pray that in the new era that is dawning, the sterling qualities of our Nurses will shine forth and light the way.

Two things need to be noticed here: first, the humility of Miss Hillyers against her extraordinary achievement in coordinating the work of Sector Vlll throughout the whole of the War; and second, the notion – for the first time – of publicly advertising the post of Matron. Whatever the intention of this innovation, in the Fellowship Meeting on 3rd November 1945, Miss Hillyers announced that Miss Smyth had been appointed as her successor. The handover was, therefore, straightforward. Miss Smyth was the granddaughter of one of the earliest members of the Fund Council, had been a Ward Sister, and had then worked elsewhere before returning in 1939 as Assistant Matron to Miss

Hillyers. The first years of the War she spent in London, and then later as Acting Matron at Hydestile.

Miss Gould looked back over *Nursing Education in Time of War* in Volume Four of the *Journal*, which summarises much of what has been written here already. She wrote about 'the nightmare chessboard movement of nurses. . . the dispositions being governed by a chart that showed in lines of different colours' how long each Set had spent in the Sector and how much in the 'Mother School' By 1944/45, six PTS courses were held every year. She paid great tribute to the Medical Staff whose senior members spent so much time on the road to get round the Sector 'and yet have invariably been ready to start their lectures at the appointed time, 9.15 am.' The syllabus did not change, with one exception: the discontinuation of the course on Elementary Science, because of difficulties in laboratory accommodation. True to the Nightingale tradition set by Dame Alicia and Miss Gullen, 'We have learnt afresh, when good practical experience was all too rare, how little theoretical teaching can avail, without that backbone of nursing education, the consistent teaching of bedside care by the Ward Sisters; and without that practical experience which gives life to the dry bones of theory.'

The retirements of key figures, so lovingly celebrated, were of: Minnie Randell who had run the Massage School since 1912; Annie Beale who became Sister Casualty in 1909; Florence Harley, Home Sister for 22 years since 1923; Miss May in charge of the Private Nursing Staff since 1920; and Miss Coode. All attracted generous appraisal.

The European War ended and a new Labour Government was elected in July. Churchill had proposed that the Coalition Government should continue until the end of the war against Japan. On 21st May Attlee, the leader of the Labour Party and Deputy Prime Minister, offered to continue the Coalition only until October. Churchill rejected this offer and resigned on 23rd May. He formed a 'Caretaker Government' to prepare for a General Election. Voting took place on 5th July; both Conservative and Labour ran more than 600 candidates; the Liberals ran 306. The results were announced on 26th July (time had to be allowed for the Services Vote to be counted). The results were: 393 Labour, 213 Conservative, 12 Liberal, 3 ILP, 2 Communist, 14 Independent.

Given the controversial nature of the programme of the new Labour Government, which in effect set out to change the whole pattern of British society, it is important to note that Labour obtained 47.8 per cent of the votes cast. This enabled Churchill to bring in the 'mandate' argument, that so small a majority of votes did not give a government a 'mandate' to embark on such far-reaching change.

Many who were associated with the serving Forces claimed to have known that there would be a swing to Labour in the Forces' vote, and it has often been maintained that this gained the Labour victory. If so, it sprang from a determination that, as against 1918, when a 'new society' was proclaimed and not realised, this time a 'brave new world' would be achieved. One of the most far-reaching changes that the new government was committed to was the introduction of a comprehensive, all-enfolding National Health Service, and this was unavoidably to have major consequences for hospitals, doctors, nurses and the training of nurses.

Without any doubt, the acceptance of such a programme and many others like it, involving transport, coal-mining and education, was made much easier by the fact that from the outbreak of War in 1939, the government had assumed direct control of every major aspect of the national life, so that 'Government control' or 'State control' had become part of the national consciousnesses. The Emergency Hospital Service, and with it the Sector system for the London teaching hospitals, is an example of this. Administrators, doctors and nurses got used to coordinated effort and lines of control: in this case, from the centre of administration in Kingston-upon-Thames, where Miss Hillyers had her Headquarters.

The free National Health Service, the pride of the whole social welfare edifice, was initiated by the National Health Service Act of 1946 (ratified only after the bitter opposition of much of the medical profession had been dealt with). The Act came into operation on 5th July 1948.

The community accepted full responsibility for the care of the sick, and nearly all the hospitals in England and Wales became publicly owned. No longer could governments play a mediatory role between a loose alliance of local authorities and an even looser alliance of voluntary hospitals. The quality of medical care, the terms and conditions of service of the staff working in the hospitals, and the power and privileges of professional bodies became all on one day matters with which central government was immediately concerned. At last it was possible for dramatic improvements to be made in the training and working conditions of the nursing profession.[13]

A major argument has developed amongst historians and economists about the wisdom of the social programme of the Labour Government 1945–1950. There is no doubt about their commitment to it; it was their 'raison d'être'. But it was embarked upon at a time when the national economy was exhausted, industry worn out, national investments spent by War, and with a tired population. There is an argument that the Government got the cart before the horse, that every effort should have been put into the reconstruction of the economy *before* embarking on the creation of the Welfare State. There is no denying that the hopes and dreams of the post-War years were haunted by massive economic crises which by the time of the General Election of 1950 brought a dramatic reversal of the position of the Labour Government. It saw Labour with 315 seats, Conservatives with 297 and Liberal with 9. In the 1951 Election, Labour had 295 Seats and the Conservatives 321.

The effect of these economic crises was seen in the indecision and changes in plans concerning the re-building and reorganisation of the Hospital and the School from the ruins of war.

CHAPTER SIX

Revival and Regeneration

From 1948 the Nightingale School was an element in the National Health Service; that is, it trained nurses who would serve in the new system. From the 1950s onwards and, markedly, in the 1960s, there were ever more radical changes in the social patterns of British life which were bound to be reflected in the backgrounds and attitudes of the young women coming forward to be trained in the School. Background still counted when it came to consideration for admission, but academic qualifications for entry also began to rise and broaden; A-Levels and a greater number of degrees make their appearance, as well as later ages of entry. The official minimum age of entry remained at 19.

Reports concerned with every aspect of the training of nurses and conditions in nursing had begun before the war, such as the *Lancet* Commission of 1932. In November 1937, another committee had been appointed under the Chairmanship of the Earl of Athlone,

> to inquire into the arrangements at present in operation with regard to the recruitment, training and registration and the terms and conditions of service of persons engaged in nursing the sick and to report whether any changes are necessary in those arrangements or any other measures expedient for the purpose of maintaining an adequate service are necessary for both institutional and domiciliary nursing.

The Athlone Committee published an interim Report in 1939; no final Report was ever issued because of the War. Brian Abel-Smith conveniently summarises the recommendations:

> Trained nurses should have higher pay and a Nurses' Salaries Committee should be established to regulate nurses' salaries. Nurses should work a 96-hour fortnight and have four weeks' leave each year. In a number of hospitals accommodation and catering needed to be

improved. More domestic staff should be employed to relieve the nurse of 'the daily repetition of routine tasks'. Unreasonable rules and restrictions affecting the nurse's life should be reviewed in the light of modern conditions.[1]

The themes and arguments of such commissions and committees did not impinge on the School or St Thomas's before or, obviously, during the war. In 1941 another Committee, chaired by Lord Horder (one of the most distinguished doctors of the time), was set up by the Royal College of Nursing – not the Government – to look yet again at what was to be termed 'nursing reconstruction'. It anticipated with great optimism, as most people did, the post-war world, confidently expecting a large-scale reconstruction of hospitals and massive public investment in the Health Service. It came out in sections over eight years.

Section I: on the Assistant Nurse (1942)
Section II: on Education and Training (1943)
Section III: on Recruitment (1943)
Section IV: on the Social and Economic Conditions of the Nurse (1949)

St Thomas's had never been involved in the matter of the assistant nurse. The recommendations on education and training caused little worry. The emphasis on the importance of the Ward Sister, described as 'most certainly the lynch-pin of the whole system', had been central to the Nightingale School since its first days; in fact it *was* the Nightingale system.

By 1949, the NHS was beginning to function, and a central machinery for negotiating and standardising salaries and conditions of work (the Whitley Council) had been set up. The Horder Committee came to see, the hard way, that the post-war years were a time of such change that it was not feasible to put forward major recommendations in any detail. Also, wartime optimism soon encountered reality, as the US Government abolished Lend-Lease arrangements, and an exhausted and bankrupt country had to begin to pay its own bills. The bitterly cold winter of 1946/47 brought the rationing of bread and potatoes, never experienced during the War, massive fuel shortages and industrial unrest.

The NHS meant, by definition, that all hospitals were seen as parts of a national framework, but it is clear that in fact the great teaching hospitals were left very much to continue as before, with their own governing boards, certainly until the Salmon Report (1966). They were outside the jurisdiction of the Regional Health Authorities and directly responsible to the Ministry. One Nightingale remembers:

> In my time the Hospital came under the jurisdiction of the NHS. At first, the only difference appeared to be the change of name on the ambulances, but gradually other changes came in which we resented; for example, a big increase in salary which left us worse off due to the fact that there was now a system of deductions.

The new Whitley Council of 1948 began to grant student nurses £100 a year as training allowance. From January 1949 this became £200, but £100 was immediately deducted for board and lodging. At the end of their first year they were to be given £5, and at the end of the second and third years £10 and £15 were added to salaries. No lump sum was paid on passing final examinations – 'The reward is that she is then a qualified nurse', said the *Journal*.[2]

Other committees followed in the 1950s and 1960s; a central issue was always to be nurses' pay. Not much attention is going to be given to this in this book, because pay has a meaning only when related to prices and the cost of living. To make one or two totally random remarks, a new well-equipped detached house in the suburbs could be bought for £600 in 1939 and a Ford 8 motor-car for £100. As soon as the War ended, inflation began, not least because there were so many shortages. A motor-car that cost £165 new in 1939 was sold for £425 in 1946, having done 45,000 miles. It could be maintained that the financial history of this country since 1945 is the history of inflation, which soared into hitherto unthinkable regions in the 1970s – 25 per cent in 1978. One further example: the fees of a particular independent school in 1960 were £500 a year; in 1970, £690; in 1980, £2800; in 1990, £9400; and in 1997, £14,250.

It could be said with justification that some of the most important preoccupations of the national committees and councils were contrary to the Nightingale ethos. Its probationers had always been shaped or formed by beginning with the lowliest of tasks – for example, to 'carry the bed-pan to the greater Glory of God'. Low pay, very long hours and imperious discipline had been accepted as central to a training into service. Similarly, affiliation with a trade union or any movement towards shortening the duration of training had been seen as inimical to the purposes of the School. It was part of the 'Establishment' and many of its candidates came from well-to-do homes, not necessarily dependent on their pay – from what Lady Antonia Fraser, in another context, referred to as 'the servant-employing Culture'. ('We were mostly middle or upper class and mixed well.' 'We were taught to cross all social barriers and to get on with everyone.') It has also been observed, ironically, that Nightingales were so exhausted by work that they had little time for spending money. Most of the questionnaires from this period – and there are many of them – give a strong sense of life in the School and the Hospital as being very much in continuity with previous decades.

> That wonderful Matron, Miss Smyth, said: 'Remember nurse, it is not the gallant acts in life that take courage, it is the courage to face the discipline of daily routine.'
>
> Punctuality, dependability and, very importantly, observation were the essentials looked for by the senior staff . . . Whilst we worked hard and long I was never aware of complaining from anyone. We were so grateful for the privilege of being trained in the Nightingale School.
>
> I know that I became a different creature when I got into that uniform. I was confident then. I left *knowing* that the Sisters were everything and the doctors were almost by the way. I couldn't believe it when I heard nurses in other hospitals call doctors 'Sir' – ours were always just plain Dr or Mr. The thing I often tell people about even today was the evening routine – the Pros went around turning off the light over every bed until only the little lamp at Sister's desk was on. Then we started our prayers, each evening the same, 'Lighten our darkness we beseech Thee, Oh Lord . . .'

This was the world of Florence Nightingale and Dame Alicia, alive and well.

One contributor to the questionnaires sent in a copy of an undated article by the military historian John Keegan, written for the *Telegraph Magazine*. It was sparked off by a ministerial attempt in the 1990s to tamper with nurses' uniforms. Keegan robustly defended the strictness of discipline, the attention to detail and the precise hierarchy of rank indicated by uniform. He spoke from first-hand knowledge because he had been a patient at St Thomas's just after the war.

> (In 1948) the day began with the day and night staffs lining up facing each other in the middle of the ward. Each nurse was impeccably dressed in a uniform that defined her state of training. At eight o'clock precisely, Sister entered, took her seat at her writing table between the rows and called forward each member of staff in turn to make a report – if she was going off duty – or receive instructions if she was coming on . . . The effect on the patients was unforgettable.

He went on to tell of a patient 'who had decided to die', whilst 'Sister Pruneface' was away.

> When she got back she recognised a situation she knew all about and decided to deal with it. The would-be corpse's bed was put next to her office, and fifty times a day she shot out to sit him up, pummel his chest, rub his back, wash him, exercise him, feed him and if necessary shout at him. When her eye was off him, he sank back on the pillows and got on with dying. When she caught him at it, she seized the spirit bottle and gave him a stinging dose of massage. The ward watched with fascination the long drawn-out battle of wills between the angel of death and the avenging angel of mercy. For a while the decision hung in the balance but in the end Pruneface won . . . A tough young south Londoner in the bed next to me summed up the ward's feelings. 'He was too frightened to die' . . . The sight of her St Thomas's uniform gave us the same feeling that shaken troops have when they know the Guards are between them and the enemy.[3]

Even so, the occasional dissentient voice begins to be heard in the answers to the questionnaire.

> The discipline was overdone and there seemed very little account taken of ourselves as people. We had to conform, or out! I was not very happy because I was still growing up and it was all very painful . . . I was glad when the four years ended.

Much the most biting criticism so far comes at this point, at some length.

141

At 18 I went into a total work-oriented setting. I never got to know a person from another profession or department . . . However, by the end of four years (1952 to 1956) I knew more about my subject than graduates knew of theirs . . . BUT I knew nothing of normal behaviour . . . unable to accept dull normality. I could have done with a lot more career guidance. Great opportunities were missed – the few late visits to factories did not overcome my inertia or lack of curiosity about the world around me . . . My ward experiences took me through a wide range of emotions including despair, humiliation and exhaustion . . . Most of us by this time had chronic boils. Note: the sectarian nature of the society – no RCs, Jews etc, few Non-Conformists, the odd atheist, three or four high-born black nurses, a handful of black domestics, two male nurses (not Nightingales) in the whole establishment. Note: no lavatories at all designated for nurses – if essential, one went to the domestics' quarters.

The same writer, however, also comments that the nature of the intake was beginning to change.

I have a feeling my Set was the first to have a mix, which included me. I would be interested to know what led to the recruitment of a wider social range, drawing from the post-war grammar school people who had never paid school fees.

Her final verdict on her time in the 1950s was that 'I knew I was learning how to nurse and was hooked by this extraordinary relationship with patients and the difference I could make to their world.'

Before the War it was characteristic of almost all education to pay little or no attention to 'current affairs' or 'politics', and no institution accepted that it had a duty to provide 'careers guidance', still less careers education. The Nightingale School was in no sense unusual in simply teaching its list of studies. Wartime brought an awakening of social interest and political awareness, which played its part in the General Election result of 1945. In the post-war world, it began to be recognised that opportunities for more intensive study should be provided, and the Nightingale School introduced the Day Block System, somewhat tentatively, at Hydestile in January 1945. But there is no evidence that the School in these years took on responsibility for a broader general education of nurses.

The Day Block System is described in some detail by Miss Gould in the Fellowship *Journal* in 1946. She acknowledged that the pioneering work had been done in the Southend General Hospital, based on developments in the United States.

The full Block System has long been advocated by the Royal College of Nursing and other educational bodies, and is in practice in a few of our Nursing Schools. It entails taking the nurses from the wards for 'Blocks of Theory' in the classroom. These Blocks would consist in the PTS period of eight to twelve weeks, and two or three other theoretical Blocks of from four to six weeks during the first three years of training.

Miss Gould went on to write that the Day Block System was being used in the Nightingale School for probationers only; Miss Gullen's original syllabus remained the basis, with additional lectures on X-rays, Pathology and the work of the sanatoria and of the Lady Almoner. Because the Hospital was still dispersed in the Sector, transporting to and from Hydestile to London took up quite a lot of time and restricted further developments. Hydestile was to remain a larger hospital than the London 'Mother House' for many years to come.

In 1948 Miss Gould wrote of the necessity for advanced planning so that undue strain should not be put on the wards, but she recognised that 'the main weight of the new experimental system has been borne by the Ward Sisters.' Block days for the different Sets followed a similar pattern: first prayers, then roll call and a lecture or revision class. At 10 am the massage class supervised ten minutes of physical exercises. A 'quick' lunch preceded individual or group study, and a lecture or demonstration. The afternoons were taken up with group practice classes and further lectures, or with group and individual study. Tea was at 4 pm, followed by visits to the wards for bathing or by further practice in the class room. The working day ended at 5.30 pm.

The 1948 edition of the *Journal* notes that Dr John Cohen, in his Minority Report published in November of that year, had written that the educational value of the Block System had yet to be proved, but that it had been found that nurses were less tired 'and are having more opportunity for outside interests'. A further result was the improvement in examination results and Ward Reports, so his reservations about the system seem surprising.[4]

In 1950 Miss Gould was saying that, whilst the Block System remained important, 'The problems which at the moment engage our special attention are the introduction of the preventive and social aspect of medicine into the syllabus and the linking of the practical teaching in the wards and classrooms.' She then outlined a truly innovative programme for the second and third year Blocks, to take student nurses into the patients' homes, into clinics, convalescent homes, factories, homes for children, homeless families, chronic sick and aged people, and housing estates.

> Some have been out with the District Nurse, others have been to see the work of Health Visitors and to see Welfare Centres . . . In this way the student nurse will be able to appreciate the preventive aspect of medicine, and also to visualise the life of her patient before and after she enters the hospital, and so to consider her as an individual with a past and present, and not just as a person who happens to be ill.

This indeed is FN's philosophy, brought into the 1950s. Many Nightingales from this time have mentioned in answering the questionnaire how valuable to them the Block System was. It was the first major curriculum innovation for many decades.

It is time to turn again to the wider context of the School and Hospital in the NHS. In 1948, St Thomas's became the nucleus of a 1,600-bed group which was to include:

The Lambeth Hospital (joined only in 1964; closed in 1976)
The South Western Hospital (joined only in 1968; transferred to Lambeth Heath Care Trust 1993)
The Royal Waterloo Hospital (joined 1948; closed 1976)
The General Lying-in Hospital (joined 1948; closed 1971)
The Grosvenor Hospital (joined 1948; closed 1976)
The Nightingale School

This was symbolised by the application for a new coat-of-arms that could be used in a Common Seal. The *Journal* records that with the advent of the NHS the control of the Hospital was removed from the hands of the old Governors, and the Mayor and Commonalty of the City of London were no longer directly concerned with the Hospital's affairs. The Act laid down that Boards of Governors were to be corporate bodies empowered to use a Common Seal, and at their first meeting in July 1948 the new Governing Body applied to the College of Arms for a Grant of Arms.

From now onwards there is very frequent reference in many different sources to the demolition of the damaged buildings of St Thomas's, the redecorating and re-equipping of wards and offices – usually in 'pastel shades' – and to what became long drawn-out arguments between Governors, the Matron, administrators and architects about the design and order of the new buildings. Much of what was proposed was never built, and argument seemed to continue indefinitely about the nature and quality of what was built. Lambeth Palace Road was re-routed and old housing pulled down. At a very late point in the writing of this book, a Nightingale who was trained in these years said that there had been serious discussion as to whether it was better to repair, make secure and rebuild such a damaged hospital, or to abandon the site and move to another – on Wandsworth Common, next to the prison. In the same conversation she remembered the many mistakes and blunders made by builders and the theoretically impossible but nevertheless real flooding of the hospital basement from the river, rats and all.

To many Nightingales, the decision in the rebuilding to raise the Great Corridor, the dominating feature of the pre-war hospital, from ground to first floor level was an historic event. In the old building it had been, so to speak, the centre of the universe, and it was felt that the change would spoil what had been so important. Similarly, the 'Deep Ward Plan', regarded as unavoidable and essential for the new buildings, would make morning and evening prayers – such a major element in the Nightingale world – no longer feasible.

In 1949, rebuilding and rearranging led to the acquisition of Chelsea Court, north of the river, to become the Nurses' Home. In 1953 a house in Ashley Gardens, adjacent to Westminster Cathedral, was bought as a home for the Night Nurses. This meant that a prominent feature in the lives of Nightingales, referred to time and again, was the travelling to and from work in special buses, and always in correct dress. One result was increased tiredness for people already made tired by work, so that the comment is made by one writer after another that there was next to no time or energy for leisurely pursuits outside the Hospital, in spite of Dr Cohen's optimism. Men were never allowed in the Homes under any circumstances; the conventual atmosphere continued into the late

1960s and early 1970s. Although the following was written to describe the early 1960s, the general pattern evokes what has been told of the earlier years.

> Having come straight from a convent boarding school, (to me) the Nurses' Homes seemed very little different. Chelsea Court was a beautiful Home. PTS had been spent at Godalming... No male visitors were allowed beyond the reception area, with the 'brown ladies' always hovering to ensure rules were not broken. Knotted sheets after 9 pm to escape to the King's Road were not unusual. Meals were at set times with tables beautifully laid with silver, and staff serving food. A book had to be filled in to confirm that you wished to eat; nothing was kept if you appeared late... A late pass was given once a week, and never if on night duty or on an early shift the next day. Any visitors were assessed on entry... and some were turned away.
>
> The Night Nurses' Home (St John's House) meant using the first day after work to transport all personal belongings from one Home to another. A coach was provided for a particular time: it was on your own head if this was missed... as one was only allowed outside the Hospital or coach if one were in outdoor uniform. The police on the river boats were always kind and my friends and I got to know them very well.

Miss Smyth was always anxious to remind Nightingales that the Fellowship was affiliated to the National Council of Nurses of Great Britain and Northern Ireland, membership of which opened the doors not only to national meetings but to the speedily growing numbers of international gatherings. (It is interesting to note the rash of visits to pleasant Scandinavian countries that followed in the ensuing years.) She also brought members up to date about the Nurses' Bill, then on its way through Parliament. This envisaged a reshaping of the General Nursing Council with an enlarged membership of thirty-four, twenty-three of whom would be nurses. Its proposed further provisions were:

1. A Mental Nurses' Committee
2. New schemes of training
3. The establishment of regional Standing Nurse Training Committees

4. The administration by the General Nursing Council of the funds for nurse training

Understandably, Miss Smyth worried about the Standing Nurse Training Committees and their likely effect on the Nightingale School. Need she have worried when the Nurses' Act was passed in 1949? In 1950 she wrote: 'It seems but the other day that the new NHS was approaching, and now we are well established within it and looking more or less the same.' At the same time she made a remark that was vastly more significant for the future: that the Minister was even then seeking ways to reduce the cost of the Service which had been in operation for two years only. There had undoubtedly been a spending spree after all the wartime shortages. So the NHS was already in crisis, and from this came the first major quarrel within the Attlee Cabinet that led to the resignation of Aneurin Bevan and Harold Wilson. The cost of the NHS within the national budget has been one of the central controversies of political life ever since.

Society itself was changing with increasing rapidity. The first beginnings of a new kind of questioning of traditions and authority was shewing in the population generally, and particularly in young people, all of whom were receiving secondary education as the 1944 Act was being implemented. Young women coming to train in the School were part of this. At the same time the increasingly widespread use of antibiotics was changing the nature of nursing. This is an interesting point, forcibly made in a letter by Miss Nuttall:

The phrase 'only good nursing will pull him through' for the patient with pneumonia has been completely replaced by 'Take these tablets and if you're not better by the end of five days, come back and see me.' No one seems sufficiently to have noticed the disappearance of this key role.

Therefore, one of the imponderable and fascinating questions is the effect, real as against intended, of the sermons that continued to be preached in the Chapel at the annual Fellowship Commemoration Service. One distinguished preacher after another put forward, in the grandest language, the ideals dear to Florence Nightingale. It was assumed that the nursing body, from probationer to Matron, was united in transcendental attitudes.

147

You whose lives have been dedicated in the highest spirit of Christian service, and to whose work your faith gives a meaning and inspiration which could be drawn from no other source . . . I call upon you to join in the greatest missionary campaign that has ever been fought in the long history of humanity.

This was Canon Spencer Leeson, former Headmaster of Winchester College and later a Bishop. Other sermons took up the Florence Nightingale theme: 'She was the greatest personality alive . . . She was sent by God . . . She was sent and then secondly she was shaped . . . She was sent and shaped in order that she might succeed – and succeed she did.' This was Canon Lloyd Hughes in 1951. He continued:

On receiving a letter which years before would have sent her rampaging, she scribbled to a friend, 'Shall I royally disregard it – or shall I give them a buster?' Now I believe of the older and senior Sisters and Nurses that sometimes they must give the Juniors a real buster. But there should never cease to appear through them that gracious nature and character which they can trace to its source.

Dean Inge of St Paul's once described a sermon as 'A bucket-full of water thrown over a lot of narrow-necked vessels'. True or untrue? There is such a strong analogy with school Speech Days, a point made in 1958 by the Matron, Miss Turner, at a Presentation of Medals and Honour Certificates:

This is an historic occasion in the life of the Nightingale Training School. For the first time parents of all Nurses receiving certificates have been invited to the ceremony . . . I am very pleased to welcome so many parents, I feel a little like a Headmistress in a School. This is the first time in my life I have had this curious feeling.[5]

The cult of being special continued and was reinforced. Mr Macmillan is said to have coined the aphorism 'The Army: The Guards; Nurses: Nightingales.' When King George VI underwent a serious operation in March 1951, three nurses, all Nightingales, were called upon to look after him, specifically asked for by the Physician to the King. On day duty there were Miss Elizabeth Perrin Brown and Miss Rosamond Hone; on night duty, Miss Barbara Tyler. Miss Hone wrote in the Fellowship *Journal* about her experience of living in Buckingham Palace to carry out this duty. (She is the distinguished nurse to whom the Fellowship has dedicated this book.) There was a massive opportunity further to enhance the Nightingale legend and the Tradition in 1954, the centenary of the outbreak of the Crimean War.

For the years from about 1950 to 1960, there has been an abundance of replies from Nightingales to the questionnaire, often with many additional comments, stories and insights. It is impossible to quote from all of them. Perhaps the writers will understand and accept that what follows is an attempt at a representative sample because so many of their experiences were shared. It is not possible to give the names of every contributor to the text. Above all, there is the preponderant sense of the privilege of being trained as a Nightingale, whatever the occasional criticism. The importance of the Set is emphasised time and again – and this was joyfully evident at the reunion in May 1996. The weariness and tiredness that came from moving around in the Sector during the course of training, the acceptance, sometimes reluctantly, of rigid discipline, tempered on many crucial occasions by tenderness, and above all the strong sense of hierarchy, stand out always. Here was a well-defined society into which they were inducted, whose pyramidical head was the Matron, and which was to end in 1970. A fairly common observation from Nightingales of the 1950s and 1960s is that they doubt if a modern generation would accept the pattern in which they lived and worked.

Susan Coventry described her training from 1951 to 1955 in her book *Images of a Nightingale* published in 1990. She tells the same story as that which can be distilled from all the questionnaires of the same period: her pride in her training and in her sense of belonging to a visible community shines through. She emphasises the 'character formation' of these years; that, in uniform, she felt a special kind of person, a more disciplined being. There is one passage particularly worth the quoting, arising from her own son's serious illness some years later, and the pain he endured.

At St Thomas' there was a completely different attitude regarding pain. It was the enemy to be fought at every level. We were taught numerous ways to relieve pain and, if they were not effective, a doctor would be found to give patients the best possible drug to make them better. In all the years of my training, I can remember not one patient who was allowed to suffer the sort of pain my son suffered . . .

That instance was perhaps the first time I had the occasion to judge one of the supreme merits of the Nightingale training. There was no room in its ethical philosophies, from base to crown, for one single item of casualness. That was what all its rules were based upon.

This was what I used to feel as I tore up the stairs with half a minute to spare before I was due on duty. If that training had not taught me that I could never be late – nothing could. But it had taught me, and I was never late.[6]

It is important, for the sake of verity, to accept that some formed different views of their training, like the following:

> It was an excellent training in practical skills, following orders and adapting without question to various routines . . . Theory was limited to learning to reproduce diluted medical information. Questioning or discussion were not encouraged; there was no guidance in making decisions or in problem-solving

> At the time I was absorbed and very happy. Looking back on my training I think I allowed myself to be protected from pain, challenge and reality . . . I have an image of myself with the bib of my starched apron acting as a shield over my heart, and keeping me immature, compliant or conformist.

Readers of this book who are Nightingales will sort out where they place themselves in the spectrum. Some further observations from these years:

> Thirty-six out of the original forty-eight completed the course.

> The terrifying responsibility for life and death that came to us at such a young age: in my second year of training I was in charge, on Night Duty, of thirty very ill patients. No wonder so many nurses left before completing their training.

> Surgical techniques improved dramatically in heart surgery. Also I was in the Ophthalmic Theatre when the first acrylic lens was implanted for a cataract operation.

> We were never trained to take blood, put up infusions, deal with the more complicated equipment.

Nurses trained elsewhere were accustomed to perform (what only medical students did at St Thomas's) e.g., taking blood from a patient, passing male catheter.

Two major things stick out. First was the *wonderful* invention whilst I was in Casualty of tubular gauze. No more bandaging fingers. It was a revolution. Also, in the Heart Unit, offering patients champagne. It was a joy to watch them have a 'pick-me-up'.

Our Set was the first one to include a nurse who married in our second year (1957). This may have been allowed because her husband went to Australia for a year after the wedding. It was the thin end of the wedge as another married and completed her four years. [Did she tell Authority about her wedding?]

I had to resign as Assistant Matron at St Thomas' *in 1968* when I married.

In 1958 we were the first Set to be joined by nurses doing a degree course at Southampton University in conjunction with training at St Thomas's . . . Hours of working changed from 48 to 44.

Education: BA Hons. King's College London, German and French. Age 22 on entering training (1958).

I think an old grateful patient deserves a mention. He was Mr Murphy who will be remembered by all Catholics at Chelsea or Cheyne in my day when it was almost impossible to get to Mass on a Sunday. He collected us in his big black taxi and took us to Mass at the Westminster Hospital and then drove like the wind to get us to breakfast on time at St Thomas's.

Miss Smyth retired as Matron in 1955 after ten years of very hard work. The *Journal* gives a detailed description and appreciation of her achievements, not least the listing of the other boards and bodies on which she served. It needs also to be remembered that she had been Assistant Matron from 1939 to 1941 and Acting Matron at the newly opened Hydestile from 1941 to 1945. She was appointed OBE on retirement. She has been described as possessing all the outstanding characteristics of an Ulster Protestant. Susan Coventry remembered Matron's visits to the wards.

The fact that these were common did not mean that they could be treated with any less respect than if they were rare . . . Even the sickest people were made to look somehow better than they were . . . The flowers swelled in health. The screens and trolleys were lined up like sentrymen in their appropriate habitats and the ventilation and temperature of the ward was perfectly balanced . . . I do not remember those visits being accompanied by any real tension . . . Perhaps it was because of the character of Matron herself. A woman of reserve, discretion and gentleness with what one felt was rock-like balance, she was the prime example of a top Nightingale. Having been through the whole hospital mill herself, she must sometimes have observed with humour the attention given to some of its least important activities and the human frailties which touched them.[7]

During her time in office, the increase in numbers and in salaries reduced the part played by the Fund Council in the affairs of the School; it simply could not afford to meet the rising bills. (It has been observed already that though these were met by the NHS from 1948, the great teaching hospitals were left with a sense of autonomy until the 1960s.) The implementation of the Block System had required an increased staff of tutors, and hence the creation of the post of Principal Sister tutor, to be held by Miss Rosamond Hone. A new Advisory Board concerned solely with education had been created by Miss Smyth and Miss Gould, called The Nightingale Training School Education Committee. It even included a Headmistress. Expansion had made it imperative to try to ensure that classroom and ward teaching were always in step, and the procedures necessary to achieve this have been a preoccupation ever since. With expansion a larger number of student nurses had to be put into the ward teams, and this necessitated an increase in the number of Staff Nurses and added to the responsibilities of the Sister Tutors.

Miss Smyth was succeeded by Miss Theodora Turner as Matron and Superintendent. Her first message in the *Journal* said that, at last, had been decided to build a new hospital rather than to repair and rebuild the bomb-damaged parts of the old one. (It was not to turn out quite as planned. The *Journal* for 1957 has a photograph of two nurses looking admiringly at a model of the new hospital, which bears no resemblance to how it looks now.) In her address at the Presentation of

Medals and Certificates in December 1954, Miss Smyth gave a comprehensive account of the organisation of the School, with a considerable backward glance to its history. She said that entries were running in the neighbourhood of 200 a year, arranged in groups of about fifty in four PTSs. She pointed out that, by taking the Hospital General Nursing Examination at the end of the third year and passing the Final State Examination, a nurse was able to enter her fourth year to qualify for the Badge without worrying about further examinations.

> Training in the Art of Nursing is then completed. Perfection in the skill lies far ahead, needing years of further study, experience and practice . . . the vast field of nursing in all its branches lies open to them . . . Nursing care of the sick will always be required but we must develop the work in the public health field for, after all, is not prevention better than cure?

Looking ahead a year, one notes that Miss Turner then announced a new contribution that the School was to make to the history of nursing, the implementation of a scheme which had been worked out by Miss Smyth and Miss Hone:

> The Minister of Health has approved the adoption by the GNC of a scheme of integrated Nurse/Health Visitor Training. This experimental scheme has been submitted by us and the University of Southampton . . . and is to be tried for a period of 5 years. The student will start her training by spending 8 months at Southampton University. She will then come back to us for 3½ years, during which time she will take her State Final and her Part One Midwifery Examinations. The student will then return to the University for 7 months. The total length of the course will be 4 years and 9 months . . . We hope to recuit our first 8 students for October 1957.

Miss Nuttall, writing in 1997, called attention to another scheme that needs to be mentioned now.

> Following the success of the Southampton scheme Miss Smyth and Miss Hone [who was to be the successor to Miss Gould] sought further advantages from experimentation permitted under the Nurses' Act. They mounted a shortened course of two years, leading to State

Registration, for graduates of any discipline from any English-speaking university.

For eleven years it ran under the tutelage of Norna Jamieson, herself an experienced tutor and a history graduate of Edinburgh University. Jamie, as she was universally known, had had a distinguished war record with Princess Mary's Royal Air Force Nursing Service, serving in a number of theatres of war. With her meagre leaving gratuity she had undertaken the Sister Tutor's Diploma of London University.

Recently (1997), 'the class of 1962' held its first-ever reunion in St Thomas', inviting Jamie to be present. In her eighties she flew down from the Shetlands for twenty-four hours. Of the fifteen graduates present, only two had stayed in nursing. Of the others, one had become a district general manager in the Midlands, while another had become a university consultant psychiatrist.

After eleven years the scheme was discontinued. As it was never evaluated, either by the Nightingale School or the General Nursing Council for England and Wales, it is impossible to say whether it or similar schemes in nurse training schools were a success.

The year 1955 saw the retirement of Miss Gould. In writing a book of this kind one comes to feel an acquaintanceship with people whom one has never met. Their names crop up so often that they become like old friends, though some of them in their photographs look decidedly formidable. This is true of Miss Gould. After nursing as a VAD, she entered the School in 1924 and received her Badge in 1928. From 1938 she is rarely out of the narrative, becoming Sister Tutor just before war was declared in 1939. Reference has been made already to her extraordinary achievement in the war years, keeping the training system in operation and up to the highest standards. She was thinking about and planning for the post-war world in the worst years of the War. She introduced the Study Day system for probationers at Hydestile and, more famously, the Study Block system. She was the Chairman of the Sister Tutor Section of the Royal College of Nursing for forty-nine years, and pioneered the Marian Agnes Gullan Trophy Contest. She was an omnipresent figure in the higher affairs of nursing.

Her successor as Principal Sister Tutor was Miss Rosamond Hone who was the first Oxford graduate to become a Nightingale. She was highly qualified, having had exceptional opportunities for studying nursing education in other parts of the world. She had visited training schools in the United States and in Canada, where she took the Course in Advanced Nursing Education at Toronto University. In 1953 she went for a year as Director to revitalise the Red Crescent School of Nursing in Istanbul.

So the 1950s moved on. The national economy was, apparently, improving all the time and standards of living, if measured by salaries, wages and possessions, made the later years of the decade quite different from anything in our social history before. There was full employment (later to be called over-manning by some) and Mr Macmillan, as Prime Minister, was said to have coined the phrase for the 1959 General Election, 'You've never had it so good'. Only in retrospect was it perceived that the Suez crisis of 1956 signified the end of Great Britain as a World Power. Certainly, against the excitable tumults of the 1960s, the 1950s seem calm. In the world of St Thomas's, there was an experiment in ward layout in 1956 described in considerable detail in the *Journal*, and Miss Smyth explained to the Fellowship the structure and purpose of the General Nursing Council, as the Nurses' Act of 1949 had been implemented. In that same year, Mrs Seymer was already beginning to plan a history of the School as it approached its centenary.

In 1958, Matron was anxious that the programme of training in the School should be incorporated into a larger plan to include the students' practical experience in the hospitals to which they later went. She emphasised the two factors that had to be borne in mind and achieved, which frequently clashed: i) that the scheme must ensure a satisfactory and complete training for the student nurses; ii) that the nurses, as well as being student nurses, do form the main part of the hospital's nursing staff. She commented that many people made the mistake of thinking that once a plan of this sort had been worked out on paper all troubles were over. She insisted that the plan should be posted throughout the hospital for all to follow, but given only to those who needed it for reference. 'From the plan are made lists of study days, study blocks, periods of night duty and holidays for all the sets. These are posted in the autumn for the following year for all the nurses to see and make arrangements accordingly.'[8]

On 2nd July 1958, Miss Gullan – the first Sister Tutor – died in St Thomas's itself, and with her passed a name even more imprinted and recorded in the School's history; she was unavoidably well-known to all who trained between 1915 and 1935. As one might expect there are many tributes to her, recalling, not least, those days 'when Study Days and Study Blocks had hardly been thought of'. It was remembered that in the years before all this, she commonly gave thirty-six lectures to first-year probationers, the substance of which was the foundation for her text book, published in 1920. 'In all her teaching she was emphatic and vigorous.' Continuous repetition over the years no doubt made her word-perfect. The indispensability of her text book is recorded by Susan Coventry. She tells of worried student nurses shouting 'Where's my Gullan?' A close confidante of Dame Alicia, 'her devotion was immense, and together they worked the scheme of training (theoretical teaching always linked with practical Ward instruction and work) . . . and together they coined the title of Sister Tutor which now has world-wide recognition.'

There was an annual competition for the Marian Agnes Gullan Trophy, a replica of the one presented to her by the Sister Tutors who followed her.

In 1958 Miss Turner recorded her struggles to reconcile the recommendations of the Whitley Council to reduce the number of working hours of nurses with the century-old tradition of detailed care. She referred to experiments with various schemes whereby the night nurses were to work an eighty-eight-hour fortnight, though it had not been possible so to reduce the day hours; it was hoped to do so in the following year. This leads on to a preoccupation of the whole decade, namely that of recruitment to nursing. The inherited attitude was to see nursing as a life-long career, indeed an unmarried one, and it is clear that young women were often put off by this as much as attracted to it. The very seriousness that came from viewing nursing as a 'calling' was at odds with the emerging social attitudes amongst some women, the majority of whom now saw marriage or 'partnership' as the norm for their lives. Once into the 1960s, the new satirical cast of mind would mock the very idea of dedication. Brian Abel-Smith, in his *History of the Nursing Profession* (1960), quoted articles in the *Observer* (1957) and the *Manchester Guardian* (1959), criticising vigorously the restrictions imposed upon nurses and indicating that a slackening might lead to a larger number of recruits and a smaller number leaving during training. He suggested that it would be wise to stop talking about 'wastage' and, perhaps, to take a less dismissive view.

Training as a nurse, even if incomplete, has some value as a preparation for motherhood and the profession might be as well advised to draw attention to this aspect of it as to imply that it is a preparation for a lifelong career. Nurse training is also a preparation for citizenship received by about one girl in twenty. She can gain from it something analogous to what young men gain from national service: some discipline, some corporate life and some sense of responsibility. It is not necessarily wasteful for so many families to have a mother or aunt equipped with some knowledge of nursing.

He developed the argument, and suggested simplifying the requirements of registration, so that there could be a two-tier profession: those with basic training and then those who would go on to a second phase of thorough and extended training.[9] Much of this kind of thinking is to be found in the answers to the questionnaire that came from those trained in these years. Interestingly a questionnaire was put out in August 1958 by the Fellowship: 2722 were sent out; 1967 answers were received. The purpose was to find out how many Nightingales were in active work and what service retired nurses were still giving to the profession. The President thought that the information might be useful 'as some form of weapon when negotiating with the Minister of Health. We are still battling for our rights where the new hospital is concerned.' The questionnaires returned, while this book was being written, by those trained in the later 1950s very much reflect the new thinking going on at this time.

The last decade of a fast-vanishing society closed. The Nightingale School and all concerned with its affairs were preoccupied in planning the centenary celebrations; only in retrospect can one maintain that they were, in fact, remembering and celebrating a disappearing world.

CHAPTER SEVEN

Holding the Line: The Last Matron

Distinctive characteristics have been claimed for the 1960s, into which the Nightingale School entered whilst celebrating its centenary. It has been said, in allusion to the beginnings of the drug culture, that 'If you remember the Sixties, then you weren't there'. Certainly some features began to appear that separate out these years quite clearly from anything that had gone before for the bulk of the population. Television became the dominant part of the media. It was the decade of disrespect and satire, epitomised in *Private Eye*. The questioning of all authority, comment made on every established area of national life, and the invasion of the private lives of public personalities became commonplace and part of the excitement. At that time only the monarchy, by and large, escaped, though the Queen was criticised for her accent and tone of voice and Malcolm Muggeridge suggested that the Royal Family was a 'soap opera'. Defiance of older conventions was most visible in the mini-skirt and in the general adoption of 'artistic' or 'ethnic' dress by the young. It may be that the contraceptive pill lies at the centre of the attitudes of this decade. Although discussion about the morality of artificial birth control had gone on for a long time, but never as a national or international issue, the Papal Encyclical *Humanae Vitae* in 1968 brought the question of sexual morality into the media and everyday public discussion. Politically, whatever idealism was engendered by the victory of the Labour Party in the General Election of 1964, when it was promised that the country would be led by a new Moses, not into Canaan but into an exciting society energised by the 'white heat of technology', soon faded away with devaluation of the pound and the development of a 'strike culture'. In 1970 Labour was defeated, as society became increasingly ragged. However, the question asked most generally in retrospect touches on none of these. It is 'Where were you when President Kennedy was killed?' This recalls not only what, somewhat misguidedly, was known as Camelot, but also the Cuban missile crisis of October 1962, when the outbreak of full nuclear war was just avoided.

Young women entering the Nightingale School in these years could hardly miss being part of or influenced by these social and political forces, the most obvious of which was the challenging of authority, an authority clearly delineated in previous chapters. This created what has been called generational tension or the 'generation gap'. At the same time there were continuing and accelerating developments in surgery and medicine and these, in turn, brought new public discussion about medical ethics; transplant surgery in particular raised many questions and there was a growing feeling that the answers should not be left to the medical profession alone.

Above and around all this was a marked increase in State intervention. The NHS absorbed the largest part of the national budget and there was a plethora of ideas on how best to manage the hospital system. The old simplicities went. By passing the Abortion Act in October 1967, the State intervened in a crucial moral issue that would now have to be faced by every nurse and doctor in training and beyond.

After such historian's generalisations, one turns to the answers to questionnaires from Nightingales who trained in this decade. The first thing to keep in mind is that these young women were trained by Sisters from an earlier generation, so that the 'system' in itself did not change. The January 1964 PTS set were the first to be allowed to wear the Nightingale cap as opposed to the stand-up cotton American-style cap previously worn. In 1965 they left Manor House in Godalming and moved back to London as the different parts of the Hospital began to be brought to one site. One notices, too, the wider range of experience and of qualifications on entry; there is some mention of resentment by many against the new and growing world of the graduate entrant, which began in 1963.

We did have graduates (1966–69) who managed to do the course in two years (I can't recall if this was an innovation). [It was.] I thought it was a bad idea as they were not nursing graduates and I felt that although they were bright they were not as good bedside nurses as we were.

The rules at Chelsea Court, much commented on, were as rigid as ever. Comfort and privacy were understandably valued.

Chelsea Court: single room [one other writer claims that 'all vicars' daughters had single rooms'], comfortable, lovely deep hot baths (bathroom next door). Strict regime. Great camaraderie among nurses. *Cheyne House*: shared top floor with friends, rather like living in a flat. *Riddell House*: luxurious rooms, rather isolated from friends. *Hydestile*: more relaxed.

The minutiae of uniform were strictly observed, and the exhausting insistence on menial tasks 'to the Glory of God' was still there. One writer, now Director of an NHS Trust, remembers after a full and successful professional life that 'another skill which has proved invaluable is cleaning – damp-dusting, sweeping, polishing, gumptioning a bath.' She is speaking of 1968.

I remember being amazed that one did what one did because that was how one did it – each Sister had special quirky treatments – no research-based practice – bottles and bottles in the 'lotion cupboards' – tidied again and again. Feeling guilty if you sat down – surely there must be a job you've missed – or go and clean and tidy something (still feel guilty sitting down today!)

One could almost begin to ask the question: where were the Sixties? One writer confesses that 'At the time I did not take much interest in political changes.' They were still living in an enclosed society – and many of them came from one. There is no evidence in the Fellowship *Journal* for these years that anyone wished to explore in any depth the rapidly changing society around them and its likely consequences for the training of Nightingales. Yet another Nightingale comments that 'We had a complete lack of street wisdom. In a sense we were still Edwardians.' The old was beginning to give way to the new, but the answers to questionnaires do repeatedly emphasise the old.

'Respect' with 'Fear' played a great part in our high standard of training. For example, if spoken to by any Sister in the corridor or anywhere we were expected to remove our cloaks before replying . . . All relationships were very well defined . . . We had many advantages in living in the Nurses' Homes as our friends were always there to provide a support and backing in difficult and testing moments in the ward, like one's first death.

However, the new was appearing.

In 1960–64 very sick patients were nursed on the wards with respirators, etc. Advent of open-heart surgery, start of routine radio-therapy with its 'sources' left in the patients on wards with attendant potential risks. Memories of terror in face of the very sick.

Endless cleaning, sewing and cooking, combined with advances in technology. One day filling water pillow to exclude air, the next handling respirators and patients following open-heart surgery. Patients gained enormous security by being in view of nursing staff. Most patients enjoyed morning and evening prayers. Patients always treated with respect. Ward Sisters and senior staff saw each patient at the beginning and end of each duty period.

Medical staff paternalistic towards patients and often unnerved them. Patients' clothes not stored in hospital which generated a feeling of impotence. Visiting hours relatively restricted . . . Patients were tacitly encouraged to give up autonomy on admission. In 63/64 Psychiatric and Obstetrics out-patients were still in basement as was Chest Department and one Theatre. In spite of this, infection rates low.

Another Nightingale writes of the years 1960 to 1964:

The way of life off the wards was akin to a convent . . . It had its advantages because no responsibility for shopping and cooking. It took me a long time after completing my training to be able to express my feelings. We coped with the most traumatic and stressful situations with no one to debrief us or provide counselling. Physically we were lovingly looked after.

The opening of the new wing of four-bedded bays altered the feeling of unity of the ward; one was no longer in contact with the whole. The lack of opportunity to talk about these major implications resulted in lack of reflection on them and a rather low level of awareness of change in the dynamics. We just got on with the job and didn't really think very deeply about it.

Lack of political and social awareness may be explained by the fact that the Nightingales were exhausted by the demands of training and nursing and had little time or opportunity for social life outside, or for reflection on what they were experiencing. Back in 1958, Miss Smyth talked about the beginnings of experiments with working hours – 'the problem of the implementation of the 44 hour week for the nursing staff.' She hoped that the reduction of hours and more time off would make possible the widening of interests. 'We make better nurses if we are good citizens.'[1] She commented that the Night Nurses now worked an 88-hour fortnight, and an experiment with a modified shift system with shortened hours in a split duty was being tried out. She indicated the difficulties, not least that an increased number of nurses was desirable to make the new system more acceptably operable. However, a Nightingale whose training ended in 1963 comments, 'I found the bussing to and from the Homes tedious, especially with the split shift system.' Far from giving more time for leisure, the system brought further exhaustion and less time, in fact, for a meaningful life outside the Hospital.

Although most of the replies from Nightingales trained in this period continue to praise the attention to detail of the ward-based training, some question the practice of putting nurses in charge of wards at night that they had not been on during the day. This is, however, contradicted by one writer.

> We often worked split shifts which meant about four hours off in the afternoon, which was reduced if work hadn't been finished within the allotted time. On the first night of night duty, which was always in a new ward, one had to report for a morning shift from 7.30 am to 12 noon in order to learn something about the patients before working that night. (1963)

To conclude, for the time being, the analysis of answers covering the early and middle sixties, one Nightingale writes of 1963:

> I never understood why we were told not to discuss hospital life with our family, and therefore to repress that one was terribly tired and at times rather frightened . . . But having passed through my training I was terribly proud of having completed it.
>
> Phases in terms of years were distinguished by change in dress colour and belt. Other changes usually were made every three months: in one year I worked on three wards and had one study block, and had some holiday. Wards/departments were allocated to

student nurses by means of a master plan. A choice could be made during the fourth year for a three-month period for which one was given a record book covered with pale blue plastic; each aspect of nursing care was supervised, tested and signed by the Ward Sister after one had been taught it in 'Block'. The practical side of training in nursing was impeccable . . . however I would have enjoyed an additional research element into one aspect of care . . . as it is best to learn about the physical background to any illness. This happened on one occasion, on Eye Care, and it was enormously valuable. In other words, I think I would have enjoyed a more academic approach rather than the hours spent cleaning my side of the ward.

(It has been pointed out by one Nightingale that blue plastic record books were for the whole of one's training and not just for the last year, as stated here. It is also thought that they were issued by the General Nursing Council and, therefore, in use nationally.)

Another writer supports the views about academic training:

With hindsight, additional theoretical knowledge should have been given . . . This is one of the real differences in nurse training today, far more academic learning and too little practical support/teaching.

Other writers criticise the sequencing of the theoretical and the practical as not always being logical and sometimes repetitive.

During these years the rebuilding and refurbishing of the Hospital was going on and the Government or the General Nursing Council were commissioning one report after another to examine every major aspect of the organisation of the NHS and the training of nurses and their pay. Though the Nightingale School moved in 1972 into the new Gassiot House, and so for the first time in its history had a purpose-built and fully equipped setting for its work, it becomes increasingly difficult to think or write about the School and indeed the Hospital as self-standing separate entities with a unitary history. What was going on there was going on in all the important teaching hospitals and, as has been indicated already, general social attitudes were changing as the economic life of the country began to move into more uncertain and disputatious times. The years 1950–70 were the most prosperous ever experienced in the western world until that time.

To deal with the simpler matters first: the great building projects were brought to a conclusion (but not completion). The first idea, of rebuiding and restoring all the pavilions, but adding two storeys, with balconies for each floor, was abandoned because the foundations would not have supported them. There were two criteria which informed the decision to build a new hospital. The first was Enoch Powell's guideline in 1964 of 3.3 beds per 1000 of the population which, when midwifery, psychiatry and the geriatric were added, came to 10 beds per 1000. The second was to get right the ratio of medical students to patients. St Thomas's was picked out and recommended as an exemplar of a hospital that closely keyed into all the health needs of the local population – it had 'a solid client basis'.

Stage One of the new hospital, known as the East Wing, was completed in 1966, to hold over 200 beds. Three major innovations were incorporated: a) a Central Sterile Supply Department – many answers to questionnaires comment on the immense benefits of this; b) an Intensive Care Unit; c) a new casualty department to be known as Accident and Emergency. Stage Two was for a square thirteen-storey ward tower holding over 600 beds together with administration and laboratories. Each floor covered an acre, with either four-bedded or six-bedded bays. Linked to this was a five-storey treatment block, which was followed by a residential block for nurses and the Nightingale Training School.

Jumping ahead, from November 1975 to November 1976 the commissioning of all the new buildings took place, including some no doubt sorely-needed guided tours for all the staff. The Mayor of Lambeth was the first out-patient, at 8.45 am on 23rd February 1976. The Queen opened the new buildings on 11th November 1976. Hydestile had been closed in 1968 and during 1976 all the beds of the satellite hospitals were transferred to the vast new ward block. The Royal Waterloo and the Grosvenor Hospitals were closed and facilities moved to the main site. (There are many memories of working in the sector hospitals. The Lambeth nurses' home was loathed by some, while startling anecdotes about the Grosvenor – which was gynaecological – tell of the small size of its lifts, which posed considerable problems when transporting larger patients, both the living and dead, on small trolleys. Even more bizarre problems arose when removing the dead through a small downstairs window.) A planned Stage Three (for another 400-bedded ward block and a new Medical School and staff facilities) was never built, and instead the old buildings were refurbished.[2]

It will be recalled how controversial was the decision to put the great corridor on the first rather than the ground floor. (It was, in fact, level with the new Lambeth Palace Road, but a large excavation had created a new ground floor giving access to what was the basement – and later, to the Museum.) The architecture of the hospital still arouses argument. Its fifteen-storey block and five-storey block alongside broke with the symmetry of the old pavilioned skyline. After all it was the 1960s, the golden age of flat roofs, plate glass and straight lines.

All this is comparatively simple when compared with the series of reports of these years, when Management (indisputably with a capital M) began to make its presence felt. In fact, change can begin to be seen as early as May 1948, when the last meeting of the old independent Board of Governors took place; for a foreseeable future of considerable complexity, their functions were entrusted to the Treasurer and the Almoner until responsibility was passed to the Minister of Health. Then a new Board of Governors was created with a new Clerk, R. Pelham Borley, who effectively became the Hospital Administrator. The Hospital was re-designated a Teaching Hospital at the centre of a group, and the group was to be known as St Thomas' (note new punctuation) Hospital. This new Board, as was recounted some time back, applied for a new coat-of-arms. The group, in all its complexity, became a very considerable employer; in the years 1964–74 the number of beds increased from 956 to 1365, in-patients from 21,200 to 32,000 a year, out-patients from 47,7000 to 63,000. The number of staff rose from 2000 to 4000. It should not be forgotten, in this welter of detail, that though the old Governing Board was wound up, the Nightingale Fund continued. True enough, its resources were less and less adequate for the complicated new developments. The management of the Hospital was the responsibility of the Treasurer, a title which elsewhere would have been Chairman.

The National Health Service Act of 1973 required the disbanding of the Board of Governors on 31st March 1974. St Thomas' and its staff became part of St Thomas' Health District, itself part of the newly-created Lambeth, Southwark and Lewisham Area Health Authority (teaching). The clumsy cumbersomeness of these arrangements led to a further change in April 1982 when St Thomas' was put under a new body called the West Lambeth Health Authority. By then the Ministry of Health had become the Department of Health and Social Security. The Area Health Authority took the place of the Governors, whose Clerk, Bryan MacSwiney, was required to resign. He stayed on, in fact, until 1975. In conversation, he made the point that the Governors were determined not to build anything new that might have to be knocked down by some further development. This was eminently sane, but caused frustration and, indeed, anger. So much had been repaired only temporarily, and maintaining the inherited ferocious standards of cleanliness was exhausting. That they were achieved, under the direction of 'that much under-rated woman, Miss Smyth', indisputably owed much to the skills which had been undeviatingly maintained despite wartime dispersion. Bryan MacSwiney is firm that the best managers in the Hospital were the Ward Sisters. There had been a history of division and tension between the nursing and medical sides, not brought out much in any history of the School. Bryan MacSwiney was committed to consultation, harmonisation and partnership with the Matron, who was the one person who had to be able to work smoothly and easily with management.

When Miss Smyth had retired in 1955, Miss Turner took over a very flourishing School which had 2000 and more applications every year for 245 places. Of Miss Smyth it was said in the *Journal* that she had been trained in Dame Alicia's time and greatly influenced by her and the 'terrifying group of Sisters'. Miss Turner had been Sister Charity, the Dame's own ward.

> There was a kind of mystique about all this; one saw the process of apostolic succession beginning to unfold. The Dame thought the world of Miss Turner and so did the medical staff, who realised that she was destined for great things and saw in her the very necessary germ of reform and hope for the future. [When she became Matron and Superintendent of Nursing,] She arrived when the wind of change was blowing and 'debunking' was the fashion of the day. Would her reign be regarded as the last of the old order or the first of the new?

In summarising her ten years in office the writer in the *Journal* felt that she had succeeded, against many obstacles – 'the forces of reaction come from unexpected places' – and was a true bridge-builder. She was also referred to as a sort of female Pope. It is difficult, at this distance, to identify the unexpected forces of reaction. As if all this were not enough, she also had to deal with the interminable architectural planning, revision of planning, scrapping of plans, new plans, all absorbing the detailed attention of not only the Matron but many of the Sisters.

The first major statement by Miss Adamson, on taking over from Miss Turner ten years later, was to tell the Fellowship meeting on 13th November 1965:

> I have received a letter instructing me to inform the staff that the second phase of the rebuilding programme could not begin until 1971 at the earliest . . . My heart goes out to all members of the planning team and especially to the two Nightingales, Miss Hayes and Miss Elliott. Both have given years of work – Miss Hayes seven years . . . Now the results of their efforts seem destined for the waste paper basket . . . Many of us have been shocked by what has happened, but we must stand up and look to the future – a far more distant future than my revered predecessor used to talk to you about. I look to the turn of the century, somewhere about the year 2000 – not for the rebuilding of the Hospital, but for the maturity of the whole Health Service. By then it will be fifty-two years old and people should have made up their minds to the sort of Service they want. Perhaps by then we shall know what has happened to London. *What does the nation want?*

Bryan MacSwiney warmly endorses this sense of exasperation abroad in 1965. Not only would many of the most skilled medical and nursing staff have retired by the time that all the new buildings were in use, but there was also a great argument about whether to build the new East Wing, a new building certainly but designed with pre-War concepts in mind such as the T-shaped ward. This shape led to confusion on busy days, when as many as seventy visitors could be coming and going, making it very difficult for the Ward Sister to be in charge. Nevertheless, the Wing was built simply to get a major new unit into operation. After that the decision was taken, which must have been a fairly dramatic one, not to continue to use the 'in-house' architects but to put the design of future buildings out to tender.

In her speech to the Fellowship in 1965 Miss Adamson continued to muse about the future, for example whether or not all the great teaching hospitals should stay in London. She then listed what she had inherited: the link with the University of Southampton; a course for the graduate student nurse. She was also 'not unmindful, and I am very grateful, that the Fund Council has a little money. Being a true Scot, I

167

have already had a heart-to-heart with the Secretary. That money is a nice nucleus from which to start a Fund of a million pounds that I shall doubtless ask for.' From all this, one can get something of a flavour of the character of Miss Adamson. It is clear that people held strong views about her, one way or another.

> To dispel any misunderstanding (the President continued), she would like members to know that she was living in the roof of the old Governor's Hall. At the moment she was not entertaining, but she hoped that in the future many would share the beauty of her panoramic view of the Houses of Parliament which she had exchanged for that of the Pentland Hills.[3]

There are many memories of Miss Adamson living in style – she had been known as the 'Duchess' in Edinburgh, where her achievements were long remembered and highly regarded. As well as always being recognised as a good clinical nurse, she was an entertaining hostess with clearly expressed views on many topics. She was the first Matron and Superintendent of the Nightingale School not to wear the traditional uniform, and though she did not abandon it immediately on arrival, it is remembered that she refused to 'wear strings'. She was in fact allergic to starch. She then put the matter to the vote that all the Sisters drop them, and it was decided to cease wearing them except for special occasions – by a narrow majority. It seems that she had a great aversion to having photographs taken of herself – so, one remembers, had FN. Always elegant but always very approachable, from what was said both on her retirement in 1970 and after her death on 25th March 1990, she was able to build up the self-confidence of those working under her.

> She had a special gift for responding to the needs of student nurses and had a lasting influence over many of them. She was an innovator, an encourager, a motivator, and possessed foresight and the ability to recognise potential. Miss Adamson was gracious, kind and imaginative – working with her was never dull. She was unique.

Many memories were assembled about her in 1970 and 1990. 'She had the grand manner and was reputed to wear the highest cap of any Matron' (in Edinburgh). She is remembered for her shapely legs, of which she was proud. She went to the hairdressers in the official hospital car – the driver said he was taking her to the 'wig-washers'. She also drove her own car, keeping a bucket and rubber gloves in the boot so that she could wipe it down before putting it away. Her special achievement was to match the colour of her OBE ribbon precisely with that of her lipstick. She enjoyed a good argument, 'particularly with Government officials', and was skilful in inducting nurses into responsibility. In 1968, she told a national newspaper:

> Undoubtedly hospitals have much to learn from industrial methods of organisation and management, which if applied to the NHS might increase efficiency and reduce costs. [What she said next deserves emphasis.] The process of adaptation from an era of dedication, selfless service and somewhat muddled but kindly organisation, to technological expertise, is bound to be difficult. *Spinsters are vanishing – hitherto, spinster ward sisters and matrons virtually ran the hospital at socially unattractive times.* Their long experience gave stability and a sense of security.

It is clear that her attitudes and policies were not welcomed by all. She was preoccupied with the nursing side and, apparently, did not find cooperation with management easy, in spite of what she had said. A strange example of this was her earliest request, to be relieved of responsibility for the Pinkies, in other words anything to do with maintenance.

Bryan MacSwiney was encouraging harmonisation and the sharing of knowledge between all those who worked in the hospital; there were more meetings, at what was hoped would be more acceptable times; and, for example, he brought Miss Garrett (to be Miss Adamson's successor in the hospital) into administrative experience. This move was supported by Miss Turner who also agreed to the appointment of nurse planning officers, working with administration. The tradition that the Governors ran the hospital, with little real consultation, was changed, and Matrons' Reports at their meetings were taken as centrally important. (Bryan MacSwiney reached the top post and achieved all this in spite of being a Catholic, though he was told privately that the Hospital would only accept one Papist at the top – Clerk, yes; Treasurer, no.)

If one looks back at the line of Matrons since Mrs Wardroper, there is first the unfulfilled promise of Miss Pringle. After her there is a succession of clearly competent women conforming to an easily discernible pattern; even Dame Alicia was a much grander version of this – an innovator in some important things but intensely conventional in her social attitudes. After her came the tormented time of Miss Hillyers – she indeed had to go through fire and water – then came the consolidation work of Miss Smyth and Miss Turner. Suddenly, when one comes to Miss Adamson, one finds silences, embarrassment, unwillingness to talk at first, and then one realises that a fascinating new type of personality is being dealt with, who aroused widely divergent reactions. Some Nightingales held and hold her in cherished and warmest memory, not least because she spotted talent and encouraged it in younger nurses who remain grateful to this day. She also was perhaps the first Matron truly prepared to delegate important tasks. For example, Mary Richardson remembers her own amazement and trepidation when being told to interview young entrants and to trust her own judgement in the full awareness that once in a while she might be wrong. She felt that she was being put to the test, but that initiative was being prompted, something hitherto not normal in the history of the Hospital and School. She was sent away from the Hospital to a recently established special course on management organised by the King's Fund; its scope was innovative and some of the financing of students had to be found, which Miss Adamson herself undertook to do. Each day she invited her assistants to have tea with her informally, and sometimes to relax with a cigarette after times of tension and trauma. She loved entertaining in her penthouse, on occasion keeping people longer than they expected. There is a strong sense from this that she felt intensely the loneliness of office.

The medical and administrative world might understandably have been uncomfortable with a non-conformist who, what is more, lived elegantly and stylishly in a different way from her predecessors. It has been put, and often, that she was 'ahead of her time' and that her return to St Thomas', which she regarded as the crown of her achievement, became overcast and sad. It has also been said that 'you either loved her or hated her', and many felt that she was a snob. Her portrait did not please her, particularly the depiction of the hands.

As one of the minor threads in this narrative has been concerned with the attitude to Catholics, one might note that Miss Adamson opened up the Chapel for Mass on Sundays and Holy Days of Obligation. A Nightingale trained from 1962 to 1966 writes:

At my initial interview I was told that I would never become a Ward Sister at St Thomas's because I was a Roman Catholic. So far as I could make out, there were two other Roman Catholics in my Set and both left after PTS. I *did* become a Ward Sister but not until the late seventies. It was an amazing statement to make to an 18-year-old. I'm never sure why I accepted my place. Was it to prove Matron wrong?

Another Catholic Nightingale (1968 to 1971) remembers, 'A group of us met each week and had a feeling of sticking together under persecution.'

Miss Adamson used her Presidential Addresses to give details of the battles that she had to fight over money and the continual re-shaping of plans. For example, in May 1966 she related how she led a deputation to the Ministry of Health to tell them that either they had to implement the plans or sound the death knell of the Hospital and School. She was told that, as things stood, the estimated cost was £16 million, from which £2½ million would have to be cut. Miss Adamson seems to have enjoyed the struggle, but pulled no punches. 'I would like to think that you would remember me as having been too pessimistic . . . Working in the Hospital Health Service today is really an attenuated programme of having your spirits dashed.' However, the buildings were built and the Hospital and School were saved. At that same meeting in May 1966 she announced that the Nightingale School would shortly be moving into the ground floor of Riddell House. By the end of the decade, with Gassiot House in the process of being built as the new home for the School, the *Journal* said:

> The new School is almost a reality . . . It has had no fewer than five homes since the end of the War . . . But Miss Nightingale's words are so true: 'Let us hail the success of other training schools, sprung up thank God so well in latter years. But the best way we can hail them is not to be left behind ourselves.'

In May 1967, Miss Adamson referred to all the difficulties experienced by those who were dealing with the young. Out of this came the decision to appoint one nurses' counsellor. She also told the Fellowship meeting that she had, for the first time in history, been invited to the Savoy to the St Thomas' Old Boys reunion. On hearing that the Medical School was contemplating the appointment of a counsellor for the students, she told them, 'Once again we retain our lead.'

In 1966 the Salmon Report, of which much more later, recommended a new career structure and the abolition of old titles. Because the Report dealt with all forms of hospital, it advised that titles and ranks indicating male or female should be replaced. For example, in the psychiatric hospitals there were Chief Male Nurses in charge of men and Matrons in charge of women. The new title of Chief Nursing Officer avoided this difference. In 1970, Miss Sheila Garrett became the first Chief Nursing Officer. Undoubtedly, she took over at a difficult time. She had reached the top by an unconventional ladder, not having been a Ward Sister, and this ruffled some feathers. On the other hand, her experience of administration prepared her to take on the implementation of the Salmon Report, more important than the Platt Report of 1964 or the Briggs Report of 1972.

Structures are one thing, but there is the underlying question, to which Dr Monica Baly has called attention more than once: What is a nurse? Definitions have changed as functions have changed, influenced as they are by scientific and technological advance. Classically, the nurse has been neither a doctor on the one hand nor a ward hand on the other, but has bridged both roles in varying proportions in different times and places – a Nightingale working in the First World is in totally different circumstances from one working in the Third, a point made by one working in the latter during the celebrations of the 11th May 1996. She maintained that in many undeveloped countries, the 'old' nursing skills are still urgently required. Recently there has been some outrage at the proposal that unskilled and untrained personnel be allowed to carry out some of the more routine nurses' duties, such as attending to patients' physical needs. It is said that either nursing is all-embracing, or its functions can be divided into the more and less important. The debate goes back to FN and *Notes on Nursing* and before, and continues.

The heart of the matter is: what should be the curriculum? By whom should it be decided? By whom should it be taught? What should be the proportions between the practical and the theoretical? Surely 'practical' and 'theoretical' are part of the whole and inter-related? (This points forward to a problem referred to by Professor Macleod Clark of the Nightingale Institute in her description of the difficulties met by researchers into the effectiveness of the contribution of each member of health care teams.) Many replies to the questionnaire have criticised in one way or another the balance between the two.

There is a tenable historical analogy between the training of nurses and the training of school teachers. In both cases and for many decades the emphasis was on the practical while theory was viewed sceptically at best and derided at worst. In the training colleges for teachers the most important post was that of Master of Method – and such colleges were concerned only with the training of elementary school and later of primary school teachers. For secondary schools, particularly for independent and grammar schools, it was not even regarded as necessary to be trained at all (and still is not, in the independent schools). University Departments/Schools of Education did not have the same academic standing as other departments, nor did their professors. A distinguished Professor of Education at Cambridge is said to have accepted the post only on condition that he was never required to lecture on Education; he wished to be free to pursue his study of Medieval Preaching. Only in the 1960s did theoretical models for teacher training begin to appear and to command attention. One might say that it was to be expected that they came in from the USA. The word 'taxonomy' – especially that of Professor Bloom – appeared and three decades of models have ensued.

In nursing, certainly in the Nightingale School, there always had been *Notes on Nursing* and associated writings by FN. But she did not see herself as proposing a model, rather an intellectual basis – 'think how to nurse' – for what was a practical, non-medical based series of routines. Only in 1914 was a Sister Tutor appointed, and only during the years of dispersal in the Second World War did her successor in the post outline the first radical new development of training, from which came the Block System. There was great pride in being Practical. Wide reading and speculation or individual research were not encouraged, nor indeed was there time for them.

In the 1960s, the first theoretical models arrived from the USA; Rosemary Long, writing in the Fellowship *Journal* in 1979, recalled the great change of atmosphere in this decade.

Nursing worldwide has been rethinking its role in relationship to other disciplines caring for the sick. One reason for this has been the explosion of medical discoveries and advancements over the last twenty years. Illness has assumed pace and reflects the speed of twentieth-century western society. It has been tempting for nurses to assume the role of doctors' assistants but, for the first time in any scientific way, nurses are beginning to re-define 'nursing' . . . Nurses are beginning, with some success, to realise who they are. American nurses have begun to spearhead this thinking and we are trying to translate their language to our own culture and our own needs.[4]

She quotes 'a famous American nurse', Virginia Henderson, and gives her definition of nursing, published in 1966:

The unique function of the nurse is to assist the individual sick or well, in the performance of those activities contributing to health or its recovery (or to a peaceful death) that he would perform unaided had he the necessary strength, will or knowledge. And to do this in such a way as to help him gain independence as rapidly as possible.

Rosemary Long continues by indicating a second need, namely to define the place of the individual in society:

In nursing this is reflected in greater attempts to see the needs of the whole person rather than primarily as a medical diagnosis . . . We have been practising various modifications of a system of total patient care . . . Briefly, this means that tasks such as 'back' rounds, 'dressing' rounds and 'temperature' rounds give place to a nurse looking after every aspect of her own group of patients and thereby viewing them as individuals.

The consequences of such changes were seen as fairly revolutionary, not least in their impact on student nurses in training.

There is now no such thing as 'junior work', making the responsibility taken by junior student nurses enormous . . . It is easy for essential routine tasks to be forgotten. Students have continually to think what they are doing and are unable to take respite away from patients and colleagues in the sluice, bathroom or linenry.

The rapid turnover of patients, complex treatment and early discharge had an impact:

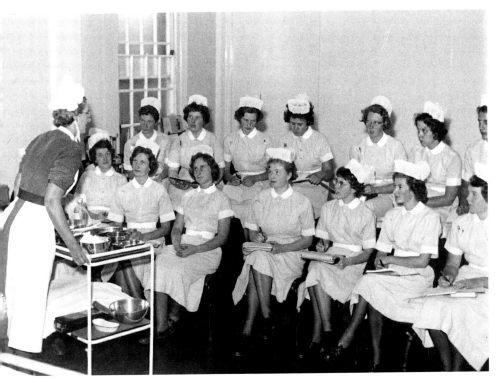

Miss Hone teaching anatomy, 1960.

Riddell House, practical classroom set out for examinations, 1960.

Morning Prayers in Elizabeth Ward: Sister, Miss Kay Riley, and nurses, 1960.

Edward Ward: Sister, Miss Mary Richardson; Charge Nurse, Miss Ann Thurston, 1964.

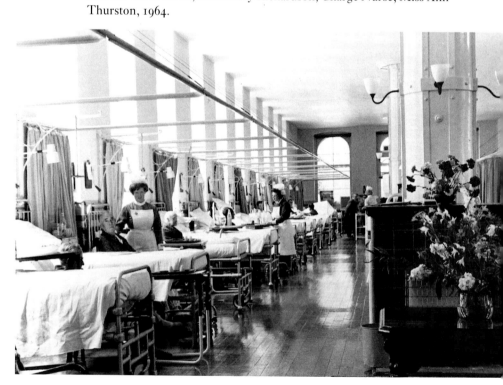

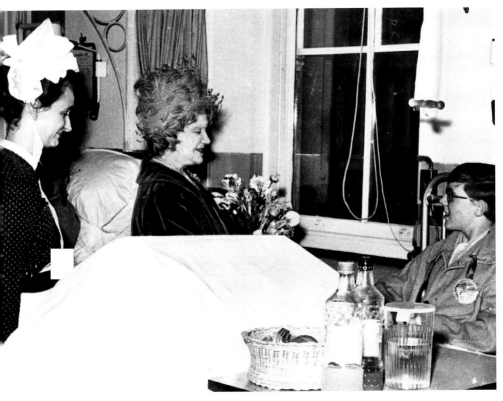

The Queen Mother in City of London Ward, 1964. Sister: Miss Barbara Rusbridge.

Outside City of London Ward: Miss Sue Critchley, 1964. Note the 'check' to keep bedclothes clean.

Miss Gladys V Hillyers, Matron, 1937-1945.

Dame Alicia Lloyd Still, Matron, 1913-1937.

Miss Margaret J Smyth, Matron, 1945-1955.

Miss Theodora Turner, Matron, 1955-1965.

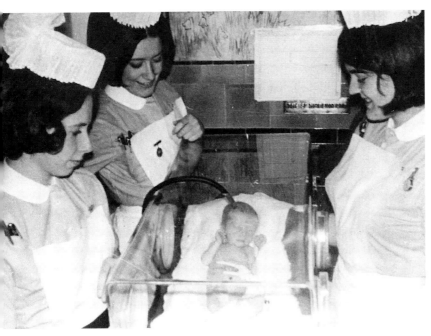

Lilian Ward night staff, 1964. Note silver 'gong' worn by Registered Nurse
Natalie P Tiddy (middle) while working for Nightingale badge.

Students and trained staff performing the Nativity Tableau, Christmas 1963.
A new-born baby from the Maternity Ward was always the focal point of these
special events.

Mr (later Sir) John Prideaux, Treasurer and Chairman of the Board of Governors, Miss Estelle I O Adamson, Matron, 1965–1970, and Her Majesty the Queen, 1968.

The April 1970 set at the start of their training when the School was at Riddell House.

The first conversion course from Enrolled Nurse to Registered Nurse, 1987.

The final set of Nightingale students, Autumn, 1992 – the last set to receive the Nightingale badge on completion of their training.

Princess Alexandra talking to Jane Easterbrook, Acting Director of the
Nightingale Training School, at the final certificate and badge presentation on
10 May, 1996.

Cutting the cake at the Celebration of the Nightingale School on 11 May,
1996: Sister Jane Leggett and Staff Nurse Katie Snell.

In the old days we could go off for a day and the ward would be virtually unchanged when we came back. Today's student may find that two-thirds of the patients have changed on her return from two days off.

One might think that this was a world away from Florence Nightingale, but in one sense at least it was not. This new world required a precision in documentation and an ability to evaluate circumstances both with patients and senior colleagues that were not easy to fit into the time-honoured methods of the Ward Sisters but which was a harking-back to FN's passionate attachment to statistics and to evaluating techniques.

In the light of answers to the questionnaire, one gets the fairly strong feeling that Rosemary Long was somewhat ahead of her time where the wards were concerned. Replies from Nightingales trained during the later 1960s make it clear that whether one experienced anything of this new world was 'the luck of the draw', and few of those who have written about these years give any awareness of change afoot. There is more emphasis on the rigidity of old routines.

We were a guinea-pig Set, with a full-time Tutor and Clinical Instructor who hounded us. Our Tutor, herself a graduate, understood us and our propensity to question her. This was not expected or encouraged at the time. On one occasion we were told, 'If I say something is sterile, Nurse, *it is so.*'

Another writes:

The School provided very good practical training on the job. We were trained in exact procedures and were not encouraged to use our initiative or think for ourselves. From this point of view, I finished my training with far less self-confidence than when I started.

It was not until the 1970s that the study of Models of Nursing became part of the programme of all students in the School, which not all found easy going. And it was not until 1979 that the Nurses, Midwives and Health Visitors Act was passed, just before the fall of the Labour Government, providing a new statutory framework to monitor and control nursing practice and education for the future. This was seen as the final implementation of the Briggs Report of 1972.

The Salmon Report has already been mentioned briefly, but before discussing it, some attention must be paid to its predecessor, the Platt Report of 1964. Its terms of reference were to consider the whole field of nurse education and training and the part which the nurse is called upon to play in the nursing service. It found the situation unsatisfactory, and worsening: 'future demands will exacerbate the situation'. It recommended a reduced number of training schools, which would be independent of particular hospitals. The intake of students should be reduced, the age of entry lowered to 17½ and the normal entry requirements should be five subjects at GCE O-Level. The course should last two years with GNC final examinations. There should be a third year under supervision as a member of a ward team. (Other recommendations do not seem to be immediately relevant to the narrative, except the one proposing that the study of nursing should become a valid university degree subject for those capable of taking it.)

Miss Turner in her Presidential Address that year said that the Report had been considered and would be again, but that the most important help that the Hospital and School could receive would be to increase the number of clinical instructors. The training of Nightingales had been ward-based from the beginning, but it now needed to be recognised that the Ward Sister could not carry the whole burden. The post of clinical instructor, first introduced to work with the experimental shortened course for graduates in 1964, had begun to be extended, for example, to the operating theatre.

The work of the clinical instructor . . . is undoubtedly helping to link more closely the ward bedside nursing with the classroom. Many may ask, 'Do the Ward Sisters accept them happily?' The answer is in the affirmative, and the reason for this is that the pressure of work in the wards and turnover of patients has increased tremendously in the last ten years and the trained staff are frustrated at not being able to supervise and teach as much as they wish or used to do. Interruptions are continuous; shorter hours of work and the short time spent in the ward by each student also make the sisters' task more difficult . . . The team of sister, clinical instructor and charge nurse can do more to keep the standard of practical work at the bedside high and ensure adequate supervision of the students' work . . . The student nurse's reaction has been most interesting . . . She gains confidence, is less nervous when supervised and often feels that she

176

can ask more advice and bring queries to the tutors through the instructor.[5]

At the same time as the spread of clinical instructors there was a change in nomenclature, from the PTS to the Introductory Course, and its members became student nurses. All were taught in the mother hospital.

The proposed reduction in the age of entry must be linked to the decision by the Wilson Government to lower the age of majority to 18, which altered the whole position of the School as being 'in loco parentis'. This was bound to undermine the requirement to 'live in' with all its consequent formality and discipline.

The Salmon Report of 1966 was the next to emerge, and when the first talks began about the writing of this book, all roads seemed to lead to it. Chronology could be dated: BS and AS. Clearly, the Salmon Report marked a watershed. The Committee was small (nine), the remit simple: 'To advise on the senior nursing staff structure in the hospital service (ward sister and above), the administrative functions of the respective grades and the methods of preparing staff to occupy them.' It tackled the complex and confusing arrangements in the country's hospitals, the various nursing grades, the tasks they performed and their relationship to one another. The implementation of its findings, so far as they were apposite, fell to Miss Sheila Garrett. E.M. McInnes sums it up thus: 'The Salmon Report recommended a new career structure and the abolition of old titles. Senior nurses would have to become administrators, and seniority lead to administrative posts rather than long service in a ward.'

In 1972, an Occasional Paper in *The Nursing Times* by Miss Garrett entitled 'Salmon – Blueprint to Reality' analysed the Report and looked at the tasks of implementation. She wrote – comfortingly – that:

Management . . . is not a technological skill – it is, in fact, a matter of people and of human relations . . . There is no blueprint for Salmon – but there are principles to be applied. An analogy can be drawn with teaching the theory and practice of nursing, when all too often one hears the cry of the student – 'It isn't like that on the wards'.

Well, it may not be, but skilled teaching of the principles of caring for patients enables the nurse to apply them . . . to meet the needs of individual patients . . . Principles can be applied with intelligence to the care of the individual . . . The skill which nurses are beginning to

177

acquire is to interpret the principles of management in the context of their own organisation and the people who comprise it . . . The principles laid down in the Salmon Report and the structure suggested give one a framework.

Writing six years on in 1978, Miss Garrett thought it no longer necessary to explain and justify Salmon to the student nurses of the day.

> The students grow up in it and it is the system they accept . . . after six years nurses should discipline themselves in the use of the proper titles for posts . . . The Hospital world has only become conscious of the need for job descriptions since the publication of the Salmon Report . . . the need to examine jobs and to set out what the job is has done more than anything to bring people face to face with the realities of responsibility and accountability, and with their relationships within the organisation.

In her secondment to the Department of Health, prior to returning to St Thomas', she had found that 'Nursing job descriptions compare very favourably with those prepared by others.' (It took the school-teaching world another decade before it faced the problems similar to those addressed by Salmon.) Miss Garrett quoted aptly from Machiavelli: 'It must be considered that there is nothing more difficult to carry out, nor more doubtful of success, nor more dangerous to handle, than to initiate a new order of things.' She also quoted Florence Nightingale, writing in 1860: 'The patient's recovery depends on the quality of the nursing and this in turn depends on the training *and* organisation of the nurses.' She reminded readers that in a later note FN had written: 'Bad administrative arrangements make it impossible to nurse.' From the point of view of the Nightingale School, the first importance of implementing Salmon was to give students from the beginning an indication of the structure of career appointment and development open to them if they were to persist.

Miss Garrett had always felt that if there were adequate supervision and reasonable stability in the training programme, there was some evidence to shew that on qualifying, nurses would be more likely to remain in nursing.

It is time to return to the central purpose of the narrative – the Training School in its life and times. What was it like on the ground? In

1968 Miss Adamson remarked that though she had recommended that the Salmon Report should be read by all Fellowship members, the Hospital had not been chosen as a 'Salmon pilot'. She observed, however, that a whole new language was having to be learned, 'curious phrases like "sapiential authority"' teased out; titles were being changed and everyone was being urged to go on management courses. Another sign of the times was that at one of its meetings Fellowship members were offered the opportunity to visit the new East Wing and saw that the post no longer went to Matron's Office; a new central post room handled all the mail. The symbolism was not lost on them.

Then came an outline by Miss Adamson of the Training School as it stood in 1968 whilst Salmon was being studied. 'It may be of interest to some to compare with their own training days, or to those with daughters showing an interest in nursing.' To summarise:

1. Nurses join the Introductory Course (old PTS) for eight weeks only, living in Chelsea Court; in the second half they work a morning or afternoon shift in the wards each week, 'under the eye of the Introductory Course Sisters, who supervise their first washings of patients.'

2. After first ward experience, some may work as Juniors on the night duty rota according to which wards they are in; all, therefore, return to the classroom for a study fortnight to concentrate on what they need to know of night duty.

3. They return to the classroom at the beginning of their second year for a six-week study block; at the beginning of the third year for five weeks' study.

4. In the second year the physiology of the cardiovascular, respiratory and gastro-intestinal systems is covered, together with related medicine and surgery.

5. In the third year the remaining systems with their medicine and surgery are completed. 'An interesting trend, especially on the medical side, is for lecturers to specialize, so that three or more lecturers may cover a course which would have been given by one physician or surgeon a few years ago.'

6. Each Set is divided into groups, each group keeps its own tutor as far as possible throughout training. Fewer formal lectures are given and there is increasing use of group work/tutorials. Tutors keep in touch with weaker members between Blocks and during the third

year; otherwise nursing care studies and the making of individual drug books are carried out between Blocks.

7. During the last year a revision week about four months before State Finals has been introduced. 'It is a gruelling week . . . The nurses want to learn, the tutors enjoy coaching' and ward and departmental sisters have small groups for revision of specialized subjects clinically in the wards, and in the clinical lectures organised by one of the senior surgeons.

Two years earlier the *Journal* had printed the details of what was required to pass with honours at the end of the certificated course:

First Class Honours: 75% of total marks, not less than 60% in any examination; 70% in Ward Reports;

Second Class Honours: 70% of total marks, not less than 50% in any examination; 70% in Ward Reports;

Third Class Honours: 65% of total marks, not less than 40% in any examination; 70% in Ward Reports;

In that year there were 1 First Class; 3 Second Class; 12 Third Class (two of whom had married during the course); 103 gained Pass Certificates.

In 1967 there was a most memorable event, the death of Miss Coode on 3rd September at the age of 94. With Dame Alicia and Miss Gullan (the first Sister Tutor in any London hospital), surely she was one of the foundation figures in the history of the School in this century, the first Sister PTS. The obituary notices were rightly long and detailed. In the light of what has been written about Platt and Salmon, and will be written about Briggs and other reports, it is worthwhile to record:

To the end Miss Coode maintained a great interest in the nursing profession. Whenever new treatments, new techniques and even new hospital buildings were described in the nursing journals, she would study the accounts and invariably ask: 'Will these innovations bring better care to the patients?' Or 'Will progress mean improvements in nursing care?'

The School was her life; she was one of that world. She was the founder of the Nurses' Musical Society, the conductor of carol services by the St

Thomas' Choral Society. A different kind of memory came back to some. 'Those of us who had been under her in the PTS could imagine ourselves again making beds to the tune of "Bottom end, Nurse, bottom end".' Another memory: 'When our PTS days finished, Miss Coode led us to the Nightingale Home and left us, in little groups, waiting for Miss Harley, while she went out like a ship in full sail. We felt forlorn indeed.' (Miss Harley, Home Sister from 1924 to 1945, had died on 6th July 1961.)

Musing over a decade in which it had been necessary to appoint a counsellor for the nurses, Miss Adamson wondered in December 1968, what was happiness, as she looked at discontinuity and change all around her.

The Abortion Bill and the Pill not only increase patient attendances but, as might be expected, raise psychological and personal problems amongst staff and students. Transplantation surgery and resuscitation units affect far more people than recipients and donors. Yet, in the final analysis, doctors and nurses have but one duty, to:

Cherish the sick
Comfort the dying
Console the relatives.

The Sixties were indeed troublesome, but the Seventies were dire. The Briggs Report fell in the Seventies, October 1972 to be precise.

CHAPTER EIGHT

Discontinuity and Change

Some Nightingales may have remained isolated from many of the main characteristics of the Sixties both within and outside the School, but this was less likely with those trained in the 1970s. The Summer issue of the Fellowship *Journal* for 1996 had a comment from the Editor:

> A pivotal time of change, both in society and in the Nightingale School was the 70s. These Nightingales who started training some twenty years ago . . . have their own tales to tell equivalent to those of earlier years on 'day side' and 'mopping'. These nurses were instruments of change as the wider world of nursing got to grips with 'The nursing process', 'Models of nursing' and all the influences of technology that changed medicine. It was a tough time for them as their teachers grappled with new theories of nursing and the aim to achieve research-based practice following the Briggs Report of 1972.[1]

The backcloth to the 1970s was an increasingly troubled social and political scene at home, and a seismic shock to the world economy as a result of the oil crisis in 1973, which amongst much else accelerated to an enormous degree the progress of monetary inflation.

To the surprise of many, and most certainly of Harold Wilson, the Labour Government was defeated in the General Election of 1970 and Edward Heath became Prime Minister. What was promised, amongst much else, was greater professionalism in administration. For example, the Civil Service College began to be used much more for the training of potential 'high flyers'. So, Management loomed larger than ever. The greatest single preoccupation of the Heath Government was to negotiate for Britain's membership for the European Economic Community after the failed attempts of earlier governments. The issue was controversial and success did not end the intensive arguments, so much so that when Labour came back into office in 1974, the decision was taken to put the matter to a referendum in 1975, in which the voting public affirmed the decision to stay in. Whatever the Heath Government might have achieved, for example in its attempts to bring a settlement in Northern Ireland, was vitiated and effectively blocked by ever increasing industrial disputes symbolised by the coal miners' strikes. Defeat in 1974 brought the return of Harold Wilson – who resigned abruptly and without warning in 1976 – and the Prime Ministership of James Callaghan saw escalating industrial and financial crises. There can have been few more doleful and wretched times in modern British history than those which culminated in the 'Winter of Discontent'; the dead unburied or uncremated, the rubbish uncollected, the frequent strikes and the financial disgrace of having to call in the help of the International Monetary Fund. From the 'Three-Day Week' to the first three months of 1979, with the catastrophic worsening of matters in Northern Ireland, surely a decade was created that few if any could ignore or be unaware of.

Dr Baly in her book *Nursing and Social Change* writes somewhat wearily about reports on the nursing service; here she echoes Florence Nightingale. She notes that all the major committees had much the same terms of reference and 'all have indicated lines of action that have been ignored . . . Nursing has its reports, but as the waters close over the next, will it move from crisis to crisis because reports are not self executive and the profession has not, like Miss Nightingale, the will to make them so?'[2]

The Briggs Committee was set up in 1970 and reported in October 1972. Its terms of reference were 'To review the role of the nurse and the midwife in the hospital and the community and the education and training required for that role, so that the best use is made of available manpower to meet present needs and the needs of an integrated health service.'

Dr Baly summarises the main recommendations:

1. There should be a single central body responsible for professional standards, education and discipline: The Central Nursing and Midwifery Council. Three Boards for England, Scotland and Wales should be responsible to the Council and under them Area Committees. For England, responsibility should remain with the DHSS.
2. For nursing education there should be Colleges of Nursing and Midwifery, each with its own Principal. Age of entry should be

reduced in two stages, to 17½ in 1973, and 17 in 1975. Selection should be by aptitude and intelligence; suitability should not be determined by academic qualifications alone. The intention was to widen the 'entry-gate'. Courses should be modular, with a prescribed amount of night duty.

All entrants would take:

i) a basic course – an introductory period and four 12-week modules in the main branches of nursing – an 18-month course leading to the Certificate in Nursing Practice.

ii) a further 18-month course, also modular, for those successful in the first. This would lead to Registration.

iii) the more able students could take a further course, either immediately or later, leading to a Higher Certificate. [Readers may be delighted to be told that education should be seen as 'an on-going process'. There should be clinical refresher courses and 'back to nursing' courses. The number of university entrants should be increased; the number of universities offering a degree in nursing should be increased; between 2% to 5% entrants might come to nursing via university; nursing should become more research-based.]

iv) there should be an increase in training facilities for mature students, with centres for advice. Labour relations in the Health Service should be improved with improved counselling services. More assistance to undertake further study and better residential accommodation with a *minimum of supervision* should be introduced.

v) at ward level work should be 'patient orientated' rather than 'task orientated'; differences in degrees of responsibility and expertise among ward sisters should be recognised by increased status and reward.

People are flattered to be asked to sit on important national Commissions and Committees; almost all of them are doomed to watch their findings either ignored, undermined, or part-implemented. Miss Nuttall has said that the nursing profession made a dog's dinner of the Briggs Report.

In a book of this kind, one of whose chief primary sources of evidence are the answers from Nightingales to the questions asked, it is unavoidable that there should be a to-ing and fro-ing in the narrative, from the adulatory and uncritical through the more measured 'emotion recollected in tranquillity' to the bitingly hostile, coming in some cases from plain unhappiness in training. From the 1920s – one of the earliest replies received – came the simple statement that though the life was tough, the pay poor and national esteem of nurses low, nevertheless, it was a wonderful experience and preparation for life, not least for its sadnesses, and the writer would happily live it all over again.

A memorably perceptive recollection of being trained in the first half of the 1970s was given, in conversation, by a nurse who went back in the mid Seventies as a Charge Nurse and taught in the School in the 1980s.

Belinda Atkinson was admitted in 1970 and left in no doubt later about the privilege of having been selected from 200 applicants. She was interviewed by the Chief Nursing Officer, a Tutor and a Teacher; her father, of some eminence, was also 'talked with'. She remembered being given an arithmetic test to be taken at home, because she had no O Level in Mathematics. She lived first in Chelsea Court: 'on parade, Nightingale cap correctly made-up, properly dressed'. The Home Sister was kind, firm and sensitive and argued for her to share with another girl who came from a long way away. This sound advice has led to a lasting friendship. The evening social life was richer than later in the new Gassiot House, where 'flats diminished the camaraderie' and there was no singing round the piano. There were three Sets in her first year and, 'unusually', only twenty-three out of the fifty in her Set finished. She remembers being initiated into various 'tricks', such as using hairspray to keep the butterfly bow on the cap in place.

She comments now that although the social patterns in society were changing, in the Nightingale School social and educational differences were still much in evidence, for example, in the absence of the cap for Enrolled Nurses and the presence of black nurses only in the Pupil Nurses' Sets. [This is also contested by one commentator.]

(It is possible to see the Enrolled Nurse, whose position was consolidated by the Nurses Amendment Act 1961, and sealed by the Nurses Act of 1964, as the linear descendant of FN's non-paying Probationer in the sense of the less qualified, as against the Lady Specials or paying probationers whose successors were Nightingales, Badge and all.)

In Belinda Atkinson's time the wards continued to be task-orientated: Back Round, Bottle Round, Catheter Bag Emptying Round, Hot Drinks Round (after carefully checking with Sister which patient was allowed one) and so on. Her belief that there was not the same level of support for young nurses as may now be found was summed up in her account of her 'first death', of performing the Last Offices with only a similarly junior Pupil Nurse to assist. The Charge Nurse (this title had a particular meaning in St Thomas': the Charge Nurse was the Sister's Deputy) looking round the curtain, briefly, to check whether she had finished, assumed that she was all right. She was certainly not expected to say that she was not, or how the experience might have affected her.

Roisin Tierney recalls a different experience, from which she bene-fited greatly and which she incorporated in her own dealings with student nurses.

> At an earlier time than that which is described here, I was asked to go and see a dead body. I was asked if I had seen one before and having said no was taken behind the curtains to look so that I could cope when I would have to do Last Offices. I appreciated this and subse-quently always asked those more junior the same question and if the answer were in the negative took them behind the curtains with me.

To continue Belinda Atkinson's story: after PTS a contract was signed and the purple uniform issued, with the White Belt – 'a great status symbol'. The duties of the First Year Student Nurses were very clearly delineated. Some Sisters regarded them as incapable of taking pulses. 'Woe betide you if you did anything more than temperatures.' Sister's authority reached to the last detail. 'At 12 noon exactly the salt and pepper trolley was put in its precise place in the ward; from then on there were no bed-pans to be handed out until it was removed after the serving of lunch.'

Personalities of teachers shine through and are remembered with affection. Their influence has lasted; their commitment and dedication made them powerful role models. The ability of one dedicated Tutor to point out an error without offending is recalled with much gratitude. 'The compassion and sensitivity of the same individual is not forgot-ten.'

In the Second Year, frightening responsibility could come suddenly when one might be left in charge of the ward and the drug cupboard while Sister went to lunch. Although 'enthusiasm was encouraged', tears in the sluice room after a sharp reprimand were not uncommon. One did not ask terrifying Sisters for off-duty times, only for duty times. However, their complete control is still admitted as having been the guarantee of high standards and enduring values.

In the Third Year, the White Belt was changed for one of blue petersham. Being a Night First meant one had to be sure to know every patient's condition and report it to Night Sister. There was more management training and practice, community placements (with Health and Practice Nurses) and more Blocks, though the criticism remains that teaching continued to be exclusively subject-related rather then ward related. After final State examinations came the ultimate status symbol of the Red Belt, the buckle for which one's parents were expected to buy.

The visits to Covent Garden to buy fruit for patients at Christmas, the PTS students' tableaux of the Nativity, the free taxi rides, the paternalism of the Metropolitan Police (whose hospital St Thomas' was) and of the Chelsea Pensioners, the Medical School 'hops' and various pranks are all remembered with pleasure.

After a short break, which gave an opportunity to stand back and reflect, Belinda Atkinson noticed on her return to St Thomas' a greater informality in the Hospital, a drift away from the tight control of her first months in PTS which had begun but had not been recognised during the time of training. Some of the old separatist arrangements persisted – dining rooms for Sisters and for Consultants. She could see then that some people had been promoted beyond their capacities – the 'Peter Principle'. A new kind of Ward Sister was beginning to be appointed – no less skilled and still commanding respect. However, the most senior posts were, until the late 1980s, still filled by 'invitation'. This was a rephrasing of the saying that Matron's Office decided everything: invitations were not refused.

Another writer's memories are more harshly critical. In the Third Year, she notes that the modules of training were *supposedly* linked to practice on the wards.

Excellent on 'mechanical needs of patients in relation to hygiene, wounds, pre and post op care.' *Very* poor guidance or support on all other aspects of life as a live-in student nurse – you were left on your own to cope with horrendous problems of adjusting, at 18 years of age, to death and disease. Ward sisters, almost without fail, VILE! No major changes, more's the pity. SLOG. No thinking, no initiative required – just cheap labour to get bodies washed and wounds dressed. I loathed it . . . a sad little story . . . I think I was so unhappy because I had been raised to question things; this attitude was not acceptable in the early 1970s.

The writer admits that she did not see herself as a born nurse and that those who did were happier. She went on to a different career and in retrospect is proud to possess the Badge. The responses from Nightingales were of a patchwork quilt nature, and though most shew appreciation of their training, when one encounters disagreement it can sometimes surprise one in its ferocity. Change was unavoidable, but the wish was strong to 'hold fast that which is good' – how did one get the balance?

In these tumultuous times, there can still emerge a sense that for many Nightingales in training the outside world was not much more than an inconvenience and that the main thrusts of the School and the Hospital were still within the patterns that have been described here in such detail. In a society that was, certainly in the major cities, inescapably multi-ethnic, one has been told on good authority of a surgeon at St Thomas' who, in the early 1970s, refused to have a black nurse in the operating theatre. All this being said, Miss Garrett was working hard to explain change, to ward off opposition and to plan a sensible way forward. She *did* realise that Management had come to stay. The *Journal* for July 1972 stated that:

> The observant reader will have noticed that reports on management courses, hitherto so regularly contributed, have not been appearing lately . . . Those of you working in Great Britain will know that [there was no diminution in courses]. The Salmon Report recommended that *all nurses should receive* management training in successive stages from the time they qualified.
>
> No longer is it the selected few who become students again. All are doing it . . . The staff at St Thomas' reflect the national trend . . . And so, since the first group of Sisters met together on a First Line Management Course in October 1969, everyone has followed suit. Proportionately, fewer go on Middle Management courses, but there is usually at least one person away. Our top executives confer with their peers in the NHS on Top Management courses.

Three reports follow, from First Line Management, from Middle

Management (Roisin Tierney) and from Top Management (Mary Laurence) with the sub-title 'Action is the Proper Fruit of Knowledge'.[3]

In the same issue the retirement of Miss Hone was noted at considerable length. She was succeeded in the title of Principal Nursing Officer (Education) by Miss Hazel Allen, a non-Nightingale. What is more, in this same rather momentous year, the Nightingale School moved on 7th August 1972 into the new Gassiot House: 'Now, for the first time in its 112 years of history, Nightingale Nurses have their own school, built to be a place of learning.' It contained both residential accommodation and the School of Nursing in two 7-storey buildings linked at either end and at ground floor level by a single-storey structure. With accommodation for 381, it was intended that it should be comprehensive, housing all ranks. It was opened by Miss Hone.

Miss Hone's retirement called for many contributions to celebrate the achievements of a truly remarkable Nightingale whose influence extended back to the early 1940s and who, in her final post as Principal Tutor, had shaped the education of hundreds of nurses. Certain words recur in the tributes: dignity, complete integrity, unfailing faithfulness, outstandingly good memory, 'a clear incisive method of teaching', unselfish, unflinching in leadership. She emerges as the quintessential Nightingale nurse, becoming increasingly important in the world outside St Thomas'. There is a Conversation Piece contributed anonymously in which Miss Hone is seen as the last of the Old Guard, the end of an era of 'personal contact and perfection in every detail'. She was compassionate but 'it's funny she's still so shy . . . I loved to see her in action. Tactics: the trouble is you never know she's won until she has.' And then, 'What about her sense of humour? So gentle, isn't it? Mark you, it took me eighteen months to recognise it.'

The outside world did intrude when the IRA bomb exploded near the Old Bailey. 'The Nightingale School sent students and tutors, and the Secretary's office arrived armed with boards to list the injured. An emergency canteen was laid on in the lecture theatre.' Another nurse remembers that there was a hush over the whole ward. 'We knew it was not anything that we had ever heard before.'

In Miss Garrett's last months of office, further major changes took place, all arising in one form or another from the Salmon Report or from implications that could be drawn from it. The direct result was to divide the Hospital into units, each with its own Nursing Officer. Wards had been grouped, and Group Sisters' meetings were to take place twice a year, held in rotation at other hospitals in the Group. Ward Sisters themselves had regular meetings with the Nursing Officer and other Sisters in their Unit. 'Uniforms are rarely worn by the most senior of the nurse administrators, and never by the Chief Nursing Officer.'

There are many references in the *Journal* for the early 1970s to continuous discussion about the implications of Briggs. At the end of May 1974, Miss Garrett retired 'from the post of Chief Nursing Officer (latterly Acting District Nursing Officer) at St Thomas'.' In the tributes, there is a sense that things were changing yet again, a point underlined by Miss Garrett in her final Address to the Fellowship on 13th May. 'It is the first time in the forty-six years since the foundation of the Nightingale Fellowship [that] your President addresses you neither as the Matron nor as the Chief Nursing Officer.'

There was a new procedure for interviewing prospective students and pupils, an area of responsibility which had been the strict preserve of the Matron.

> The candidate is now interviewed by three people including the Selection Officer, a representative from the School and a representative from the service side. These last two vary so that all officers receive an opportunity to select. Candidates are taken around the hospital on arrival and . . . have lunch with nurses in training. Pupil candidates take a short written examination which includes mathematical problems, the meaning of words, and a short essay. Student candidates are given a topic to discuss in their own group and are observed by the interviewers . . . The session lasts practically all day.

The Final State Practical Examination also disappeared. Practical Assessments were now undertaken in the wards and trained nursing staff, approved by the GNC, acted as assessors. Students were to take the following practical assessments: a) aseptic technique; b) drug round; c) total patient care; d) ward management. They had to be successful in all four before taking the State Written Paper. All student nurses were to wear the blue and white striped uniform; pupil nurses were in mauve and white striped dresses; in both cases the colour of the belt indicated the stage of training. Student nurses needed only to complete six months after taking their State Finals in order to qualify for the Badge; during this period, there were two 3-month allocations. The burden of work on the Ward Sisters increased.[4]

1972 was seen at the time, and increasingly so in retrospect, as a pivotal year. There was an old world, and it was giving way to a new one. Natalie Tiddy has written 'Some Memories', mainly about her work from 1988 to 1991, but she introduces them by returning to 1972.

Until 1972 the allocation of student nurses for the practical aspects of their training was undertaken by an Assistant Matron in Matron's Office, and then by a Nursing Officer Allocations. This part of the work was moved into the Nightingale School in 1975 and housed in the office which dealt with recruitment. Everything therefore came into the responsibility of the Principal Tutor, and as she was accountable to the Matron it made sense anyway. The appointment of Hazel Allen, as the first Director of Nurse Education (that is, no longer Principal Tutor), continued this arrangement, now completely part of the School. A Nursing Officer Recruitment and Selection and a Nursing Officer Allocation were added as new appointments. In the early 80s Jean Peacock was appointed as Senior Nursing Officer to oversee these, herself accountable to the Director of Nurse Education.

It was not until May 1975 that Miss Garrett's successor, Miss Mary Laurence, had the opportunity to explain what all the latest reorganisations had really meant, though she was delighted to have been greeted 'most mornings in the corridor by Mick the dustman, by "Good morning Sister". It is still the greatest privilege to carry such a title.' In her post she had as her Deputy Joyce Skues, a Senior Nursing Officer who was 'virtually the Matron responsible for the day-to-day management of St Thomas'.[5]

Firstly, Miss Laurence was the 'District Nursing Officer' in the reorganised Health Service, responsible for the administration of nursing in the St Thomas' district, but not responsible for the School. It had taken her a year to put key people in new posts with new titles. It has been seen already that Miss Hazel Allen, appointed as Director of Nurse Education, had been promoted to the post and title of Director of Nurse Education, which meant responsibility for the training schools of *all* the hospitals in the Sector – to which Tooting Bec Hospital had just been added. She was the first non-Nightingale to be appointed to high position, and no Nightingale has been appointed to run the School since that time. What is the significance of this, given the high esteem in which Nightingales were held and in which they held themselves?

The traditionalist line was broken; an outsider in authority perhaps could more easily oblige the School to notice what was happening to the academic side of nursing, world-wide. 'Models of Nursing' were foreshadowed in the last chapter, but they became a reality in the second half of the 1970s. There have been so many changes since these years, with many Nightingales no doubt confused about the complexity, and it was interesting to receive the Fellowship *Journal* for Winter 1997 and to find that at last a full Glossary of Terms, entitled *Nursing Terminology Today* had been thought necessary and compiled. It would have helped the present writer considerably to have possessed it earlier on. 'Models of Nursing' are described as

> Ways of thinking about nursing that call upon particular knowledge and skills. The Nursing Process is used within this framework (assessment, planning, implementation and evaluation). The most frequently used models are by Roper Logan and Tierney; Roy; Orem; Johnson; Rogers and Neuman. Orem's self-care model, for example, emphasises self-care and the promotion of ways to achieve independence.

The Activities for Living model was put forward in 1980 by Nancy Roper, Winifred Logan and Alison Tierney, based on the findings of a research project on the clinical experiences of student nurses published in 1976.[7] The work looked back to the definition of nursing put forward by Virginia Henderson in 1966, already quoted. She had given her own description of nursing under fourteen headings. Helping the patient with the following activities or providing conditions under which he can perform them unaided:

1. Breathe normally.
2. Eat and drink adequately.
3. Eliminate body wastes.
4. Move and maintain desirable postures.
5. Sleep and rest.
6. Select suitable clothes – dress and undress.
7. Maintain body temperature within normal range by adjusting clothing and modifying the environment.

8. Keep the body clean and well groomed and protect the integument i.e. the skin.

9. Avoid dangers in the environment and avoid injuring others.

10. Communicate with others in expressing emotions, needs, fears or opinions.

11. Worship according to one's faith.

12. Work in such a way that there is a sense of accomplishment.

13. Play or participate in various forms of recreation.

14. Learn, discover, or satisfy the curiosity that leads to normal development and health, and use the available health facilities.

One has been told that this analysis of nursing was well-accepted by British nurses and that Henderson's 'concept' was developed into a 'model which focussed on the activities people engage in to live'. This all seems a rather ponderous way of stating the obvious. The model assumes the acceptance of a set of beliefs and values, which needless to say, all models must. It is concerned with 'living throughout the life-span' and, interestingly, in the definition of 'lifespan' comes the statement, 'An individual is seen to begin living *at conception*, and to end it at death' – another somewhat obvious fact perhaps. (However, not to everyone: the arguments between the pro-life and pro-choice groups are intensifying, and bring to the forefront the values on which they are based.)

It would seem unchallengeable that models help to concentrate the mind powerfully. On the other hand, many felt, and still do feel, that they were restrictive and that the claims made for them are unproven. In an article in the *Nursing Standard* in 1990, Norah Casey examined the state of play. She wrote that 'the use and abuse of models is now provoking more and more debate and taking its rightful place among the top-ranking topics of the day.' She referred to the 'models band-waggon' that had been the subject of the second *Nursing Standard*/Royal Marsden Hospital Debate. She summarised the course of discussion: models did little to improve nursing care, their use was potentially damaging, they inhibited the development of nursing. 'While nurses are drowning in a sea of theoretical ideology, they lose sight of the real goal of nursing.' Few nurses were adequately prepared to put a theoretical framework into practice. The argument about models distracted from tackling the real thorny issues: 'Education, skill/mix and staffing – all essential components of quality care.'

The model became the scapegoat and was seen as something from the world of fantasy, bearing little relevance to the realities of nursing. Norah Casey herself did not see things in quite this way. She thought that it was not always the ideologies that were the problem but imperfections in putting theory into practice. She continued:

> There can be no one model, no absolute rights or wrongs in nursing practice. There is no reasoning behind our continued use of North American models or our insistence on their strict interpretation. The rigid enforcement of an alien model into nursing practice without forethought and planning is doomed to failure.

The article concluded by saying that the supporters of models had not done enough to prove their case. There had not been sufficient evaluation of the impact of their use on the quality of nursing care, and until such time as something more definitive could be said, the arguments would continue. Having looked at some of the literature about models and the models themselves, one can certainly understand the perplexity of student nurses, and see the truth of what Norah Casey said.

Professor Macleod Clark, in conversation in 1996, made the point that in the new Nightingale Institute the task is to extend the boundaries of nursing beyond 'models' into new territory, not necessarily to the liking of the doctors. As in Education so, in nursing, American theories, models and taxonomies, often advanced in a version of English that seems to have been rather badly translated from the German, tend to be worn down by English pragmatism. It has been remarked more than once, that models were part of the movement to make nursing 'academically respectable', and that patients were sacrificed to them. A senior Nightingale has said, 'I don't think that there is much evidence that we have ever evaluated or reflected sufficiently on the care that we have given (neither by the old guard or the new).'

During the first years of her tenure of office Miss Laurence confessed to the shock of having to deal with the Area Health Authority that had replaced the Board of Governors, and with The Community Health Council, a body which was much respected. Suddenly, she had found political attitudes affecting her responsibilities. 'To hear our Health Authority Board members arguing that because Cow and Gate Milk Producers have South African connections, they should not have their products on sale in our Maternity and Child Welfare Clinics is an education in itself. The Council members are very politically orientated.' One of her proper preoccupations was with whether all these reorganisations had improved nurse training and patient care, a question to which she could give no neat answer, only hope.[8]

In January 1976, Miss Allen wrote at length about 'Changes in Nurse Education at St Thomas' '. She listed some major worries:

1. Though more students were commencing training nationally, there was an increase in the number of 'discontinuations': from 37,196 beginners, 13,265 dropped out – spread across all the years of training.
2. The wastage rate of teaching staff had worsened: in the six year period 1968–1974, 783 nurses registered as tutors, but the number in post had increased by only 115. 'The outlook for traditional nurse training is unhappy quite apart from any major development such as envisaged by Briggs.'
3. In the Nightingale School itself, over the three years April 1971 – April 1974, 14% of the students had discontinued, and 'we only just managed to keep our establishment of tutorial staff. Both learners and teachers have different priorities from the traditional outlook and both have expectations which if not met mean withdrawal of service.'

She therefore outlined her proposals for retaining learners and tutors, commenting on the reasons for dissatisfaction.

The role model of ward sister and tutor is not encouraging to students. Many do not wish to be either. Why? Why can they see little job satisfaction in being cogs in a wheel, subservient to a system of conflicting loyalties and pressures which increased professionalism and consensus management appear as yet unable to deal with to any degree of satisfaction?

Miss Allen proceeded to a cold analysis. The position of the Ward Sister as the centre of teaching had been reduced. 'Regrettably, a dichotomy has occurred between School and Ward through divorce of theory from practice.' The time had come for a new marriage of the two. Therefore, henceforward, students would be admitted in two groups in March and September to be educated in modular form, starting with ward experience of eight to twelve weeks, and then going into the classroom. A new curriculum study group of Ward Sister, students, teachers and an educationalist was rethinking objectives and methods. A learning resources centre had been opened to allow for more personal study 'instead of the blanket coverage of the past'. For the first twenty-four weeks after the introductory course, three hours a week were to be spent in the classroom to correlate theory with practice – on either Tuesday or Wednesday afternoons. From January 1975, students were going to be required to have experience in community or obstetric nursing and geriatric or psychiatric nursing; this would reduce by 17 per cent the amount of time that could be spent at patients' bedsides (not a Nightingale but a nationally statutory requirement, stemming from an EEC directive). The Community Course of six weeks was to be based at the South Bank Polytechnic where students from King's and Guy's would also go.

She went on to give a warning that 'there is no doubt that we shall not be able to supply the same amount of service as in the past.' Doctors would have to accept this; no one would gain if students and ward sisters were exhausted. The third year was to be spent in consolidation of experience in two allocations of six months' duration each, one in Medicine and the other in Surgery. Miss Allen hoped that this rationalisation would lessen stress, increase the time for practice and study and enable some forward planning. 'The price of failure will mean fewer students and tutors and ward sisters of tomorrow.' Her conclusion was to quote Florence Nightingale: 'Let whoever is in charge keep this simple question in her head – not how can I do the right thing myself but how can I provide that the right thing shall always be done.'

In the Fellowship *Journal* for 1988 Sister Anita (Elizabeth Morris) wrote about the cultures of communities, particularly of large hospitals, maintaining that each hospital had a distinctive character. She claimed that the aspect of the School and St Thomas' that stood out most for her were 'the care for the individual, the appreciation for a person's dignity and the passing on of high standards and teaching . . . St Thomas' always seemed to have time.'[9]

Not time generally, not time for standing and staring, but time 'to get priorities right'. She picks out one incident that, for her, summed up everything that mattered. A particular Ward Sister, Miss Riley, was in charge of a 'very mixed bunch of patients'. One of them was an elderly woman, dying of cancer, who seemed to have neither relatives nor friends; barely conscious, she kept muttering under her breath. Sister Anita asked a Staff Nurse what she was saying, and was told it was 'just the drugs'. Even so, she bent down to listen. The old lady was saying over and over again: 'I am afraid. I am so afraid.' She felt bound to tell the Ward Sister, known to be formidable.

> Sister regarded me solemnly . . . She rose and came round the desk. Without a word, she picked up a chair in one hand, and took me by the other. We went over to the patient's bed. Sister put the chair down beside it and sat me on it.
> 'You do not leave here', she said, 'until you are relieved.'
> She told me the things I could do for the old lady, and the things which would make her know she had someone with her . . . There was a time and motion exercise on at the time. Sister remained unruffled. She had her priorities right.
> That old lady died two and a half days later, and she was not left alone night or day. On the last morning Sister herself came early on duty to relieve the night staff.

Miss Riley provided that 'the right thing was done.' It is difficult to believe that this incident could have happened only in St Thomas', and indeed the claim would be vehemently rejected, but it is clear that here, as in so many other examples quoted, someone who was trained in the School thought it special.

The answers to the questionnaire for the earlier 1970s sometimes give, as one might expect, a confusing picture, because of the experience and attitudes of individuals and also because the pace of change and the new flexibility allowed – and began to require – some variation in patterns of training. The downside of this was that some of this experience was in other hospitals in the Group, not all of them thought to be of equal standing and standards. Some described this as a 'culture shock'. But

> wherever we worked, we took our 'chart' (a log book), in which procedures were signed off at the end of our time on the ward or department – a tick when something had been observed, and an initial when we ourselves had carried out the procedure. Training was EXCELLENT.

Not all those who were the first to follow modular programmes regarded them as equally successful, nor those who were affected by them.

> As a Charge Nurse this made running a ward more difficult as there

was no longer a cross-section of students from all years. The new students did not have the experience to feel confident and needed a lot of extra teaching in practical tasks. We missed the seniors who were doing their specialities, so the wards were less balanced.

One memory, from someone trained between 1975 and 1978, was of

being taken to see the hospital computer which consisted of dozens of fridge-sized boxes humming and buzzing and churning out volumes of paper – all housed in two large rooms. I remember looking around the iron lungs, indeed I remember having a go in one.

These were the young women who, living in a time of spiralling inflation, were part of a School and a tradition in which it was not 'the done thing' to protest publicly or too much. (There was an incident in which some took part in a protest across Westminster Bridge about salaries.) The Halsbury Commission did tackle nurses' pay, and some of those who answered felt reasonably well paid by the end of the Seventies.

One strong feeling – it was there in previous decades but not so pointedly – was that they were used as an underpaid labour force in the wards. Another, again expressed in earlier years but now felt poignantly, was the awareness of the difference between them and contemporaries in other forms of higher education. The realisation that there was a gulf between nurses in training, who were dealing with death, suffering, misery and deprivation in their late teens and early twenties, and the often callow immaturity of their friends in universities, comes through forcibly. Some, an increasing number of them, were graduates, and there is evidence that the immediate school-leavers felt slightly uncomfortable in mixing with these older students.

The old world was still present.

On my second ward allocation on Grosvenor Ward: 'You will never make a true Nightingale – you answer senior staff back' – just because I asked questions. You have to laugh – so old-fashioned – but wonderful, wonderful years. I am proud to be a Nightingale.

Another reply brings in a certain bitterness that 'the modern world' has abandoned so much of value.

The whole feeling of the Nightingale School was one of pride and privilege. Pride to belong to such an establishment – morale was high because we felt that although we'd all done well to get in, we were privileged to be having our training there. This feeling never left me. Sadly, I totally suppress it nowadays, because it means absolutely nothing to the new generation of nurses.

The September 1973 Set were the first to be required to wear the paper American-style cap until their third year, when the Nightingale cap was awarded.

I enjoyed the old-fashioned discipline and tradition which are not so well observed today. We would never have dreamed of addressing each other by Christian names within earshot of Sister.

The privilege of being a Nightingale could be double-edged. In these answers, as in so many others, there are instances of resentment met when working in other institutions. Some even decided not to wear the Badge to avoid comment – no doubt pushed by incidents such as when a Consultant, on seeing a Nightingale with Badge, exclaimed to the assembled group: 'Thank God, a real nurse.'

The real hastening of the pace of change came in the later 1970s, and it is to the answers from this period that one needs to look for evidence of the acceleration. Needless to say, certain themes recur, as they do throughout all the answers right through to the end of the School. First, the intense pride of being a Nightingale – always with a few, but only a few, exceptions: 'Everyone I've ever met has been impressed that I'm a Nightingale and I try to justify their "awe" and be gracious about it.' 'Training was *superb*. We led the field in the "total patient care method".' The one element in the training that receives fairly unflattering comment is Psychiatry, but as one said, 'We did learn it for real in practice.' Another comment is:

We had a 'fast-track' of graduate nurses who provoked a lot of jealousy until they qualified ahead of us and then used to come running asking for advice. This was, I guess, a taste of things to come, of Project 2000.

Another way of expressing the sense of the specialness of the Nightingale School is to say that it saw itself as 'the Oxbridge of training schools'.

199

The nursing process arrived to stay during my time. Its implementation depended on the ward sister, so as a result it sometimes worked more efficiently than others. Many found themselves spending more time updating and recording nursing care than actually with patients.

Someone else commented similarly on the major changes during her time:

Above all the move from task-based work – that is the bed round, the bottle round etc. – to the concept of 'Total Patient Care' and then the introduction of the 'Nursing Process'. Ward sisters took to new ideas with differing views, so as you moved from ward to ward you had to adapt pretty quickly between the old and new models of work.

The same writer reflects how she learnt always to strive for excellence, but often in fear of doing the wrong thing or of not knowing the correct answer. 'I found the responsibility overwhelming at times.' She remarks wryly that, 'On reflection our training taught us great practical skills but counselling and psychology were never mentioned.'

It would seem that student nurses were much more affected by changes than the pupil nurses, one of whom, trained between 1975 and 1977, simply records that 'The only major change was that the final exam was changed from a written exam to multiple choice questions.' The old order was giving way to the new, but the old order was still there – even for someone whose training ended in 1981 there was an appreciation of the routine of back rounds and bed-pan rounds. She finds it hard to see how other methods are better – yet another comment pointing at what are perceived as the deficiencies of Project 2000.

For the rest, there are the nostalgic reminiscences of social life as it was. 'The inter-com to remind us we still had a guest in the room.' 'The inter-com system was too intrusive and having my fiancé to stay was impossible.' The intrusiveness of some of the pastoral care, the friendliness of the Metropolitan police and the taxi drivers, the excellent 'social life with the medical students', like being at a cross between university and finishing school, are all remembered and relished, so that one is left wondering if the rules and restrictions gave a quality to life that cannot be appreciated in today's free-for-all.

I met my husband just before starting training and we were married in my third year (1978). This was very much frowned on.

Miss Allen left the School in 1977 to become Deputy Director of the King's Fund Centre, where she established a project called, surprisingly, *Preparation for Ward Sister* to examine the role of the Ward Sister and to identify the needs for her training. After extensive evaluation, the results were published in 1984. In anticipation of this, in 1982, she edited a book for the general reader, *The Ward Sister; Role and Preparation.* The article about her in the *Nursing Times* for 28th September 1983 indicates fairly clearly that she was a controversial person who did not shirk argument. One student, an Honours Graduate – there was only one Graduate Set each year and this was the two-year course, 1970 to 1972 – certainly reacted to Miss Allen, finding her 'combative and provocative'.

She brought the first major changes in the Nightingale School because the entire dynamic was altered. It was a sea-change that affected every aspect of life and the School's relationship with the wards ... Hazel Allen's era was the period when the School was made to jettison many of its old ways – I think we sometimes threw the baby out with the bath water.

Miss Allen later set up a 'nursing policies study unit' which 'should be able to design an alternative career structure for clinical nurses.' She advanced the notion that 'nursing is changing from a subservient to a thinking profession ... With this move away ... comes the acceptance of accountability by nurses.' Readers will see in a later chapter how some of these ideas were incorporated and developed, not least her hope to attach nurse training directly to a university. She may be regarded as controversial, but then it is likely that anyone holding her position after the time of Miss Hone would be so regarded.

In May 1978, the Fellowship celebrated its Golden Jubilee in some style. After the President's welcome, Miss Smyth, Miss Turner, Miss Adamson and Miss Garrett 'spoke for about five minutes each to the delight of their listeners, and audible murmurs of "My Matron" were heard all around the hall.' Each, understandably, reflected on their time in office. The cake was cut by Miss Clare Parkes, the first ever Hon. Sec. to the Fellowship, and Mr Leslie Graham, the first male Nightingale, who had completed his training in 1974 – a training about which he has written amusingly and wryly. He wrote to the author about being 'spared the ordeal of being "washed" by my fellow students and given a real-life patient to practise on from the start. I was spared the mysteries and . . . the miseries of trying to make the perfect Nightingale cap.' Patients were confused about what to call him.

Miss Gould was not present because she was preparing for her eightieth birthday celebrations in Winchester, but she was one of the contributors to a series of 'Memories of Training' – Miss Bocock revealed that she was 'an elementary school teacher in the East End of London when I visited St Thomas's to enquire about nurse-training . . . I was accepted on the spot, testimonials allowing. I was told that to enter the Nightingale School I *must* grow my short hair.' (This was in 1927.) Miss Hone and quite a number of others added their own memories.[10]

By then it was recognised that, with three types of ward design, spanning more than 100 years in the Hospital, it was necessary to commission an evaluation study. Most of its conclusions did not affect directly the training in the School, but it is interesting to note that opinion from Sisters, Nurses and patients came down in favour of the large open ward in which everyone could be seen and cared for most easily. By then, the new buildings were in operation with their wards divided into bays and the Hospital has had to live with a 'mixed economy' ever since.

As 1978 came to a close, Miss Laurence wrote about the Bill based on the findings of a Royal Commission 'to unify the standard of education, training and professional conduct for nurses, midwives and health visitors' that had had its first reading in the Commons. This was the beginning of implementing the Briggs Report. The main purpose of the Bill was to establish a United Kingdom Central Council, with four Boards to oversee education and training. Most interestingly, there is also the first reference to some consequences of belonging to the EEC; some changes were necessary to comply with Article 57 of the Treaty of Rome, concerned with the free movement of labour. Clearly, there had to be a mutually acceptable standard of training and competence in each member country. 'To achieve this syllabus we will have to allow every nurse to gain experience in psychiatry, obstetrics and community nursing, in addition to medicine, surgery and paediatrics.'

Miss Laurence was sure that all these skills and experiences were available within the Health District but needed to be coordinated. She made the first proper mention of putting everything on computer disc. These new responsibilities fell to Miss Cackett, the Director of Education, who had just returned from a lengthy study course in other EEC countries.

The Callaghan Government ran increasingly into trouble, its continued existence dependent on an uncomfortable alliance with the Liberals. But as part of what it thought was a response to a popular demand, it planned to introduce a combined Devolution Bill for the four constituent parts of the United Kingdom – the Kingdoms of England and Scotland, the Principality of Wales and the Province of Northern Ireland. It was abandoned because the Government's own criteria were not met, and separate Bills were introduced for Scotland and Wales with further accompanying criteria for acceptance insisted on by parliamentary back-benchers. Such planning unavoidably involved health, the organisation of hospitals and the training of nurses. The Act to implement these health proposals was passed; what Miss Laurence had not referred to in the previous year was that it also made proposals – indeed they had become centrally important – about what would follow if the Government's intentions about referenda on devolution had been passed by the planned pattern of voting. The failure to get them accepted was one of the many catastrophes that the Government faced. The Bill concerning health became an Act in spite of its problems.

The UKCC and its Boards were given the task of bringing together the organisation and training of Nurses, Midwives, Health Visitors and District Nurses. They were, with their different perspectives on training, dragged 'kicking and screaming into centrally organised bodies', in the words of an eminent executive. The most reluctant were the Health Visitors, who considered that they were already the most highly trained.

With the incoming Thatcher Government came a new severity in looking at finance and efficiency, which increased the drive towards rationalisations. To the outsider, this means further bewildering changes both in organisation and in nomenclature. It came to be realised that with its unique concentration of major teaching hospitals, the capital was over-supplied. Twenty per cent of the national health budget was being spent on fifteen per cent of the nation's population. Attention was to be rightly directed to the use and function of each major hospital and, understandably, a model of best practice was to be sought. It was found in Guy's Hospital, which had become the first

NHS Trust, 'the flagship', and so was used in the Tomlinson Report. St Thomas' was never a Trust in its own right, but for a time it had to act as a 'shadow Trust'. Given the proximity of Guy's to St Thomas' there was to be some heart-searching about the use of each institution. Opinion was to veer strongly towards the development of Guy's and the running down of St Thomas'.

Local politics played their part, certainly in St Thomas', where a vociferous left-wing element on Lambeth Council expressed itself through representative members on the Hospital's committees. It has been said that the spiteful verbal abuse at meetings, and the resentment shewn to the Hospital and the School, were because they were seen as 'élite'. According to one eminent teacher, the Left was out to destroy a centre of excellence. Banners baiting the Government prominently displayed directly opposite the Houses of Parliament, in partnership no doubt with the GLC's hanging from County Hall, did not endear the hospital to government ministers. These were unhappy times. But whilst these deliberations were being held, other rearrangements, of no concern here, were to deprive Guy's of its catchment area and were to swing matters greatly in favour of St Thomas'. (One is put in mind of similar unco-ordination in the schools' field, of splendidly-equipped new secondary schools being completed just as they were being deprived of their catchment areas – in Liverpool on one occasion, as the Lord Mayor declared a school open, the bulldozers, 200 yards away, began to knock down every house in sight.)

The result has been the running down of Guy's to a point where it will have 157 acute beds – the rest of the site, to be called the Thomas Guy House, is to be developed as a 'high-tech' unit for specialised treatments, with a swing back to St Thomas' to give it 1100 beds, with all the concomitant costs, running into many millions of pounds. The implementation of much of this, so one is told, is dependent on possible changes of direction by the new Labour Government. For those in favour of St Thomas' it all appears to be good news, though there remains an active pressure group in Guy's. As Professor Macleod Clark is reported as saying in the final chapter, the amalgamation of these two great historical institutions – Guy's did, quite simply, grow out of St Thomas' in the 18th century – has had its moments.

Mrs Thatcher was the determined opponent of many of the chief characteristics of British administration since 1964. She was against consensus politics, she was committed to the undoing of what she called 'the nanny State' and was not afraid of abrasive confrontation. Above all, she introduced, with some ruthlessness, the policy of the Free Market. A completely new style of government came in, whose criteria were based on those of private enterprise, particularly large-scale private enterprise – Education was measured against Marks and Spencers, and it has been suggested that Sainsburys was the model for Health. In conversation in March 1997, Miss Cackett observed that one contemporary Health Region employs as many people as all Sainsburys nationally, underlining her point that the Health Service is the largest of all national enterprises, and that there have been, understandably one supposes, many attempts to 'get the management right'. All these reorganisations, particularly in the 1970s and 80s, cost vast sums of money; there seems to have been no public assessment as to whether they improved the quality of care for patients.

CHAPTER NINE

Battles Won and Lost

In 1980, through all 'the changes and chances of this fleeting world', there was a Nightingale School recognisably in line with its own past. Its traditions were cherished and intact, its rituals largely continued. It still saw itself as a separate entity with a unique character, even though it was part of an NHS sector, titles had changed, and the administrative and management systems had altered to fit in and keep pace with what was happening in the hospital world generally.

Sue Norman, who had trained in the School from 1966 to 1968, was appointed Nurse Tutor in 1978 by Miss Cackett, who had taken over as the School's Director in 1977. Sue Norman held her post until 1987. In an interview she maintained that in Miss Cackett's time a major set of changes was introduced to enhance the professional status of nurses; it was necessary to move away from the 'apprenticeship model', which had kept nursing at a low level of professional and public esteem. One move towards this was the plan to introduce computer-assisted learning which she had been sent to the United States and Canada to study. The School was one of three pilot sites for this but, according to a number of senior Nightingales, not an entirely enthusiastic participant. Sue Norman was also charged by Miss Cackett with developing the 'Nursing Process'.

By 1986 the system of teaching nurses in the clinical setting had been phased out; its worth, at its best, was very considerable, and perceived as such by many nurses in training. In this time of transition, some of the Ward Sisters were relieved because they thought that the Clinical Teachers undermined their authority; others appreciated them, but not necessarily for the right reasons. This is another example of the question, not yet resolved, of who integrates all aspects of training, more difficult now that clinical expertise has expanded and become more complex.

One school of historians will always seek for significant figures, from a conviction that such people shape events (and are not part of an impersonal process). A fair number of such women have come into this book, and a meeting with Miss Cackett in March 1997 established that she had read the times well. She made the following points:

1. It has taken sixty years and eight major Reports to achieve student status for nurses and to remove them from being a cheap labour force on the wards.
2. The change has been phenomenally expensive, with much wastage on the way.
3. The years 1985–1995 saw the biggest revolution in nurse education since the Registration Act of 1919.
4. The tension between theory and practice should not exist if services are managed properly. Far from being over-managed, there is a need for more and better management if the services are to be held together. This reflection came from her review of just how often politicians and others have arranged and rearranged the Health Service. Change, time and again, was politically and economically led, without sufficient ground work to prepare people and systems for what was about to happen.
5. Her experience in running the School led her to a determined policy of in-service training, not least to broaden the perspectives 'of those in the service area'. She became more frustrated later as Chief Nursing Officer, when she found that public relations and marketing loomed larger than getting anything done.
6. All through, she wanted to bring together service and education, she sought out 'potential' in the staff, and saw the need fully to explain changes to those who were to be involved.
7. Problems were exacerbated by 'too much being done far too quickly' in response to the Health Authority's insistence that the School should be 'more educational'. (Another senior nurse has added that, in particular, some of the local political members wanted a greater representation in the School of people from the local community).

Natalie Tiddy, the President of the Nightingale Fellowship, in her reflections underlined the same confusions and worries brought about by so many changes; the words 'Project 2000' loomed larger and larger. The School was seen to be slow in implementing it and pressure was brought from the Department of Health to get a move on, but as Natalie has said, 'a whole series of training programmes had to be devised for trained staff and students to begin to understand what Project 2000 really required.' She pointed out, as Jane Easterbrook was to do, that 'such enormous change over such a short timescale lost many staff and I fear the quality of care delivered was sorely tested.'

The middle years of the 1980s seem to have been full of tensions, but it was the first time that changes in nurse education were seen to be as important as all the other changes in the National Health Service. By the end of the decade the School had almost gone – it ceased to exist in 1991 – and the final ceremonies of May 1996, when its last graduates received their Badges from Princess Alexandra, were emotional, retrospective and symbolic. It is not an easy task, in fact it is plain difficult, to plot one's way through this decade.

One of the most surprising realisations in writing about the 1980s was that a Report of great significance, published in 1985, seems to have been lost in limbo. Keeping in mind Dr Baly's remarks about the fate of most Reports – that after all the toil, the excitement and the expense their findings have been usually shelved or disregarded – a reading of the Judge Report nevertheless reveals it to be of true significance in any study of the development of nursing in recent times. It was commissioned by the Royal College of Nursing and its title proclaimed its findings: *The Education of Nurses: a New Dispensation. Commission on Nursing Education* (April 1985). The first thing to be remarked upon is its delightful style. Dr Harry Judge was the Director of the Department of Educational Studies in Oxford University, widely experienced in educational matters in Europe and in North America, who, along with his distinguished committee, 'approached venerable questions in a spirit of freshness, to review all possible options, and [came] to a conclusion that fundamental change, without fudging or compromise, is now needed.' In other words, a group consisting of perceptive outsiders and insiders examined the state of affairs in nursing. 'We want the rest of the world not just to care about nurses – it does that already – but to know about them and the education they receive, and the one they deserve.' The position seemed to be that the problems were not new, although they were becoming progressively more urgent. They had not been effectively addressed because nurses themselves had not agreed either upon their nature or their cure.

Palliatives have been proposed, but the underlying conviction of this

Report is that nothing less than fundamental reform can now be effective. The changes which are proposed will appear to many as dangerous and threatening, but should not (for that reason alone) be rejected. Failure to undertake radical changes will, in any case, be even more dangerous.

The Report in its analysis exposed all the concerns and problems that the writing of the history of the Nightingale School has already encountered, and it could be quoted verbatim now and still hit many targets. Its writers published a statement of key issues in the summer of 1984 and invited responses from all relevant bodies. These responses, when analysed, formed the basis of the recommendations, which covered support for student status, closer integration of education and service with mainstream education, the need for a single basic qualification, the need to reduce the number of unqualified nurses, the need for teachers of nursing to carry clinical responsibility, the need to identify a common body of knowledge, attitudes and skills appropriate to a basic nursing qualification. Opinion was 'hung' in the matter of an all-graduate nursing profession – educationalists least in favour of it – and as to whether there should be an increase in undergraduate degree places in nursing, whether colleges of nursing and midwifery should have independent governing bodies, and as to the advisability of creating a new body to advise on the supply and education of nurses. Vested interests clashed and a well-argued and documented Report joined the rest, to be largely forgotten, 'one item in a long agenda' of proposals for change.

Miss Laurence, who had succeeded Miss Garrett in 1974 as Chief Nursing Officer, retired in March 1985. At that time, yet another general review (the Griffiths Report) of the management of the Health Service was being undertaken and some major questions were as yet unresolved. Miss Laurence was able to say to the Fellowship Meeting on 11th May 1985 that her position was to be handed on to Miss Cackett, adding, 'As you know she is not a Nightingale, but is a full member of the Fellowship and has had responsibility for training Nightingales.' Miss Laurence has written:

I never had jurisdiction over the School in my time as CNO. That was in the hands of the Director whom I met on a fairly regular basis . . . I felt it important to be very much in touch with developments and progress and to use the skills of the Director and tutors. The

Community Nursing Services came under my jurisdiction. They welcomed this and were happy to introduce me to their responsibilities in Nursing and Health Visiting (and hence Midwifery, although this came under the Principal Nursing Officer for Midwifery) – they found they could 'blossom' as a service when they were no longer responsible to the Medical Officer as they had been. Psychiatric nursing at Tooting Bec came into my responsibility. Initially there was great suspicion but they found it an advantage to have a nursing head outside their own hospital.

Miss Cackett's tenure of office in the Health Authority was short. She left her post in 1987 to become a Nursing Officer for Education at the DHSS. Her departure, first from the School and then from the Hospital, introduced and coincided with difficult times. She had appointed Ursula Cowell to be Director of Nurse Education in 1986, and she remained in place for the next four years. Natalie Tiddy was Acting Chief Nursing Officer until her appointment was confirmed in 1988. In 1991 the post, by then called Chief Nursing Adviser, was ended. In that same year Jane Easterbrook, who had taken up her first post in the School in 1982 as Senior Tutor Staff Development, became Acting Director of Nurse Education – Acting because no one could see far enough into the future. In her words, it was a time of 'holding the edges together.' The post of Director was advertised once, but 'no one bit the bullet'. She and Natalie Tiddy had to carry the main responsibilities for piloting the School through its last few years. She found herself in this position because Miss Cowell had resigned, the immediate cause of her resignation being her opposition to the merger with Guy's Nursing School. Miss Cowell felt that the School, with its history and traditions, was well able to continue to stand on its own. 'What is the Nightingale School philosophy?' she asked during our interview. 'Caring is valued for its own sake and so is the pursuit of excellence.' Her tenure of office was full of tensions and problems resulting from her conviction that, in order to maintain this heritage, fundamental reforms had to be undertaken.

The post had been twice advertised and she confesses to her surprise at being appointed, the third outsider in succession to Miss Allen and Miss Cackett before her. At her interview, she had stressed the need to introduce management skills to a point much beyond where they had reached so far. Her first task, as she saw it, was to introduce and run an interim curriculum that would be the transition to Project 2000. Then immediately it was necessary to rationalise the various documents that existed on her arrival. The situation was serious. On a visit to the English National Board to meet the Education Officer responsible for the Nightingale School, she was told somewhat abruptly that a new curriculum was overdue and that already a year had been lost. 'It was made abundantly clear to me that time was running out for the presentation of a new curriculum and that discontinuation of the Nightingale School as a training institution was imminent.' No wonder she was surprised and shocked. Inquiry revealed that curriculum development was the responsibility of 'the inevitable curriculum committee which had been meeting for over a year with a great deal of debate but with little to show in terms of constructive results.'

She wanted to involve the Service Staff as well as the School in everything that was going to happen and to strengthen partnerships, but she faced a race against time. Resistance, it would seem, came quickly; not everyone was convinced of the necessity for such a far-reaching 'new look'. Her method to achieve her purposes was to write a paper for the teaching staff indicating what had to be done to avoid withdrawal of recognition. With Jane Easterbrook, the Head of Continuing Education, she organised time management training of all the staff, because an analysis had revealed an unbalanced and disproportionate use of time. (It had emerged that less real time was spent on administration than had been thought, not least because an 'open door' policy to students in effect had distracted many staff.) Ways of achieving reorganisation had to be developed. Teaching staff were formed into curriculum groups and taken out of the School for days of discussion and planning. The chief purpose was to construct a curriculum that would be thematic, and would cover as a unity all the years of training – it appeared that, because of the time of entry of different Sets, three schools within the School existed separately, and this, as has been noted, had to be ended. An Examination Board, chaired by Miss Cowell, was set up to sanction the questions and procedures, with Carolynn Williams in the new position of Senior Tutor Curriculum Design and Development. Miss Cowell paid a particular tribute to Nicola Grant, who became Senior Tutor Operational Management.

The result, through heroic efforts on the part of all concerned, was that we achieved a new curriculum. We did this by working together, despite lingering reservations on the part of some members of staff.

The Nightingale School retained its status as a training institution, and more importantly the curriculum anticipated what were eventually the published requirements of Project 2000.

The English National Board insisted on a merger with other schools. However, 'A merger of the Nightingale School and the Great Ormond Street School – with which there had been profitable discussion – was not permitted despite the fact that we had provided clinical placements for each other's students for years. Only geographical mergers would be allowed.'

Miss Cowell posed the question that this book cannot answer: 'How much political pressure was being exerted?' She pursued the idea of loose federation as against merger in the hope ultimately of collaboration with a university medical school; 'such a federation would pave the way for Nursing and Midwifery to become all-graduate professions.' What was made clear instead was that the Nightingale School should merge with the Nursing School at Guy's, and that this was inevitable.

Within the School she required every student to be taught First Aid. This move came from her realisation on meeting new students that their worst fears came from feelings of inadequacy in coping with emergencies, such as haemorrhage or cardiac arrest. An examination conducted by St John Ambulance Instructors enabled students to feel more confident and 'senior students to bemoan the fact that they had missed out'. Even more importantly, students were to be given courses in management skills which would go beyond what hitherto had been confined to their last year. These were to include the psychology of management and leadership and 'how you manage people and get the best out of them.'

Miss Cowell soon encountered what had already taxed her predecessors: the charge that the Nightingale School was WASP (White, Anglo-Saxon, Protestant) and exclusive. The Brixton Access Course, referred to below, was already in place. She aroused considerable controversy and animosity by her position on necessary standards for admission to the School. There was a local feeling that the School should consider lowering its standards to accommodate the problems of achievement that might be found in ethnic minority groups. Her stand on this was supported by the Commission for Racial Equality. 'I refused to bring people into the School to fail.' She won her point, and such students as were admitted were successful and passed – 'You are special,' she told them. Another interesting problem arose in the admission of Jewish students, some of whom, having presumably accepted the 'house rules', tried to avoid work and duties on holy days. An accommodation was reached, through the Chief Rabbi, with the Hospital Rabbi.

Her view on the matter of 'stand-alone' training schools and on whether degree courses, degree and higher diploma courses could be introduced and achieved without amalgamation has already been explored, but linked to this was a question, still relevant, of subsidiary qualifications for what would, in effect, be ancillaries. Miss Cowell was no friend to the newly-emerging National Vocational Qualification; she did not see how it could become a professional qualification of the kind that she thought necessary, and she had her doubts about proposed methods of assessment. She objected, for example, to the idea that 'you don't need qualified staff to nurse the elderly' – something that, in her opinion, has gained ground and has diminished the standards and the status of nursing of the elderly.

In spite of all these enumerated difficulties a curriculum was put together to prepare the way for Project 2000. Many members of the tutorial staff were put into small task forces in specific subject areas, of which the three main ones were: 1. Applied Behavioural Sciences, 2. Applied Bio-physical Sciences, 3. Nursing Studies. A course was planned, to be divided into four separate phases:

Introductory phase: entirely theoretical – the study of basic human needs and of ways of helping people of all ages in the community; first aid, caring for the sick – certificates to be awarded by St John Ambulance.

Phase One: forty weeks of a mixture of theoretical study and supervised practice within the community and other areas where community met hospital, e.g. in the Out-patient Departments.

Phase Two: eight weeks, in which learners would undertake protected clinical practice within the hospital; they would help care for patients with acute and chronic conditions and with terminal illness; 40 per cent of the time was to be spent on theoretical study and the remainder in practice.

Phase Three: twenty-seven weeks, for the gaining of greater responsibility and autonomy; experience in Accident and Emergency Departments and in particular illnesses; increased knowledge and skills in the art of nursing. Teaching and management skills to be developed in preparation for becoming Registered General Nurses; 10 per cent of the time to be spent in theoretical study.

Catherine Mann, writing about this, which came to be called Curriculum 88, hoped that the first intake of 75 students would be admitted in October 1988.[1]

These changes undoubtedly brought friction. Miss Cowell is aware that she was regarded as controversial and that her Territorial Army background and training were perceived by some to be not quite in tune with the ethos of the School. Nor were her relationships with management easy. Her vivid account of her final disagreement with it, resulting in her refusal to take part in amalgamating the School with others, recalls a turning point in its history. She cares deeply about nursing and, although a non-Nightingale, about the place of the School in the history and future development of nursing. This is disputatious territory and argument is fierce. At the heart of it is the question whether such great reforms in nurse training could have been achieved through her idea of a loose federation of independent schools, or whether not only financial but ideological reasoning required the decisive move to take nurse training fully into Higher Education as part of the university world. Miss Cowell's opponents hold strongly that her intentions for nursing were right but that they could not have been achieved by her policies. For her part, she thinks that 'The Nightingale School was destroyed', and goes further – that 'nursing itself has been destroyed'.

The Fellowship was, no doubt, in need of an explanation of what was going on in the School and the Hospital and Miss Garrett, who returned to act as its President in the interval between Miss Cackett and Miss Tiddy, told a meeting in May 1987:

> Miss Janice Cackett resigned on leaving for another post . . . At that time there was some uncertainty as to whether the West Lambeth Health Authority intended to retain the post of Chief Nursing Officer since it was known that a number of Health Authorities have taken the view that this post is no longer necessary within the present management structures . . . In the event, the Health Authority decided to appoint a Chief Nurse, the post was duly advertised and Natalie Tiddy was appointed as Chief Nursing Adviser in March.

Another two new titles. Miss Cackett had already described in May 1986 what further changes in organisation had been introduced:

1. A District General Manager was responsible to the Authority.
2. There was a Nurse on the Board of the Authority: Mary Richardson first, then Daphne Millward, also a Nightingale.
3. The Authority had four units:

   a) The Mental Health Unit at Tooting Bec Hospital, covering both in-patient and community services for people with mental health problems. The Director of Nursing was Martin Brown, the Unit General Manager Ray Rowden, a nurse.

   b) The Community Unit, covering services for the elderly and all Community-based services such as Health Visiting, District Nursing, School Nursing, and Therapies and Services for Adults with a Learning Disability. At this time, the Director of Nursing was Dr June Clark and Caroline Langridge was the Unit General Manager.

   c) In 1987 Elizabeth Winder, a Nightingale, was appointed Unit General Manager of the Acute Unit, covering all services on the St Thomas' site, with Elizabeth Stevens as Director of Nursing and Mary Lansdell Director of Midwifery Services.

   d) The Unit for Central Services included the Nightingale School, the Olive Haydon School of Midwifery, the Physiotherapy and Radiotherapy Schools and all District Headquarters activities.

Miss Cackett in her Fellowship address of 9th May 1987 said, 'We are particularly pleased that a Nightingale should be appointed as the first Unit General Manager to St Thomas' Hospital. I am sure Florence Nightingale would rejoice to know that the entire St Thomas' is run by a nurse.' Elizabeth Winder held this post until 1991, when she became Executive Nurse and Director of Quality for the Shadow Trust of St Thomas' Hospital. She was succeeded in 1993 by Wilma Macpherson, who was appointed to the position of Director of Quality and Nursing for the newly-formed Guy's and St Thomas' Trust.

In Natalie Tiddy's first Presidential Address to the Fellowship on 7th May 1988, she explained her remit as Chief Nursing Adviser and Director of Consumer Affairs:

The role encompasses all non-medical education, that is, nursing and midwifery education, physiotherapy and radiotherapy schools together with the development of consumer affairs. This latter is the reflection of the patients' view and information for users of the service. In addition, the CNA is charged with the responsibility for nursing advice to the District General Manager, Dr Stephen Jenkins, and the Health Authority.

She outlined the many achievements of the Nightingale School, including the validation of the first national integrated theatre course enabling RGNs to gain specialist experience throughout theatres, recovery and anaesthetics. In addition, with the growing interest in the development of nursing and nurses, both a Diploma Course and a Certificate in Management Studies Course were being undertaken in conjunction with the North-East London Polytechnic. She further announced that the first intake of nurses to the fifty-two-week Conversion Course from Enrolled Nurse to Registered Nurse had achieved a 100 per cent success. Plans were already in place to begin a Conversion Course from Enrolled Nurse Mental Health to Registered Mental Nurse in 1989.

Natalie Tiddy confirmed that thanks to a private donation of £100,000 for the benefit of nurses, a fitness centre was to be commissioned in Gassiot House; this decision had been taken after discussion with students and staff, who felt that such a facility would be in their best interests. She went on to describe how staff had to work at a time when there were so many changes in buildings and services: the refurbishment of Block Seven in the South Wing to accommodate St John's, the Institute of Dermatology, the two Wards in Block Six for the Dreadnought Seamen from Greenwich, the development of a purpose-built crèche adjacent to Canterbury House to support staff with children. At this time, Clinical Directorates were being discussed as the 'way forward' for the management of services. 'This means dividing the Hospital into a number of small units of management with a Senior Nurse and an Administrator undertaking the day-to-day coordination under the direction of an appointed Clinician.'

She went on to say – her listeners may have been as disheartened then as this writer is now – that 'There may well be further changes in the forthcoming year.' Making one's way through the long intricacies of one reorganisation after another added to the sense of bemusement of outsiders trying to grasp what was happening.

It is a relief, after all this, to turn to the work that had begun on the Florence Nightingale Museum in the undercroft of the School in the October of 1987. It was hoped to open the Museum within a year: this was achieved. Miss Laurence has written:

I suppose my main personal achievement was the Nightingale Museum. I had only just taken up my post as CNO when the Nightingale material came out of store. I found I was responsible for it, and many visitors wished to see it. It was obviously taking a fair amount of 'nursing time' and I started a Nurses' League Fund better to display what we had. The hospital architect took this up and today's museum is the result.

The Nightingale Museum Trust was set up:

1. To establish a museum in conjunction with the School for the preservation and the wider display of the collection of 'Nightingalia' at present in St Thomas' Hospital.
2. To receive donations of suitable items for the collection or to purchase them.
3. To provide facilities for research into the history and work of Florence Nightingale, particularly in relation to the founding of the School, and consequent developments in the nursing profession.
4. To award grants or bursaries to graduate nurses for postgraduate study/research in this country or overseas.

It has become evident in the course of writing this book that the Museum project has not received universal approval. On the other hand, it was noted at the time of the Appeal that much support could be expected from the United States and Japan, where FN's work is held in great reverence – indeed, it is likely that many of the visitors are from these countries.

Among so many other changes – Natalie Tiddy noted twenty-eight different building projects in hand – new uniforms were introduced. Nurse learners were to wear lavender and white stripes. On qualification the uniform changed to blue and white stripes. Navy and white spots remained, and the denim. Caps were to remain, though there were real difficulties in ensuring the quality of Sisters' caps. This last matter surfaced again when a ballot was held. Natalie Tiddy informed her readers:

Following considerable pressure from many senior and other nursing staff a ballot was undertaken to decide whether caps should be worn. It is clear from the results that a greater proportion of the nursing staff do not find the cap to serve any useful or significant function. It has always been my intention to involve nursing staff in decisions regarding their uniform. *Therefore, I must confirm that caps do not form part of uniform from 1st May.*[2]

Caps went as the School was going. It is important to add that, in Natalie Tiddy's words, 'Clear written guidance was issued to staff outlining what was expected when wearing uniform, which included length of hair and dress as well as the requirement not to wear any jewellery apart from a wedding ring.' As no mention has previously been made of the male nursing staff in general, it can be said now that they were to be provided 'with grey trousers with a white tunic and epaulettes bearing the same colour as the female dress; additional stripes on the epaulettes reflected the belt colours of the female nurses to indicate what stage of training they had reached.' A rhyming lament from Cicely Barnes appeared in the Journal for January 1991:[3]

> Starched collars and cuffs have long vanished;
> Hem-lines a mere matter of taste;
> Will our belts be on the next casualty list
> To accommodate post-canteen waists?
> No more ward shoes like flat-bottomed barges,
> Our stockings, a kind of 'see-through';
> Shall we one day be bare-foot, I wonder –
> To health-cranks that concept's not new.
>
> George, the hernia in bed number seven, –
> Gets confused, having known 'the old days' –
> May well beckon some visiting girl-friend:
> 'It's my false teeth again gone astray,
> And I can't eat my dinner without them';
> Then, stifling a near-uttered curse:
> 'Forgive me, my dear, I mistook you
> For someone once called – was it "nurse?"'

A further major change that affected the School was the discontinuation of courses for the qualification of Enrolled Nurse; the final Set qualified as 'Second-Level Nurses' in 1988. It was realised, immediately, that there should be a proper opportunity for such nurses to convert their qualifications so that they could continue their career with promotion prospects. This move was approved by the English National Board and the first conversion course introduced in 1987, a national First. Subsequent conversion courses were approved for EN (Mental) to RMN, and EN(G) to RSCN (Registered Sick Children's Nurse). Furthermore, an 'open-learning' package was devised to enable study at variable times, pace and place. This did not come free, and generous help was given to the School by the Special Trustees of St Thomas' Hospital and later by the Health Authority. The *Nursing Times*, in collaboration with the Open University, introduced a two-year open learning programme to increase the opportunities for nurses to convert from second to first level registration. Those already in nursing who wished to 'convert' faced a charge of £2000 (it has gone up to £3000), for which the Trustees hoped to be able to provide interest-free loans. In 1988 Fiona Rodden made the point that if this course should cease, it would mean a loss of workforce – in the case of St Thomas', of forty-five nurses a year. She observed a shortfall of at least one hundred and twenty nurses at St Thomas' at the time of writing.

A second new course was approved in 1990 called Alternative Access to Nursing Course. This formalised the scheme that had originated in 1983 in Brixton College to encourage people from the multi-ethnic society of that area who lacked formal academic qualifications. It was to be a twenty-one hours a week course, and had ten students in formal training at the time. This reflects a particular aspect of the continuing debate about the nature and requirements of education for nurses. Standing as the School did in an area with an increasingly diverse multi-ethnic population, it was felt, not least by political members of Lambeth Council, that the student body should be more representative of that local population. Pressure was exerted to reduce the educational requirements for entry:

> The national requirements stood at five GCE O-Levels. Previously, candidates with A-Levels had been sought and the O-Level subjects expected were Mathematics, English Language and Literature, Biology and another Science, History and Geography. A working knowledge of a foreign language was considered helpful. (Without a qualification in Mathematics an arithmetic examination had to be passed successfully.)

So writes Natalie Tiddy. She points out that the training of the small groups on the Access Course required much individual tuition and special support, and was expensive in terms of tutor costs.

Everyone agrees that Jane Easterbrook took on a formidably difficult task after Miss Cowell's departure, amongst all the uncertainties about the future. There is unalloyed praise for her achievement. Project 2000 henceforeward became the focus of all the arguments and worries about the future of nursing. Jane Easterbrook recalls the number of attempts which were made to get it in place; they failed because the bids could not have matched up with the criteria and there was not enough money. A routine audit by the ENB had indicated weaknesses, tending towards the conclusion that the School was too small to 'go it alone' – or 'stand alone' in a later usage – in rapidly changing circumstances.

Jane Easterbrook, reflecting over the failure of the bids for Project 2000, has concluded that the explanation must lie in decisions taken elsewhere concerning mergers. (Curriculum 88 was a stepping-stone towards Project 2000 which, however, was not embarked upon until the Nightingale Institute had been formed.) Failure did increase the inclination for a major shake-up in the School, and the Basic Programme was 'brought up to date'.

The move of fundamental importance that had been so opposed by Miss Cowell, nevertheless was approved in 1990. From 1st April 1991, the three Schools of Nursing and Midwifery in the West Lambeth Health Authority and Lewisham and North Southwark Health Authority were amalgamated: the Nightingale School; the Olive Haydon School of Midwifery; the Thomas Guy and Lewisham School of Nursing. This meant the creation of a new college with a new Principal. On 8th May 1991, the Nightingale and Guy's College of Nursing and Midwifery was launched by Stephen Dorrell, then Junior Minister of Health. The new Principal was Maureen Theobald, whose office was in Gassiot House.

It is difficult to write precisely of where the driving forces for accelerated change in nursing were to be found. There were senior civil servants with strongly held ideas; there were senior nurses in the Department of Health; and undoubtedly there were administrators within the service – all of whom were pushing for changes on the grand scale. It has been said, forcibly, that matters were not helped by the fact that many of the prominent movers 'wore two hats' and often could not decide which was the more important. It appears that the chief dividing line was between those who were essentially educators and those who were managers, and there was a failure to recognise that they were working to different time-scales. Any innovation in education needs five years at the very minimum to begin to take effect, whereas managers expect to see change within one or two years.

The authors of Project 2000, which had been submitted to the Government in 1987, claimed that its whole reason for existence rested on a determination to concentrate on the patient as the focus of care, requiring a great deal of knowledge of the background and of the likely future. It proposed a radical change in nursing education in that students should be supernumerary for two years, then have a year's specialisation. If this be what was intended then there are those who felt, and feel, its essential purpose – patient care – has been sidelined by the concentration on making nurse training an academic subject. One senior Nightingale has gone so far as to say that 'the patient hunger' of students is not satisfied by academicism, and that nurses 'have had a hand in digging their own grave.' This view is supported by a male Nightingale who went on to be a university academic. After his time he noticed what he thought was a deterioration.

> I have not come across any similar fellowship in the training schools of any colleagues. The style of training during our time was very enjoyable (entered 1981)...Modern nurse training is pushing nurses away from the patient and into management. It is not the vocation that I answered and I am very sad.

Such far-reaching proposals for change were bound to cause debate and disquiet, not only about the plans themselves but also as different kinds of possible consequences were explored. These were commendably summarised by Fiona Roddan in the *Journal* for July 1987. The plan was to have:

1. A new registered practitioner, with three years' training: competent to assess needs, to plan, give, monitor and evaluate care.
2. Specialist practitioners: with experience and qualifications in particular fields to teach and act as team leaders.
3. A new grade of helper called an Aide: to work under the direction of the practitioner.
4. The training of registered practitioner: two-year common core foundation, with final year in a particular area of practice.

She wrote that students should be supernumerary and not 'pairs of hands'. The consequences were likely to be that, at a time when recruitment was in crisis, 'the number of trained nursing staff must increase if we are to achieve supernumerary status for nurses during training.'[4]

Writing in 1990, Natalie Tiddy reported that a Working Paper 10 had been published, which would require major work to project future nurse staffing needs, when student nurses would no longer be part of the work force. There was insufficient national funding for more than one Project 2000 demonstration site for each region, and the pressure for merger was increasing. In addition, Wards and Departments were faced with the challenge of new ways of training nurses and it was necessary to plan a series of programmes for staff already trained, for them to begin to understand what Project 2000 really required.

The pressure towards a merger was increasing all the time, but it did arouse very strong feelings amongst those who treasured the history and achievements of the Nightingale School. Natalie Tiddy wrote, 'My view was that the Nightingale School should lead on the merger and that we should find the best way forward for continuance of our special heritage. It was made clear that 'stand-alone schools' would not exist that it was my job to ensure the most satisfactory compromise.' It has already been said that Miss Cowell felt forcefully that the School could achieve a great deal on its own. Natalie Tiddy writes of her:

> She had a clear vision for nurse education and its development and was totally opposed to a Nightingale School merger with any other institution. The curriculum that she developed was similar to that of Project 2000 but with considerably more practical experience and a central focus on close collaboration between School and Service. I supported the development of the innovative curriculum and my role was to ensure that its details were understood and accepted by the Health Board at a time when the pressure for merger was being driven by South East Thames Region.

One can see what the tensions were, but discussions did begin with Guy's and the Lewisham School of Nursing to find the best way forward. This was a landmark decision, a tacit recognition that this famous and historic School was no longer seen as capable of continuing to be independent in a time of financial rationalisation and concern with balancing the books and value for money. South East Thames Region confirmed that Project 2000 would not be approved without amalgamation. In a new emerging world, the School was seen as élitist, and the reasons for which so many of its members had been proud were unsentimentally pushed to one side. This really marked the end of the Nightingale School. What followed was a series of amalgamations based on new thinking.

Jane Easterbrook has also recalled in conversation her difficulties at this time, when students both in the School and then in the Nightingale and Guy's College of Health were not clear as to why they were not getting the new diploma status and were not too much interested in the detailed reasons. They wondered what the course they were following would be worth when it was not of Diploma Status – generally regarded as being two undergraduate years – and when it would not open the gate automatically to degree studies. They would have to negotiate the credit-worthiness of their course with individual universities.

In view of the many staff changes within the District and the funding arrangements within Units, together with the clear desire of most students no longer to accept the requirement that they remain within the District for a further period of experience, it became clear that staff nurse posts could no longer be guaranteed. It was therefore agreed that trainees of the Nightingale School should be awarded the Badge and Certificate of the School on successful completion of training and should be free to apply for vacancies wherever they appeared. What is more, living in London was no longer seen as desirable by all.

The appointment of Maureen Theobald in 1991 inaugurated the newly formed Nightingale and Guy's College of Nursing and Midwifery. She had already been involved in the explanations about amalgamation before she took up the post. One option discussed had been a merger with the King's College Medical School. Within a year the name had been changed to the Nightingale College of Health. The English National Board agreed to validate work for Project 2000 but this was overtaken by the move into the University sector; the curriculum, so carefully prepared, was not put into practice. The decision was taken for the new Nightingale Institute to adopt the model already in progress in Normanby College.

The College of Health had only a brief existence but it was an important transition, beginning degree programmes in Nursing, Midwifery and Learning Difficulties, and establishing a Research Forum that could draw on a college-wide research directory. Its programme included:

a) Validation of the ENB framework and Higher Award leading to the degrees in Nursing and Midwifery awarded through King's College London

b) Conversion Courses for Enrolled Nurses

c) Health Care Assistant Training, and National Vocation Qualifications Training

d) Two Diploma Courses in Higher Education in Midwifery

e) A Diploma in Higher Education in Nursing (commonly known as Project 2000) validated by King's College and beginning in October 1993.

f) A B.Sc. in Learning Difficulties

Arguments about Project 2000 did not end then. The view has been met increasingly that this title is a misnomer, and that it is more accurate to call it the Diploma Programme, as do some colleges. However, it remained a point of controversy even for those Nightingales trained from 1992 to 1996:

> A year after our training began Project 2000 courses were commencing. There seemed to be a lack of interest in our course. Lecturers were being moved or made to retire early. No one really knew what was going on.

> We saw the introduction of Project 2000 in the School and on the wards . . . Many of our lecturers had to move on and the atmosphere became quite unfriendly towards us . . . As Project 2000 became more important it seemed as if no one apart from our remaining tutors was interested in our course.

> Project 2000 was introduced in the next Set that started after us. Therefore there were 200 students starting twice a year. This meant classroom space was being fought for by tutors. There was occasionally hostility from these students – jealousy I think, as a lot of them wanted to do the pre-Project 2000 Course.

Those students who were caught in the transition obviously felt strongly, though with different emphases.

> Changed from Nightingale School to Nightingale Institute via three other names. No consultation with students. All decisions were dictated.

Move from 'traditional' course to Project 2000 – mixed feelings, particularly about lack of accreditation about the course I did. Moves to join with other schools to some extent left on sidelines.

In *The Times* newspaper for 26th December 1996, Nigella Lawson wrote an extended article in which she addressed the problem of the shortage of people who want to be nurses.

> We seek, reasonably enough, a financial explanation. Everyone knows that nurses don't get paid enough . . . After all, the spirit of the age hardly embraces the vocational selflessness that earlier produced generations of hard-working, ill-paid nurses. [She went on to argue that, more to the point] What is really keeping students out of nursing colleges is something called Project 2000. This is the plan to make nursing training more academic and theory-based. And, frankly, can anything be more idiotic than that?

Nigella Lawson attacked the demand for academic qualifications for entry – five or six GCSEs at Grade C or above – and the ensuing life of taking and passing more examinations.

> There is a huge dropout rate among those who do start their training – simply because the qualities that make people good nurses are not the same qualities that make people good at passing exams. [The attack continued, that student nurses] read papers and papers and have to learn about what research says, how it leads to which findings and why – and then the students end up on the wards and don't know how to give an injection or take someone's blood pressure.

All this is not seen as flattering to nurses, but insulting – the quest for academic status is 'silly'; a false academicism has been applied to nursing. The example is given, to illustrate her point, of Radio Four broadcasting part of a lecture on 'The Philosophy of Nursing'. She felt strongly that, if seriously ill, she would wish to be nursed by someone with skills and the right temperament rather than by someone with a degree.

The two are not mutually exclusive, surely? It was a long article which one would have while one would have expected to provoke a long-running correspondence, but it did not: just a few letters in the usual for-and-against mode.

225

The much-referred-to Project 2000 had begun, officially, in 1990 when the first students in the Demonstration School for the South East Region began training at Normanby College. It led to a Diploma of Higher Education in Nursing Studies, plus Registration in a particular branch. Five years later the decision to review and revalidate was taken; this was to be carried out by the English National Board for Nursing, Midwifery and Health Visiting (ENB) and King's College, London (KCL). The targeted recruitment numbers were fully achieved in the autumn of 1995 when three hundred students were admitted. (Do remember that four Schools merged into one.)

The rapidity and complexity of so many changes was bound to provoke the sort of reactions given already, and to act as a springboard for reminiscence and recollection. For example, the restoration of the Governors' Hall and Grand Committee Room, opened on 21 October 1991, allowed the re-hanging of a number of portraits, including those of three memorable Matrons – Dame Alicia Lloyd Still, Margaret Smyth and Theodora Turner – and opened up the chance to assess their achievements.

The restoration was magnificent. The contents of the display cabinets are a reminder of the connection between the Governors of the Hospital and the Freemasons. There has never been any lack of speculation about such connections, and some have suggested that they were a strong element in the School's exclusivity – the real cause why so few posts went to Catholics and Jews. This has been firmly denied by others. The best of the portraits in the Hall is undoubtedly that of Miss Smyth by Dame Laura Knight. A recent decision has been taken to hang the portrait of Miss Adamson, the hands of which she disliked having been repainted.

The question posed again and again circles round whether or not 'real nursing' continues or has been washed away. Madeleine Cuff, writing for the *Journal* in July 1992, attempted to see where things stood. She felt that the growth of nursing theories should enable nurses to be more precise in knowing what to do, how to do it, and whether it could be done better. She observed that the role of the nurse is obviously allied with the role of women in society. She accepted willingly a better informed public that would want to be more involved in health care – 'patient involvement [is necessary] because the vast majority of today's illnesses are lifestyle-related . . . It takes a strong confident nurse to relinquish control of the patient to its rightful owner – the patient.'[5]

Before all these new proposals and plans had been activated, there was one of the most powerful reminders of a different past: Miss E.M. Gould (Molly) died on 4th July 1984 and her Memorial Service was held in the Chapel of St Thomas' on 16th August. Miss Hone gave the Address, in so many ways an evocation of the Nightingale world that has occupied previous chapters. Miss Gould's father was a clergyman and among her forbears were an Archbishop of Canterbury, a Bishop of Winchester and a Bishop of Guildford. She had been taught by Miss Coode and Miss Gullan in the days of Dame Alicia. After gaining experience in India and various hospitals in this country, she returned to the School just before the Second World War broke out. An earlier chapter has described the circumstances and conditions of training in Basingstoke, Chertsey and Hydestile. Miss Hone recalled affectionately and wryly Miss Gould's inexhaustible energy in maintaining standards and routines in all the circumstances of dispersal and blackout.

Miss Gould had a motor-bicycle which she rode with great courage and presumably with great skill, battling in all weathers but arriving always with a smile and making nothing of the discomforts. In due course she was allowed to run a car . . . She really enjoyed driving and was always absolutely sure of her own rights on the road. Her passengers and other drivers were not always as happy as she was.

It was Miss Gould who pioneered the Block System in the Huts behind Riddell House; she was 'Boss of the Huts' or, more properly, Principal Tutor. Miss Hone continued:

St Paul, like Miss Gould, had strong convictions which caused uncomfortable differences of opinions, as with Barnabas and the young John Mark, and I do not think it wrong to recall that her convictions also caused distress on occasions to members of her staff or to those on committees with her . . . She never courted popularity for herself – it never entered her head to do so. She commanded respect and affection naturally . . . She was an enterprising walker and loved anything to do with water, especially rowing. She had excellent binoculars and cameras and enjoyed painting either landscapes or flowers. Nothing daunted her, and after a strenuous day in the open and a leisurely evening meal she was ready to play Scrabble or some other clever word game and usually won.

One could linger in thought over such a personality, one of those who made the School the memorable place that it was. She was not the only notable figure from that – long-lost – past whose life was celebrated and death commemorated. Miss Smyth died on 17th November 1991, aged 94.

It may seem something of an anti-climax after so much recording of transition and new forms to come back to the fact that, during all these years, Nightingales were trying to get on with their daily lives, some aspects of which had not changed much. For example, Nightingales still 'lambasted Lambeth'.

I lived in Lambeth New Home. This could be summed up as 'horrendous'. Tiny rooms, no showers, one kitchen for forty people and one cooker and fridge. Cockroaches galore.

In January 1993, Natalie Tiddy told members of the Fellowship that discussions to effect the merger of St Thomas' with Guy's were nearing a conclusion; they would form a new NHS Trust, and it was hoped that this would be in place by April. The Editor of the *Journal* for the summer of 1993 wrote

One of the unfortunate effects of change is the redundancy of so many senior nurses in the process of reorganisation, be it as a result of Project 2000 or the formation of clinical directorates.

Yes, clinical directorates! It is not only older Nightingales who scratch their heads at this new term.

Rosemary Morris went on to explain that a clinical directorate could be managed by someone who could come from any discipline – medicine, nursing, physiotherapy – or from a non-health service background.

For nursing, this has meant the virtual abolition of the senior nurse post that arose as a result of Salmon in the 1970s, replacing Matron. The practical effect of this may be a return to the key role of the ward sister and charge nurse. What, then, happens to the career path? What are the lines of accountability? Does this open the way for the nurse practitioner? How do nurses gain experience in senior management?

Sue Norman called attention to what, if one were feeling charitable, could be called faulty drafting, otherwise malice aforethought, in the new NHS regulations concerning Trusts. They were so worded as to forbid Hospitals from having on their premises any activities and buildings not to do with patient care. The result was to disenfranchise the Schools of Nursing, and to make inevitable the creation of self-standing institutions of teaching that would have to find their place in the world of Higher Education. The Nightingale Institute, in this sense, was the only way forward.

Natalie Tiddy described in considerable detail, in her paper to this writer, the background to and personalities involved in the negotiations towards creating a new foundation.

Without Jane Easterbrook and other Senior Teaching staff, the merger would not have been effected . . . From the first, Jane and I were determined that the Nightingale name would remain, but clearly we had to be diplomatic . . . We wanted to see the development of a Nightingale Institute which would enable all training to come under one roof, with a common foundation, with Medical Students, Nursing, Midwifery, Physio and OT students all joining together for the first year. This seemed to be a worthy way forward and one which would have been welcomed by Florence Nightingale.

After the first year, we envisaged that students would stream into their chosen paths, but they would have started together and learned the important lesson of team work. We felt strongly that quality care for the patient depended on multi-professional team work, and that the sooner this was understood and learned the greater the benefit to the patient. The Nightingale and Guy's College of Nursing and Midwifery was formed after only one year and Maureen Theobald was appointed as Director. At this point she was also appointed Chairwoman of the English National Board. Accountability to the Chief Nurse ceased . . . All training of nursing and midwifery staff is quite separate from Hospital and Trust management . . . These massive changes were forced upon us from the centre and the UKCC with the intention of achieving 'professional status' for nursing and midwifery . . . I am not sure that this has been the result, and I am sure it is not what I wish for nursing and midwifery myself. There is a clear role of caring for the nurse and if anyone is in any doubt as to what nursing is, then the *Notes on Nursing* by Florence Nightingale should be mandatory reading. [She added later that] an increased qualification is essential but not at the cost of losing the ability to undertake the essential role of the nurse in holistic care of the patient/client both in hospital and in the community.

The Nightingale Institute was established on 1st April 1993, as part of the Division of Nursing and Midwifery at King's College in the University of London, in company with other departments in the School of Life, Basic Medical and Health Sciences, now one of the largest in Europe. The undergraduate prospectus states that:

> In order to encourage collaborative research and teaching across traditional subject boundaries, the departments have been grouped into four divisions – Biomedical Sciences, Health Sciences, Life Sciences and Nursing and Midwifery . . . This organisation has enabled us to widen the choice of course-units open to students in their second and third years whilst enabling them to continue to identify with a group of lecturers who reflect their core academic interests.

Thus, 'the multi-disciplinary learning environment' that Natalie Tiddy and others wanted so much was to come into existence. An article in the *Journal*, with the jargon very much in place, put it thus:

> The health-care practitioner of the future is likely to require a portfolio of study options . . . The nurse manager of the future will be focused on directing health-care provision . . . Practitioners will be equally comfortable in all health-care environments . . . Skillmix management will be vital.

(Skillmix refers to the ratio of trained to untrained staff. Belinda Atkinson, managing the Intensive Care Unit in Southampton, noted that most Trusts are working towards a 70/30 mix. The Government target in Project 2000 is a 60/40 mix.)

In the College of Health, Maureen Theobald was to be in charge of the new arrangements. Students were to follow a Common Foundation Programme for eighteen months, covering psychology, sociology, basic science and theories of nursing. Then they were to divide into four branches of nursing: adult, children, mental health, learning disabilities. After this they would receive the Diploma in Higher Education in Nursing in order to register with the UKCC, a pre-requisite to qualified practice.

The Fellowship meeting in May 1994 was told by Natalie Tiddy that the last group of students from the traditional course would qualify in October 1995. 'All courses completing after this time will have received their practical experience across a range of hospital and community units and will perceive their focus to be the university as opposed to any particular hospital.'

At the AGM of the Nightingale Fellowship in May 1997, it was agreed that graduates trained in the Nightingale Institute would be able to apply to join the Nightingale Fellowship. All graduates from the Nightingale Institute are now offered the opportunity to join any or all of the three Fellowships and Leagues.

The *Journal* for the winter of 1996 contained 'a guide for today's nurses' by Rosemary Morris. Its purpose was to induct the last young Nightingales into the language of the world gone by. It is rather like the 'fags' exam' or initiation into the private language of some of the older boys' public schools, though the young nurses would not have been punished for failing the test. After such a long journey through so many chapters, it may help many to be reminded of or to recall what older Nightingales (and not so old) have written, in loving detail, into answers to the questionnaire:

1. Probationers were on probation. They had three allocations of their daily routine. Shifts were split, usually with three hours off in the morning. 'Day Side' and 'Night Side' were the left and right side of the ward, going back to the time when day nurses cleaned the left and night nurses cleaned the right side of the ward. The day began at 7.30; windows were flung open regardless of the weather.
2. Beds were pulled out and dusted behind, and then the Ward Sister said prayers at the centre desk, after having received the report from the night nurses.
3. Breakfasts were served, bedpans distributed and collected; final cleaning was done between 9 and 9.30 and ended on the stroke of Big Ben. Lockers and bedside tables were cleaned. 'Hot dusting' – using a string cloth 'of which the central third was immersed in boiling water and wrung out' – was for the lockers, bed tables' surfaces and window ledges. These were then dried with a soft cotton cloth. 'Day side' was responsible for the sluice.
4. 'Night side' was responsible for the bathroom. 'Thirds' were responsible for the kitchen and a number of other tasks, including

the checking of oxygen cylinders and the boiling of thirty eggs on Sundays.

5. Nurses had to know everything possible about patients: name, age, religion, diagnosis, treatment and nursing care. No written records were allowed; all information was solemnly recited, after supper, to the Ward Sister. Notes were made on the back corners of starched aprons; pocket notebooks were forbidden but were used surreptitiously. The 'copper porringer' was a round copper tray used for small dressings and inhalations and polished on Sunday afternoons.

6. 'Blue Belters' were third years; 'Gongers' were fourth years wearing their St Thomas's SRN Silver Badges. (The 'State' Examination was seen somewhat dismissively – the Hospital Examination that made you a Nightingale was the one that mattered.)

There have been so many references in earlier chapters to the general sense of 'yours not to reason why', and the Editor of the *Journal* went on to give a telling anecdote.

> Questioning was not encouraged and I remember rebelling against being told to wash a wall in Surgical Out-patients. I did not think that this was the job of a nurse at 7.30 in the evening and had the temerity to say so. My report was a one-liner: 'This nurse represents the transition from the old school of nursing to the new.'

It is a sad but extraordinarily apposite fact that Miss Rosamond Hone, the Nightingale who has come to epitomise the traditions of the old Nightingale School, and who was their superb exponent as a teacher, died on 4th August 1995.

The author's meeting with Jane Easterbrook in January 1997 not only clarified a great deal but, rightly and unavoidably, led to some further reflection. It has been seen that, in fact, the School in its historical sense ended when it became part of the College of Health, but when this College became part of the Nightingale Institute, it was a symbolic and geographical move to a new world. The absorption into the University of London via King's College, with a University Professor as Director, makes the change very clear. This is where the drive towards first management, then rationalisation, that began when Miss Garrett undertook to implement the Salmon Report, ends – for the time ' being. The tension between academicism and practice was created and continues. In fact, the ENB prescribes that not less than half of the time should be spent in a 'practice setting'. The conviction held by Jane Easterbrook is that the best result of the new courses will be 'the knowledgeable doer' – that knowledge is necessary to inform practice. The test will always be what happens in the wards and in other clinical areas. Her important question is (as it was for others before her): Who is the link between the two sides of the training, between theory and practice: who integrates the knowledge and who monitors the areas for practice? Or, are the links 'ad hoc' and dependent on who the individuals are, and on how nurses have been taught to observe and to learn. (Once upon a time there were Clinical Tutors, and before them the Ward Sisters, who undertook the teaching.)

Belinda Atkinson's view is that more work needs to go into the training on the wards, or in FN's words, to 'learn nursing practice where it happens'. At the moment, and predictably, the situation varies from hospital to hospital. PREPP (the Post Registration and Practice Project) recommends that newly-qualified nurses should have a mentor, but this is not yet fully implemented. Her experience of Project 2000 students is that they are notably enthusiastic and bright, but they frequently have difficulties in the clinical area where 'real learning' must come from experience. She also argues that aiming for an all-graduate profession could risk losing the good-quality carers who may not be able to pass exams. It seems inescapable that there will be a two-tier system. The trouble is that graduates usually are not self-conscious about their degrees, but non-graduates may be self-conscious about not having them. Tensions do develop in all institutions that are two-tiered by nature. Nevertheless, as Miss Cackett observed, the more qualified will be needed to head the teams.

The management of resources, including 'human', is crucial. The merged Guy's and St Thomas' was approved as an NHS Trust from April 1993 and therefore entered into a new relationship with the College and later the Institute, namely that between purchaser and provider. The purchaser is bound to be in the stronger position and its requirements will shape curricula.

More than one reference has been made to the appearance of models of nursing, mainly American and much criticised here. Many attempted to deduce from FN's writings what could be called the sanitary/environmental model, which was sanctified by long usage. It was to be overtaken by the Medical/Biological. Then came the Biographical, where the uniqueness of the patient was paramount. Latterly there has arrived the Populist Model, rather too often expressed in a certain kind of jargon about patients' 'ownership' of their own health. Thinking upon this, Jane Easterbrook perceives that matters are coming full circle: the environment is again being taken fully into account. (There is an ironical reminder in some of this of FN's view that hospitals can be rather undesirable places in which to be ill.)

Jane Easterbrook also applauds the move towards looking at common areas of knowledge between subjects and training modules, something which she had attempted earlier, but for which people were then not ready, isolated as some of them were in their exclusive subject areas. Her desire to cross boundaries also shews in her concern that student nurses should be aware of professional issues and matters concerning the management of the NHS, both nationally and locally, which affect their professional lives. It is necessary for them (and for others) to understand how Trusts manage their budgets and how the professional nurse, as well as the Health Care Assistant, is being used in hospitals, and increasingly in general practice.

Running through the decade, as it has through the long history of the School and Hospital in one form or another, is the drive to convince the doctors that nurses' knowledge is as 'legitimate' and to be as much valued as their own. The identification of men with medicine and power and women with nursing and compliance was (and perhaps to some extent still is) powerfully present in some minds. The medical side, it is often claimed, saw nursing as being unscientific. Many nurses even in the 1980s continued to see nursing pre-eminently as 'looking after sick people', and mainly as task-orientated. Concentration on tasks could protect nurses from stress because they were not necessarily called on to be responsible as individuals for individual patients. However, during these years the way was being paved for the health nursing model which came to form the basis of the teaching of the new Institute. There are arrangements in some areas of the curriculum to teach nurses and medical students together. The medical model of nursing had been driven mainly by the advancement in medical science and by the advances in technology. The health model of the 1990s looks to people's whole environment, to return them to health as soon as possible, or to make bearable and manageable the living with illness, or to help towards a peaceful death.

In Jane Easterbrook's view, all the many changes in the School and, later, the College were managed as successfully as possible and 'people were more prepared than they thought they would be'. The changes had, she summarised, been driven mainly by employment legislation with its emphasis on equal opportunities; by the need to broaden the 'entry gate' so that the School was no longer recruiting from the social categories from which it once had – 'admission no longer based on accent'; by amalgamations of Schools and Midwifery establishments into larger units; by movements towards Diploma and Degree Studies for basic and post-basic students and Degree status for teachers; by 'up-sizing and down-sizing' at different times and for different reasons; and, crucially, by the 1990 Health and Community Care Act which resulted in NHS Trust status for some hospitals and Directly Managed Units status for others. There were also reductions in the numbers of 'acute beds' provided in London hospitals at the same time as the College was moving towards the establishment of the Institute. There were many financial tangles resulting from so much change and pressure for change. Not surprisingly there were some crises. Natalie Tiddy records that

> At one stage the District Management Team took the decision to cancel a student intake at six weeks' notice owing to a funding shortage within the Acute Service. I returned from leave to find that the next intake were to be notified that their course would not commence. Having been unable to change the view of the Chief Executive, I met the Chairman of the Health Authority and a Special Meeting was called. Fortunately, the Health Authority agreed that the intake should not be cancelled. This was largely due to the high success rate of Nightingale School students compared to the national average, and the large numbers retained within the Health Authority on completion. Without the relevant statistics [shades of FN] to support the request the decision could have so easily been different.

Jane Easterbrook pays great tribute to Mary Laurence, Janice Cackett and Natalie Tiddy, whose work covered so many years of complicated change. They, with the Health Authority, steered everything and everyone through; their aim was not to hurt people, and to disrupt careers and curricula as little as possible. The redundancies when they came were in the main voluntary – only four were compulsory. They were not as a result of moving into Higher Education, and were not in the hands of the University.

To sum up the sequence of events:

1. 1991: the Nightingale School ceased to exist (current students were still able to work towards the Badge).
2. April 1991: the Nightingale School, the Thomas Guy and Lewisham School of Nursing and the Olive Haydon School of Midwifery amalgamated to become *The Nightingale and Guy's College of Nursing and Midwifery*.
3. 1992: The name was adjusted to *The Nightingale and Guy's College of Health*: throughout most of its life the College operated in six centres on three sites (St Thomas', Guy's and Lewisham).
4. 1993: Nightingale and Guy's combined with Normanby College of Health within King's College, University of London, to form *The Nightingale Institute*, (for which a new badge was struck).

The answers to questionnaires that were sent out to Nightingales, and which have provided an invaluable resource for the writing of this book, tailed off for the 1980s and 1990s. One can only hazard an explanation. Jane Easterbrook has said that she took great care to explain the number and rapidity of changes to students, and their political and economic implications, but it may be that, even so, many students felt left out – 'we were not consulted'; as they were being trained an ever-increasing pace of change altered the identity of the School, and eventually led to its official disappearance. In such circumstances it must have been difficult to achieve the sense of proud loyalty and of being special that so characterised the replies from those trained in earlier generations. It remains to be seen whether the Nightingale Institute, with its own Badge, will build up a new but similar sense of pride.

This book was written to mark the end of an era as well as the history of one training School for nurses. That School was distinctive and unique in its connection to Florence Nightingale. Those who were trained in it and went from it, not only to St Thomas' but to hospitals all over the world, in a very large number of cases gave their whole working lives to what many saw as a dedication. One recalls Miss Smyth's words to a young nurse, 'You are giving your youth to the sick'. The changes described in this chapter have deeply grieved and upset many Nightingales, who feel they have witnessed not only the death of their School but the death of nursing. Against this sadness must be placed the optimism and self-confidence to be found in the Nightingale

Institute. Here, there is a conviction that they are developing the only tenable ways forward for nursing.

It will be recalled that FN and the Fund Council always intended that there should be a missionary element in their work. Most Nightingales were to work in St Thomas', but many went out straightway or on promotion to posts elsewhere, many to exceedingly influential ones. The Book of Ecclesiasticus contains words often used because they are so appropriate. (The Old Testament uses 'men', but the words apply equally to women.) 'Let us now praise famous men . . . All these were honoured in their generations, and were the glory of their times. There be of them, that have left a name behind them, that their praises might be reported. And some there be, which have no memorial; who are perished, as though they have never been . . . But these were merciful [women], whose righteousness hath not been forgotten . . . The people will tell of their wisdom, and the congregation will show forth their praise.'[6]

Here follows a representative, but in no sense whatsoever all-inclusive, list of Nightingales who did good work, received Honours and, in many cases, made their name further afield from the School and the Hospital.

Olive Baggaley MBE, Eileen Baldock ARRC, Dorothy Bannon CBE, Louise Bell OBE, Daisy Bridges CBE, Mary Carpenter, Dorothy Coode OBE, Lucilla Crichton, Barbara Cozens DBE, RRC, Janet Craig, Muriel Cullen, Kathleen Douglas, Muriel Edwards MVO, Ruth Furze, M. Gannon, Lucy Duff-Grant, Anne C. Hayes OStJ, Norna Jamieson ARRC, BEM, Agnes Jones, Gwyneth Ceris Jones, Gwendoline Kirby LVO, Charlotte Kratz MBE, Mabel Lawson CBE, Mabel Liddiard, Baroness Lucy Mannerheim, Elizabeth Merry, Marjorie Mudge MBE, Helen Parsons, Minnie Randell MBE, Mary Richardson OBE, Lady Annie Riddell, Cicely Saunders OM, DBE, DSG, Agnes Saxby MVO, Lucy Seymer, Marjorie Simpson OBE, Amy Squibbs, Rebecca Strong OBE, Eunice Tattersall OBE, Joan Thompson OBE, RRC, TD.

The Institute

The book's last chapter had a strong sense about it of an unavoidable 'trudge' through a time of massive change wherever one looked – in the buildings, on the building site, in administration, management and finance, in the curriculum that was taught in the School, and even in the clothes worn by those in it. To an outsider it was a considerable challenge to make sure that it had been got right – one hopes that it has. Beneath all the changes in job descriptions and the personalities behind them, a sense that one was dealing with a living and immensely diversified organism had to be kept in the forefront of one's mind. The transition from the School to the Institute has now been made, and since 1993 Professor Macleod Clark, the Institute's Director, has kept Fellowship members up to date with what is happening there.

All Schools of Nursing Education are now committed to Project 2000, leading as it does to a University Diploma. There is some division of opinion as to whether more or less all who take the Diploma should see themselves as progressing towards a degree. Some feel uncomfortable lest the totally necessary aspects of nursing, namely patient care, should be seen as less important and left to be carried out by less qualified people – for example, those with the NVQ (National Vocational Qualification) training. At the time of writing, the argument continues about the wisdom of this; there has certainly been an acknowledgement that it would lessen the pay-roll and so help towards lowering the cost to the Health Service. Does the vexed and difficult matter of recruiting from the ethnic minorities come into this in some parts of the country? (There were, at the time of writing, the inflammatory comments about 'fair-haired, blue-eyed Finns' coming into Hackney.) The Director says that the Institute has a good record in recruiting from minorities.

The Nightingale School from its beginnings in the 1860s through to the early 1950s was a world 'entire unto itself', clearly defined and in a very close relationship to the Hospital. From the implementation of the NHS in 1948 it began to be part of a larger and continually enlarging medical world, though its identity began to slip in the 1980s – with the threat that it might be closed.

Miss Garrett, in the new role of Chief Nursing Officer, took the School and the Hospital into a much larger association. The creation of Sectors in anticipation of the outbreak of war in 1939 was the fore-runner of this process, a reasonable pattern to confront what was antici-pated to be massive disruption. But such a mode of organisation, once created, was never abandoned, and from the 1950s onwards it has become more and not less elaborate; Regional Health Authorities have their ancestry in the idea of Sectors. Mr Attlee, in the earliest days of his Prime Ministership in 1945, broadcast to the nation (and it was filmed for cinema news-reels). At the centre of his policies to create a Welfare State would be a National Health Service that would transform the health of the nation; it was the heart of the Socialist dream. Its costs were a matter of dispute and disagreement in his Cabinet within two or three years. The unpalatable and often unaccepted truth is that there is not and never has been enough money, and never will be unless the electorate is willing to pay higher taxes, one way or another. The Health Service has been controversial ever since its inception.

Miss Garrett felt that 'management' had been invented in the 1960s, but in the 1980s onwards it was surpassed by 'rationalisation', a preoccupation with the efficient best use of resources leading to group-ings and amalgamations when necessary. No student of politics, or anyone else for that matter who has worked near the centre of power, can be unaware of the desire of incoming Secretaries of State or Minis-ters to do something memorable during their brief tenures of office. The NHS and all to do with it experienced this as much as any other Department of government. Part of the seemingly endless processes of rationalisation was the amalgamation of St Thomas' and Guy's Schools of Nursing and Midwifery. It was one thing to legislate for amalgama-tion and quite another to assume that two separate very strong histories and traditions would merge easily, and the evidence indeed supports this. In the formation of the Institute a considerable number of staff took voluntary redundancy or early retirement, but there were few compulsory redundancies. Approximately two-thirds of the original staff members of the Schools were retained, but it can be seen by the merest observer that the task of creating something new from all this was formidable indeed.

It was decided, after strong argument, to call the new establishment

The Nightingale Institute, even though it was to be housed away from St Thomas'. This decision was a recognition of the uniqueness of Florence Nightingale's place in the history of the training of nurses, and those in charge of it have expressed their determination to ensure that the Institute should be unsurpassed in the quality of what it offers. Professor Macleod Clark has stated firmly that 'FN's philosophy and ethos underpin it'. Symbolically, a bronze bust of Florence Nightingale stands in the ante-room of the Director's offices. She pins her trust in recognising that it is FN's principles that matter, not the details of organisation. The new Institute, in its place as part of King's College in the University of London, was the first of its kind – a fully integrated unit; it is seen as the flagship and it is intended to keep it so.

From one year's training to three, from 'Specials' to 'Probationers', from a normal age of entry from 19 to 18 with very few late entrants, there has come about a completely different 'world'. Although most students undertake three years of training for the Diploma, those entering at 18+ are no longer in the majority. It is anticipated that many will continue to study after qualification on a part-time basis to gain a degree from London University. At present approximately 20 per cent of recruits are men. There is a definite move towards an all-graduate nursing profession at specialist practice level. Entry requirements at 18+ are five GCSEs at a minimum of Grade C, to include English Language, Mathematics and a Science. Applications are encouraged from those with A-Levels or with higher qualifications. All courses commence in the September of each year so that students start their university career alongside other students – a complete change from those days when Sets arrived at different points. The number of available places for the main intake is approximately 350 in any one academic year.

It is increasingly the case, however, that the greater number of entrants will be mature students. These may be people in their second careers, or women entering when their children have gone to school or moved away. Those who have graduated already in another discipline related to Health Studies will follow a shortened course. Many will continue with specialist studies from a long list on offer that may well lead to higher degrees. Furthermore, every year there are over 1000 already qualified nurses and midwives studying part-time modules and courses leading to higher degrees and qualifications. Another important innovation in the late 80s is the Diploma in Midwifery Practice, a three-year course 'designed to enable students without a nursing qualification to achieve the standard required of a Registered Midwife.' Those who so wish can take their studies further to acquire an Honours B.Sc. in Midwifery. It was remarked very early in this book that FN regretted that she had not given more attention to this field.

The new kind of nurse is already and will continue to be a member of a partnership, making an accurate assessment of patients' needs and the kinds of interventions required, and playing a part in their delivery. In such circumstances it is held not to be tenable that the nurse be less qualified and of lower status than the others in the partnership, and this in itself is the case for bringing nursing into higher education; student nurses are university students, keeping university terms, living and mixing with students from many other disciplines. Their teachers are no longer adjuncts to a hospital but academic members of a university staff, with the same contracts and terms and conditions as other university teachers.

Such a transition was bound to bring difficulties. There were problems of industrial relations; understandable fears among some nurse tutors that they would not hold their own in the academic world; there were the inherited rivalries from previous institutions. It is maintained that these difficulties have been surmounted, and that the tutors have brought strengths to university teaching. The change of culture has meant a move from the strict and confined hierarchy of the training schools to a new freedom and responsibility within a larger university framework. The lecturers are members of a Common Room and the students are part of a group of three hundred rather than of twenty. In common with general university practice, first-year students have accommodation provided and then make their own arrangements. A very little reflection shews how far this is from Chelsea Court, from Home Sisters and from the rigid discipline of the old pyramidical society. There is bound to be regret on the part of some at the extent of these changes, and that those entering at 18 should not now be in the majority; such would maintain that the mixed age range and the variety of backgrounds mean that cohesiveness has gone; 'there is no norm of practice, no common sense of vocation on entry'.

There is no escaping the division of opinion. Certainly, in the first three years of the Institute's life the five teaching sites brought difficulties, and some of the buildings are very unattractive. But by the year 2000 all the work of the Institute and its associated partners will be under one roof. It is maintained, though some disagree, that what has not been put at risk is the basic tenet that training should be 'practice-based' and 'patient centred'. The Director holds firmly that if students are not interested in 'caring' then they are out of place and will not survive. FN's emphasis that nursing calls for education and not simply for training is strongly pursued. Those who now run the Institute are absolutely convinced that it is only under the present arrangements that the future of the profession of nursing can be assured; no intermediate form of affiliation, still less an attempt to 'stand alone', would have survived. The fundamental question is and will be what is the quality of the experience of patients in or out of hospital – hence the ripples in the pond created by Nigella Lawson and others. The new organisation of health care teams has not yet been fully and professionally evaluated. There are many groups involved in the evaluation, as one might expect these days in a 'research-based industry'. The difficulty has been, Professor Macleod Clark says, in measuring the contribution of each of the different elements in the team. A number of false trails has been followed, but the question remains and is being addressed in a spirit of optimism.

A growing number of lectures, seminars and tutorials in the Institute are held jointly with medical students. One may ask how easily this is achieved. Entry to medical schools is difficult and competition is fierce, and their students cannot necessarily be thought to be compatible with those coming in with those qualifications necessary for nursing. However, in the Institute the question of 'what is nursing?' – a question raised by FN and asked in every decade since – has now acquired a new importance, because it is clearly envisaged that a number of nurses will be competent to undertake many of the lesser medical, surgical and diagnostic responsibilities. Indeed, according to one General Practitioner, with further in-service training many practice nurses may be better briefed and more competent to deal with specific health concerns than the GPs with whom they are working.

The general policy aims at holistic nursing, which goes well beyond the patient to the family and to the social context in each case. This belief that nursing is concerned with the promotion of health as well as the care of the sick again returns one directly to FN, and to other prominent teachers in the School in times past. Miss Gould instituted a programme of sending students out into the community and pioneered health care and nursing in the neighbourhood; then it was seen as a startling revelation of social realities – 'we had no idea that people lived like that'.

In the first phase of the history of the School it was understood that its students would not only be trained in St Thomas' but would work there on qualifying; they had a contractual obligation to the Hospital in this matter. The present state of affairs is completely different. One of the major lessons of recent years has been that a completed training does not guarantee a nursing post in St Thomas' Hospital, though many do not wish to work in London for all kinds of reasons. The Institute educates, trains and sees students through to a wide range of qualifications. It is a provider. Nine Trusts are the purchasers of what is provided, and separate liaison teams in the Institute are working in partnership with them 'to meet their needs for education and help with their forward planning'; this seems to be in contrast to some other examples given to the writer, where the purchaser indicates what is required of the provider. Professor Macleod Clark maintains that negotiation is at the heart of the process. But as the market system is maturing, the relationship between education and service provision is strengthening, and this is particularly true of the Institute and its Trusts.

These great changes range so far and wide that the old Nightingale practices that lasted to the 1970s have more or less disappeared. With so much to study and learn, the former preoccupations with absolutely basic routines of cleanliness and hygiene may appear to have diminished. Few nurses in training now would be willing to accept the old autocracy of the Ward Sister, but this very autocracy, which could be harsh and unsympathetic, was, as has often been emphasised, the guarantee of standards, some of which are now under question. Hence the recently-heard cry: 'Bring back the Matron.'

The new policy is to encourage and indeed to rely on the ability of students to grow into self-discipline, but what happens if they do not? There is a difference now in what is expected of a student and of a newly-qualified nurse. The rigid sense of hierarchy is visibly diminished. In its place, there is a conviction that the more informal relationships within the Institute and with the medical staff help rather than hinder. Students and nurses are encouraged to be more assertive and self-confident. Some people feel that they have developed too great a sense of what they will not do, as well as what it is their duty to do. From this comes the lament that 'the future lies with the new breed of carer, the less academically-qualified and less well-paid Health Care Assistants, the product of

243

the NVQ.' The Director points out, however, that most of her students are welcomed and appreciated on the wards, particularly by those who understand the reasons for the changes and approve of them. One has to recognise, as an outside writer, that there is a cavernous divide between those who do approve of what is taking shape and those who grieve, at times bitterly, for 'the world we have lost'. They see casualness, scruffiness, lack of full commitment; many go as far as to say, and not only in the questionnaires, that the new nurses are more able or willing to communicate with each other than with the patients in the wards. Some go further and lament the death of nursing. Perhaps it is fair to ask whether all this should have been expected in the transition from the notion of vocation to that of a career.

The positive point of view about the present state of affairs would maintain that the old order forced young women into maturity; at a very early point, far too early by this reckoning, they met all the realities of life and death. This is also made clear time and time again in the questionnaires. The new order operates on a longer time scale. Nurses in training are no longer counted as staff on the ward; there is more time to grow up for entrants at 18, and for the other older students to grow into the job. Up to 40 per cent of nurses will not wear a uniform at all because it is felt to be a barrier in some important aspects of work, particularly psychiatry.

Some chapters back, Miss Nuttall was quoted as saying that 'nursing ended with the coming of antibiotics'. What she meant in this aphorism was that the introduction of more and more new drugs, and the new developments in surgery, together not only reduced greatly the amount of time that most patients would spend in hospital but also thereby altered and reduced the nature and function of nursing. Professor Macleod Clark is entirely in agreement with those who say that whilst nurses will continue to care for the acutely ill, their role must also be to prepare patients for reduced stays in hospital and a rapid move back into the community.

In this new world taking shape, the place of authority and discipline has to be re-examined. The School was founded in a hierarchical society. Patients may have been 'honoured guests', but were not invited to be partners in their illness by the ward sisters. Observation and care were not to be accompanied by any blurring in position or rank. One eminent Nightingale has commented ruefully on her perplexity over how to deal, in the outside world, with ordinary people who had been her patients. The concept of partnership between the sick and those who care for them has been introduced by many who have contributed to this book. This means negotiation, and an acceptance of variable portions of responsibility. There are clear instances where partnership is proper and effective, and others where authority is necessary. But what happens when the dividing line is not so clear?

In 1893 FN wrote: 'We are only on the threshold of nursing. In the future which I shall not see, for I am old, may a better way be opened. May the methods by which every infant, every human being will have the best chance of health – the methods by which every sick person will have the best change of recovery – be learnt and practised.' Moses saw the Promised Land but never entered it.

In the Fellowship *Journal* for Summer 1996 Professor Macleod Clark gave an up-date of how things stood when 'the last students from the old training graduated' and all academic and support staff of the Nightingale Institute – Nightingale, Guy's College of Health, and Normanby College of Health Studies – had become fully integrated members of King's College in London University. (This means, all who graduate from the Institute receive their diplomas and degrees at the King's College Graduation Ceremony.) She talked about all those who had been granted their Badges in the last year as 'traditional pre-Project 2000 trained nurses'; this ended an era of one hundred and thirty-six years, but 'just as surely confirms the start of another.' To mark this a new Badge had been decided upon, after a competition which had been won by a Nightingale, Anji Waring, a lecturer in the Institute. 'Our new Badge is now in production and I know our graduating nurses will be proud to display a symbol of our exceptional role model, Florence Nightingale.'[1]

On the 11th May 1996, at the ceremonies marking the formal end of the Nightingale School, Peggy Nuttall said:

We have reached the end of the beginning. Care is moving out of hospital and into the community. It's time to say goodbye to so much that we knew and which is so familiar. Perhaps we need to remind ourselves of Miss Nightingale's words: 'While having devoted my life to hospital work I have come to the conclusion that hospitals are not the best place for the sick – except, perhaps, for surgical cases.'

245

The variety of education and training in the new Nightingale Institute gives some indication of the range of work into which the new graduates may go. Sue Norman, in her speech in May 1996, risked a forecast.

> The trends in health and social care are fairly plain – much less emphasis on acute care; a power shift towards purchasers and GP fund holders; greater emphasis on primary and community care; minimally invasive surgical and diagnostic techniques; gene therapy; taking health care to the population . . . much more long-term care for an increasing percentage of the population.

A whole series of new opportunities will open up, unavoidably bringing a blurring of professional role boundaries. She felt – and in this would be supported by all the generations of Nightingales who have been written about in this book – that the central feature must remain the value placed on caring. As always, this will be provided by 'confident, accountable practitioners who are able to articulate and demonstrate, through their care, the contribution professional practice makes to the health and welfare of all.'

Project 2000 so far has been seen, with some reservations, as the necessary way to raise the status of nursing and to establish it as a separate partner within the medical profession. It has its own reputable qualifications at Diploma level and the implication increasingly is that this, in turn, may lead to an appropriate Degree. However, on 17th April 1997, a consultant writing under the pseudonym Hippocrates Spratt in a *Sunday Telegraph* supplement launched a violent attack:

> The best nurses have quit . . . abandoning the asylum to the lunatics. To be fair, not all of the remaining nurses are insane. The vast majority of them fall into one of three categories: the embittered, the stroppy and the irredeemably stupid. The decline in nurses' common sense and overall brain power coincided with the profession's attempts to improve its intellectual standing. Project 2000 took student nurses off the wards and put them into classrooms. It promised them a university degree at the end. But everyone knows that a few letters after your name make you reluctant to get your hands dirty.

Unlike Nigella Lawson's earlier article, this one provoked a correspondence. Its opinions were not universally refuted and a genuine concern emerged about where nursing is going. The complete tale is not yet told, but it is certain that the argument will go on. It has been put that, by the time it is resolved, the whole system of health care provision will have changed beyond most present conceptions. At the very time of writing this, a new Secretary of State was announcing yet another 'thorough-going' review of the NHS, which is bound to have its effect on nurse training and supply.

There is a temptation at the end of a book to attempt to tie it up neatly with the beginning. First it was felt necessary to revisit Florence Nightingale, and it was natural to assume that her spirit and her principles would pervade the whole history and development of the School. One realised with surprise that the original dynamic died either with Miss Pringle who resigned in 1889, or at any rate during the time of her next two successors – Miss Gordon (1889–1902) and Miss Hamilton (1902–1913). The point was made that the 'legend' was very likely invented by Dame Alicia during her long reign from 1913 to 1937. What she created was an organisation that became more and more stylised as the decades went by, totally hierarchical, running smoothly on principles of strict obedience and perfectionism all down the line. This remarkable institution produced great pride in most of those trained in it; the Badge came to symbolise this, and gave confidence that those who wore it were in a direct line of succession.

Both spirit and organisation were put to the test in two world wars; the School held together and functioned with extraordinary efficiency in the most exacting times, particularly in the Second War – one remembers the Sectors, Miss Hillyers driving round and round them, Miss Coode looking optimistically to the future when the days were darkest, and Miss Gould working out the Block System and ways of making probationers more aware of a world outside most of their own social experience. Miss Hone, in her austere undeviating dedication, has come to represent to many Nightingales all that was best in the School in its last two decades. (It is something to dwell on, that all her successors, in a renamed post, were not Nightingales.) From the beginning, the relationship between theory and practice in nurse training, and between nursing and the medical side, were problems to be solved. They are still there, sharpened by developments within each of them.

Annually, probationers/students and nurses were preached at in the most lofty manner by a succession of prelates who always referred to FN in one way or another in their discourses, but one has been told that in everyday life in the hospital, she was hardly mentioned outside PTS/initial training. One can read her writings carefully and marvel at some of them; one is also told that extracts from *Notes on Nursing* are read each year to entrants to the Nightingale Institute, although one can be reasonably certain that what was central to her thinking – the relationship of nurses and nursing to God – is played down. The School bore her name proudly, the Badge was worn with honour, and the Institute uses her profile in its own Badge.

The relationship of Founders to the Orders or Institutes that bear their name differs. Sometimes there is a Rule to be followed, such as that of St Benedict; sometimes there is a stupendous personality whose life is the source of inspiration, as with St Francis; sometimes the Founder is there for general reference, a source of pride through connection. For 'Rule' read 'Model'. Models of nursing have been encountered: one was even told that there was a Nightingale Model – but there was not. She herself was firm on the point: 'To furnish a cut-and-dried prospectus of my plans . . . is what I would not if I could, and could not if I would.' Nightingales have had her, therefore, as the general exemplar – more a St Francis than a St Benedict. She demanded, on the one hand, highly detailed standards of cleanliness and organisation; on the other, single-minded dedication and the highest principles. Generations of nurses have had to work out what happens in the everyday realities between the two.

APPENDIX I

The Programme for the Celebration in Commemoration of the Nightingale Training School 1860–1996 Held at St Thomas' Hospital on Saturday, 11 May 1996

11.30–12.15   Chapel Service, for Nightingale Fellowship members only

12.30–2.30   Buffet Luncheon, in marquee, Thames Terrace

Speakers at Luncheon

Natalie Tiddy, President, Nightingale Fellowship
Sir Kenneth Eaton, Chairman, Guy's and St Thomas' Trust
Miss P Nuttall, OBE, OStJ, FRCN, a Nightingale
Miss S Norman, Chief Executive and Registrar, UKCC

A Replica of the Nightingale Badge was unveiled by Miss M Laurence, OBE, Vice-President, Nightingale Fellowship
Toast to the Future of Nursing and Midwifery: Tim Matthews, Chief Executive, Guy's and St Thomas' Trust
Members of the Guy's and St Thomas' Music Society Wind Ensemble played a selection of music during luncheon.

3.00–4.15   Annual General Meeting, for Nightingale Fellowship members only, Nevin Lecture Theatre

4.30–5.30   Tea in marquee

APPENDIX II

A List of Senior Staff

St. Thomas's Hospital: Matrons and Superintendents of The Nightingale Training School, 1860–1970

Miss Sarah Wardroper	1854–1887
Miss Angelique Pringle	1887–1889
Miss Louisa Gordon	1889–1902
Miss Harriet Hamilton	1902–1913
Miss (later Dame) Alicia Lloyd Still	1913–1937
Miss Gladys Hillyers	1937–1945
Miss Margaret Smyth	1945–1955
Miss Theodora Turner	1955–1965
Miss Estelle Adamson	1965–1970

St Thomas' Hospital Group, 1970–1974

Miss Sheila Garrett, Chief Nursing Officer	1970–1974

St Thomas' Health District (Teaching), 1974–1981

Miss Mary Laurence, District Nursing Officer	1974–1981

West Lambeth Health Authority, 1982–1991

Miss Mary Laurence, Chief Nursing Officer	1982–1985
Miss Janice Cackett, Chief Nursing Officer	1985–1987
Miss Natalie Tiddy, Chief Nursing Adviser	1988–1991

The Nightingale Training School for Nurses Superintendents, Home Sisters and Tutors in Charge, 1860–1993

Miss Sarah Wardroper, Matron and Superintendent	1860–1885
Miss Elizabeth Torrance, Home Sister	1872
Miss Fanny S. Parkinson, Home Sister	1873
Miss Maria Machin, Home Sister	1873–1875
Miss Mary Crossland, Home Sister	1875–1896
Miss Florence Haig Brown, Home Sister	1896–1903
Miss Dorothy S. Coode, Home Sister	1903–1910
The Hon. Gertrude Best, Sister, Preliminary Training School	1910–1913
Miss Dorothy S. Coode, Sister, Preliminary Training School	1914–1924
Miss Marion A. Gullan, Sister Tutor	1914–1935
Miss Mabel Lawson, 1st Sister Tutor	1936
Miss Gwyneth Ceris Jones, 1st Sister Tutor	1936–1939
Miss Marion E. Gould, Senior Sister Tutor	1939–1954
Miss Rosamund A. Hone, Principal Sister Tutor	1955–1972
Miss Hazel O. Allen, Director of Nurse Education	1972–1977
Miss Janice S. Cackett, Director of Nurse Education	1977–1985
Miss Ursula M. Cowell, Director of Nurse Education	1986–1990
Miss Maureen Theobald, Nightingale & Guy's College of Health	1991–1993

Names of the Final Set of Nightingale Students, Photographed in Autumn 1992

Front Row: Catherine Hunter, Imelda de Guzman, Jane Worsh, Catherine Mullen, Andrea Hunt, Nadiya Moores, Cathy Freeman, Kerenza Swinfen, Maria McMillen, Zara Barnes.

Second Row: Emma Harley, Joanna Gibbons, Keren Ling, Dorte Humlebaek, Michelle Ray, Todd Davies, Richard Walker, Jeremy Pearce, Hannah Lee, Susan Kerr, Paula Tindale, Claire Elbourne, Ruth Hartigan.

Third Row: Donna Burnett, Tracy Hilton, Fiona Pilkington, Zoe Baines, Ruth Ordway, Laurence Parker, Darren Murphy, Susannah Whitehouse, Helen Clitherow, Emma Brown, Delyth Davies, Elizabeth James.

Fourth Row: Katherine Palmer, Sophie Bates, Eunice Chanakira, Sally Anniss, Andria Christian, Claire Butcher, Barbara Hall, Katie Snell, Claire Ragan, Katrina Miller, Kerry Havis, Claire Moore, Fiona Snadden.

Sources

Any research into this period must keep in mind the vast miscellany of material in the Greater London Record Office. The Admissions Registers are of first importance, though the early ones were far from accurately kept. There is also a great number of letters, including letters and memoranda from FN herself which range from her messages on many occasions to her beloved nurses to her scathing, excoriating comments on some of her collaborators. In addition, there are the records of the training of probationers and syllabuses: nurses' files, examination and time books, diaries, Matrons' Addresses and correspondence, accounts, interviews with past Nightingales, papers relating to the Fund Council and the Fellowship, records of special occasions, appointments of key staff, reports from other hospitals about Nightingale nurses. The thirty-year rule applies to some of these papers. There are, in particular, the papers concerning Arthur Hugh Clough and Henry Bonham Carter, the first two Secretaries to the Fund Council. The thirty-three packets of Bonham Carter papers have a covering table of contents. To quote from this gives an indication of the range of some of his work:

> the training of Nightingale nurses, the allocation of trained nurses to suitable hospitals, applications from prospective nurses, enquiries from hospitals seeking trained nurses, requests for help from clergymen and others about the provision of district nurses and midwives, accommodation for Nightingale probationers, matters concerning Nightingale nurses and the Royal Victoria Hospital at Netley, the founding of the Midwifery School at King's College Hospital, the training of nurses in Workhouse Infirmaries.

There is so much more, at the British Museum, the British Library, the Wellcome Institute, the Wilton House Archives concerning Sidney Herbert, and so on, including in the United States. There are also unpublished doctoral theses. What might be called an international 'Florence Nightingale industry' exists by now, especially in the United States.

In addition to these papers, there is a substantial collection of photographs and prints, though very few of FN herself. It is known that she was not fond of being photographed or of having her portrait painted, or of any resemblance in bronze or stone. She did not wish to be 'memorialised'. Her work was to be her memorial. She was not only a prolific writer – of at least 200 books or major memoranda, and nearly 14,000 surviving hand-written letters – but also kept copies of most of her writings. On many of them she scribbled heavily underlined instructions, such as 'Burn' or 'Destroy' or 'Most Private – Burn'. When she was 44 (1864), she wrote: 'I have taken effective means that all my papers will be burned after my death.' She relented in later life and one result is that the British Museum Library holds 10,000 of her letters, along with other personal papers. It is said that a further 4,000 letters exist in archives or in private hands.

FN did consent to record her voice in a brief message on a wax cylinder on 30th July 1890, made by Thomas Edison to promote his new recording machine. There are only two sentences: 'When I am no longer even a memory, just a name, I hope my voice may perpetuate the great work of my life. God bless my dear old comrades of Balaclava and bring them safe to God.' (This comes from a tape-recording kept at the Royal Victoria Museum at Netley.) Her words give a perfect confirmation of the view that the Army came first in her thoughts, and not the School.

The life stories and reminiscences of Nightingales past and present form a particularly important element in this book. Oral history 'took off' in the 1960s as tape recorders became more and more portable, so that a new seam of investigation has opened up to historians in the matter of evidence. The questionnaire devised for Nightingales to answer in connection with this book has led to an abundance of replies that creates a unique archive for present and future use.

The chief general sources are the Fellowship *Journal* since its inception in 1927, the answers to the questionnaire, the Fund Council Minutes, the Doctoral Thesis of Dr Monica Baly (University College London, 1984), and various writings of Florence Nightingale. To these must be added the very substantial number of interviews with Nightingales and others connected with the School, the Museum and the Hospital. The Fellowship *Journal* is not always easy to use. Individual issues were collected and bound into volumes, leaving the page numbers of each issue intact – therefore, in any one volume one might find five or six pages similarly numbered. Until very recent times, the twice-yearly *Journals* were labelled January and July; now Winter and Summer. In earlier volumes it is sometimes only possible to know in which year issues were published by finding the date of the report of the Annual General Meeting which comes at the end of the issue. Difficulties in wartime led to contents pages being omitted. The complete volumes are kept in the Fellowship Office, as are the answers to the questionnaire.

The Questionnaire which was sent out to a large number of Nightingales and then printed in the *Journal* was as follows:

THE NIGHTINGALE TRAINING SCHOOL

Your Experience

To write the history of the Nightingale Training School it is important to receive in writing and/or orally the memories and the reflections of a wide number of Nightingales.

To begin with written evidence: would you be kind enough to fill in such details as you think fit in answer to the following questions.

Name (as in address list: but may we follow the practice 'Smith/Jones' i.e. before and after marriage?)

Telephone number

1. Years of training in the Nightingale School
2. Education and Qualifications before training, and age on entering training
3. What led you to enter the Nightingale School – why did you choose it rather than another?
4. Could you describe the aspects and the phases in the training and how long was given to them? How would you assess your training?
5. Did you live in any of the Nurses' Homes? If so, which ones? Would you describe the pattern of life. What did you think of it?
6. What pattern did your professional career follow on completion of training? What reaction did you encounter in your hospital/nursing work to being a Nightingale?
7. Did any major changes take place in the School or in your training during your time there? What were/are your thoughts on these changes?
8. Will you be kind enough to proffer any further reflections on your training, its social circumstances and patterns of relationships in your time – for example, in comparison with present circumstances and in comparison with any of your friends who did not nurse?

Please would you add anything else that you think important to be known in writing a history of the School?

Introduction

1. Orchard Gillian M. IBVM (ed), *Till God Will: Mary Ward Through Her Writings* Darton, Longman and Todd, 1985, pp. 56–7.
2. Woodham-Smith C., *Florence Nightingale 1820–1910* Reprint Society by arrangement with Constable, 1952, p14.
3. ibid. p 61.
4. Florence Nightingale, *Notes on Nursing (Revised, with Additions)*, Victor Skretkowicz (ed.) Scutari Press, 1992, p165 and p164.
5. Baly M., *The Influence of the Nightingale Fund from 1855 to 1914 on the Development of Nursing* 1984 Ph. D. thesis, published in book form as *Florence Nightingale and the Nursing Legacy* Croom Helm, 1986.
6. Terry N., Lecture printed by The McGill Institute for Learning in Retirement.

Chapter One

1. Holroyd M., *Lytton Strachey* Vintage, 1995, p430.
2. ibid. p428.
3. ibid. p318, (letter from Lytton Strachey to his mother, 15th January 1914)
4. ibid.
5. Annan N., *Our Age: The Generation that Made Post-War Britain* Harper Collins, 1995, pp113-114.
6. Woodham-Smith, op. cit., p203
7. Le Fanu *The Times*, 18th January 1996
8. Vicinus E. and Nergaard B. (ed), *Ever Yours, Florence Nightingale: Selected Letters*, Virago, 1989, p135
9. Skretkowicz V., (ed) op.cit., p63
10. Baly M. article in the Fellowship *Journal* No. 109, July 1983
11. Bingham S., *Ministering Angels* Osprey, 1979, pp23–25
12. ibid. pp25–26
13. Howlett B., *The Origins of the Nightingale School* Florence Nightingale Museum Resources Centre Paper.
14. Nightingale F., *Subsidiary Notes as to the Introduction of Female Nursing into Military Hospitals in Peace and in War* 1858. Presented by request for the Secretary of State for War.
15. Woodham-Smith, op.cit., p227
16. ibid., (letter to Madame Mohl), p506
17. Bibby J., *Notes Towards a History of Teaching Statistics* published privately, John Bibby Books, pp34–36
18. Selanders L.C., *Florence Nightingale: An Adaptation Theory* Sage Publications Inc. 1993, Chapter Two
19. ibid. p12

20. Woodham-Smith, op.cit., pp411–412
21. ibid., p411
22. ibid., pp400–401
23. Bingham S., op.cit., p72
24. Woodham-Smith, op.cit., p26
25. ibid., p381
26. Bibby J., op.cit., p36
27. Woodham-Smith, op.cit., p395
28. Vicinus M. and Nergaard B., op.cit. Introduction p10

Chapter Two

1. Greater London Record Office (GLRO), Fund Council Archive, File No. 13.
2. Baly M., Doctoral Thesis, London University, pp315–320
3. Hibbert Christopher, *London, The Biography of a City* Longmans, 1969, p187 (see also Roger Hudson and Joe Whitlock Blundell, *The London Guides, Covent Garden, Trafalgar Square and the Strand* Haggerston Press, 1996, p89)
4. Baly M., *Florence Nightingale and the Nursing Legacy* Croom Helm, 1986, p57
5. McInnes E.M., notes made towards her history of St Thomas' Hospital.
6. From an exchange of letters between Bridget Howlett, Assistant Archivist at the GLRO and Alex Attewell, Curator of the Florence Nightingale Museum, May 1996
7. Baly M., *A History of Nursing, The State of the Art* Croom Helm, 1985
8. Baly M., 'How the Nightingale Fund Influenced Nursing Education', The Fellowship *Journal* Vol XI, No. 109, July 1983, p342
9. Vicinus M. and Nergaard B., op.cit., p340
10. McInnes E.M., *St Thomas' Hospital*, Second Enlarged Edition, published by the Special Trustees of St Thomas' Hospital, 1990, p114
11. Carpenter Turner B., *A History of the Royal Hampshire County Hospital*, Phillimore Press, 1986, p91
12. Fellowship *Journal*, Vol 3, (Number missing, not printed), July 1940, pp11–12
13. van der Peet R., *The Nightingale Model of Nursing*, Campion Press Edinburgh, 1995, p49
14. Nash R. (ed), *Florence Nightingale to Her Nurses*, Macmillan 1914
15. Baly M., *Florence Nightingale and the Nursing Legacy* p61
16. ibid., p 44
17. Baly M., article in The Fellowship *Journal*, July 1983
18. Baly M., ibid. p223
19. Baly M., (ed) *As Miss Nightingale Said . . .* Scutari Press (now defunct)
20. Bingham S. op.cit., p66
21. ibid., p71
22. McInnes E.M., op.cit., p146

23. Vicinus M. and Nergaard B., op.cit., p331

24. Seymer L., *Dame Alicia Lloyd Still, A Memoir*, printed for the Nightingale Fellowship, May 1953, p2

25. Parsons F.G., *The History of St Thomas's Hospital* in 3 volumes, Methuen 1936, Vol I, p152

26. Baly M., *Florence Nightingale and the Nursing Legacy* p181

27. Baggalley O., article in *Nursing Times:* 'The Wider Influence of the Nightingale Training School', 13th May 1960

Chapter Three

1. Letter from Florence Nightingale to Henry Bonham Carter, 3rd September 1865. GLRO

2. Vicinus and Nergaard, (ed), op.cit. p380

3. Baly M., Ph.D. thesis, p274

4. Bingham S., op.cit., p75

5. ibid., p76

6. Hampson S.E., 'Reflections of St Thomas's in the Eighties' Fellowship *Journal*, Vol. 2, July 1935, p13

7. Masson F., 'Old Days at St Thomas's' Fellowship *Journal*, Vol. 2 July 1935, pp 10–11

8. Baly M., *Florence Nightingale and the Nursing Legacy* Ch. 10

9. van der Peet R., op.cit., p27

10. Hampson I.A. et al. (ed), *Florence Nightingale: Nursing of the Sick* 1893, reprinted McGraw-Hill Book Co., 1949

11. van der Peet R., op.cit., p28

12. ibid., p74

13. ibid., p33

14. Skretkowicz V., Florence Nightingale's *Notes on Nursing*, Scutari Press, 1992, p17

15. ibid., p33

16. F.N. wrote extensively, in three Volumes, on her religious position in 1860. Volume One was addressed specifically to the 'Artizans of England'. Volumes Two and Three were addressed simply to 'Searchers After Religious Truth'. All were published by George E. Eyre and William Spottiswode.

17. Skretkowicz V., op.cit., Introd., p xi

18. Weintraub S., *Albert, Uncrowned King*, Murray, 1997, p435

19. Baly M. *Florence Nightingale and the Nursing Legacy*, p178

20. Nash R. (ed), op.cit., p80

21. ibid., p81

22. ibid., p83

23. ibid., p146

24. Baly M., op.cit., p203

25. Redl F.T., 'Some Impressions of the Nightingale Home' Fellowship *Journal*, Vol 2, July 1935, p21

Chapter Four

1. Seymer L., op.cit., pp8–9
2. Vesey E.M., Fellowship *Journal*, Vol 2.
3. Seymer L., op.cit., p10
4. Routh M.C., 'The Nightingale School, 1919–1935', Fellowship *Journal*, Vol 2, July 1935, p34
5. Fellowship *Journal*, Vol 1 p28
6. 'Times Change' (no author given) Fellowship *Journal*, Vol 1, January, 1931, p14
7. ibid.
8. Baly M. *Nursing and Social Change* Heinemann Medical Books, 1973, p166
9. Nolan C. *A Bride for St Thomas* Constable, 1970
10. Seymer L., op.cit., p25

Chapter Five

1. Cockett F. and D. (ed), *The War Diary of St Thomas's Hospital 1939–1945*, Starling Press, 1991, p17
2. Allen C., 'PTS in Wartime', Fellowship *Journal*, Vol 3, January 1941, p27
3. Allen C., ibid., p27
4. Andrews L., *No Time for Romance*, Harrap 1977
5. Hillyers G., Presidential Address, Fellowship *Journal*, Vol 3, July 1941, p29
6. ibid.,
7. Schofield: 'The Hospitaller in Wartime', Fellowship *Journal*, Vol 3, July 1942, pp2–3
8. Andrews L., op.cit., p152
9. Taylor A.J.P., *English History, 1914 to 1945* OUP 1965, pp583–584
10. Cockett F. and D. (ed), op.cit., p34
11. Fellowship *Journal*, Vol 3, Articles on hospital bombing and 'Casualty May 1941', Vol 3 January 1942
12. G.M. Hillyers, Presidential Address November 1943, Fellowship *Journal*, Vol 3, January 1944.
13. Abel-Smith B., *A History of the Nursing Profession*, Heinemann 1960, p191

Chapter Six

1. Abel-Smith B., op.cit., p146
2. Fellowship *Journal*, Vol 4, January 1949, p37
3. Keegan J., *Telegraph Magazine* – cutting sent to author, no date attached. © Telegraph Group Limited, London.
4. Cohen J., *A Minority Report* quoted in the President's Address for November 1948, Fellowship *Journal*, Vol 4, p38
5. Turner T., Fellowship *Journal*, Vol. 7, No. LXI, July 1959, p8
6. Coventry S., *Images of a Nightingale* Beauclerk Publishing 1990.

7. ibid., pp62–63
8. President's Address, Fellowship *Journal*, Vol 6, no. LVIII, p26
9. Abel-Smith B. op.cit., pp249–251

Chapter Seven

1. Presentation of Nightingale Medals and Honour Certificates, no author given, Fellowship *Journal*, Vol VII, July 1959, p7
2. McInnes E.M., op.cit., pp182–184 (with two new chapters by J.M.T. Ford)
3. E.Adamson, Fellowship *Journal*, No 74, January 1965
4. Long R. 'Nursing Care for the Individual in the 1980s', Fellowship *Journal*, Vol XI, No 101, July 1979, p7
5. M.S Lee, M.I. Rikof, G.M. Woodard, Fellowship *Journal*, No. 73, July 1965, pp24–26

Chapter Eight

1. R. Morris, Editorial, Fellowship *Journal*, Vol 16, No. 135, Summer 1996
2. Baly M. *Nursing and Social Change* p161
3. Laurence M., 'A Top Management Course: Interim Report', Fellowship *Journal*, Vol IX, No. 87, July 1972, p366
4. Lawrence H., 'Changes at St Thomas'' Fellowship *Journal*, No. 91 (Volume No. not given), July 1974, p8
5. Lawrence H., Fellowship *Journal*, Volume Numbers 91–100, No. 94, January 1976, p193
6. Casey N., *Nursing Standard* 1st August 1990, Vol. 4, No. 95
7. Roper N., *Clinical Experience in Nurse Education*, Edinburgh: Churchill Livingstone, 1976.
8. Laurence M., Fellowship *Journal*, Volume not given, No. 93, July 1975
9. Morris E. (Sister Anita), 'The Unique Culture of St Thomas'', Fellowship *Journal*, Vol XII, No. 119, 1988
10. Fellowship *Journal*, Vol X, No. 99, July 1978

Chapter Nine

1. Mann C., Fellowship *Journal*, Vol XII, No 118, January 1988, pp394–395
2. Tiddy N., Fellowship *Journal*, Vol XIII, No 123, July 1990, p623
3. Barnes C., Fellowship *Journal*, Vol XIV, No 124, January 1991, p655
4. Rodden F., Fellowship *Journal*, Vol XII, No 117, July 1984, p303
5. Cuff M., Fellowship *Journal*, Vol XV, No 127, July 1992, p776
6. Ecclesiasticus, Chapter IV, King James Version

Postscript

1. Fellowship *Journal*, Vol XVI, No 135, July 1996, p80
2. Baly M., *Florence Nightingale and the Nursing Legacy*, p15

Index

Jowett, Benjamin 31, 43, 44, 45, 46, 49
Judge, Dr Harry 208

Keegan, John 140–1
Kirby, Gwendoline 237
Knight, Dame Laura 226
Kratz, Charlotte 237

L.F.P. 92
Laurence, Mary 209–10, 216–17, 249,
    250, 251; response to change 189, 191,
    194–5, 202–3, 235
Lawson, Mabel 237, 250
Lawson, Nigella 225, 242
Lees, Annie 57
Leeson, Canon Spencer 147–8
Le Fanu, Dr James 47, 48
Liddiard, Mabel 237
Lieven, Princess 125
Lloyd Still, Dame Alicia 251; appearance
    111, 112; appointed Matron 93, 94;
    appreciations 110–13, 114, 170; and
    Archbishops of Canterbury 129; con-
    tingency plans for Second World War
    110; death and funeral 114; devises
    syllabus 94, 156; earlier career 84; FN
    gives Charge as Sister 70; on forma-
    tion of Fellowship 108; honours 100,
    106–7; length of tenure 69, 94; por-
    trait 226; and Royal College of Nurs-
    ing 99, 106; Territorial Matron in
    First World War 97; and Tradition 14,
    114, 115, 134, 247; and ward charts
    99–100; and young applicant 125
Logan, Winifred 192
Long, Rosemary 173–5
Luckes, Eva 84

McEwan, Sir William 61
Machin, Maria 250
McInnes, E.M. 54, 56, 60, 78–9, 80, 177
Macleod Clark, Professor Jill 53, 172–3,
    194, 204; on developments at Institute
    238, 240, 242, 243, 244, 245
Macmillan, Harold 148
Macpherson, Wilma 215
MacSwiney, Bryan 165–6, 167, 169
Makins, G.H. 74

Mann, Catherine 214
Mannerheim, Baroness Lucy 237
Manning, Cardinal Henry Edward 20, 27,
    32, 68
Mary, Queen of Great Britain 108
Masson, Flora 81
May, Kathleen 134
Medhurst, Emily 57
Merry, Elizabeth 237
Milnes, Richard Monckton 45
Minet, W. 94–6, 99
Montagu, Lady Elizabeth 125
Moore, Mother Clare 36
Morris, Elizabeth (Sister Anita) 196–7
Morris, Rosemary 229, 231–2
Mudge, Marjorie 237
Murphy, Mr (taxi driver) 151

Nash, R. 62–3
Newman, Cardinal John Henry 68
Newman, Katherine 114
Nightingale, Florence 19–25, 27–50;
    Army as first preoccupation 24, 33, 37,
    40, 52, 87, 253; biographies 27–9, 51;
    'calling' to nursing 21, 22, 30, 31, 32;
    concept of nursing 62–4, 248, (reli-
    gious) 19, 21, 22–3, 25, 40, 41–2,
    62–3, 89, 91–2, 248; in Crimea 27,
    31–2, 33, 36, 47; on disease 85–6;
    early life and education 23, 30; on
    education for nursing 41, 74–5, 242;
    and Home Sister 43, 75; and India 37,
    40, 44; invalidism 47–8; involvement
    with School 24, 42, 70, 78, 85–9, 247;
    and King's College Hospital 40; maid
    12; manipulative character 32–3, 48,
    49; and Matron's power 43, 56, 71, 75;
    miasmatic theory of infection 42,
    85–6, 87–8; old age and death 49–50;
    and Miss Pringle 81; Order of Merit
    50; planning and organisation of hos-
    pitals 24, 33, 37–8, 43–4, 55, 61, 85,
    87, 178; and Poor Law nursing 35, 38;
    recording of voice 253; recruitment
    policies 42, 58–9, 59–60; and register
    of nurses 89–92; religious beliefs 41,
    62, 67–9, 82, 85–6, 86–7, 89, 30, 31,
    32, 36, (see also concept of nursing